M000309108

ZAGATSURVEY®

1998

SAN FRANCISCO BAY AREA RESTAURANTS

Edited by Anthony Dias Blue

Coordinated by Carol Seibert and David Gadd

Published and distributed by ZAGAT SURVEY, LLC 4 Columbus Circle New York, New York 10019 Tel: 212 977 6000 E-mail: zagat@zagatsurvey.com

Acknowledgments

First of all, we want to thank the over 2,000 respondents who took the time to fill out the San Francisco Bay Area questionnaire: without you, there would be no *Zagat Survey*. Thank you for your intrepid restaurant-going and for your keen wit. Special thanks are also due to Kathy Blue, John Burciaga, Lorraine Gallagher, Jorge Martin, Mark van Tricht and Jack Weiner. Finally, a warm thank you to all the San Francisco Bay Area chefs and restaurateurs whose dedication makes this the best place on earth to find a great meal.

Contents

Introduction

Here are the results of our *1998 San Francisco Bay Area Restaurant Survey* covering some 714 restaurants from the wine country in the north to the Monterey Peninsula in the south.

By regularly surveying large numbers of local restaurant-goers, we think we have achieved a uniquely current and reliable guide. We hope you agree. This year, more than 2,000 people participated in the *Survey*. Since the participants dined out an average of 3.5 times per week, this *Survey* is based on about 364,000 meals per year.

We want to thank each of our participants. They are a widely diverse group in all respects but one – they are food lovers all. This book is really "theirs."

Of the surveyors, 50% are women, 50% are men; the breakdown by age is 19% in their 20s, 27% in their 30s, 24% in their 40s, 19% in their 50s and 11% in their 60s or above.

To help guide our readers to San Francisco's best meals and best buys, we have prepared a number of lists. See, for example, the Bay Area's Favorite Restaurants (page 11), Top Ratings (pages 12–16) and Best Buys (pages 17–18). On the assumption that most people want a quick fix on the places at which they are considering eating, we have tried to be concise and to provide handy indexes.

We are particularly grateful to our editor, Anthony Dias Blue, the nationally syndicated food and wine radio and television commentator and columnist, and to his associates, Carol Seibert and David Gadd.

We invite you to be a reviewer in our next *Survey*. To do so, simply send a stamped, self-addressed, business-size envelope to ZAGAT SURVEY, 4 Columbus Circle, New York, NY 10019, so that we will be able to contact you. Each participant will receive a free copy of the next *San Francisco Bay Area Restaurant Survey* when it is published.

Your comments, suggestions and even criticisms of this *Survey* are also solicited. There is always room for improvement with your help.

New York, New York   Nina and Tim Zagat
November 17, 1997

Foreword

Glance at any diagram of the Internet. The San Francisco Bay Area is a large, brightly lit node with lines leading in from all directions and out again to all points on the globe. The same can be said of San Francisco in the culinary schematic. Since the rise to prominence of California cuisine well over a quarter of a century ago, food is one of the factors that has put and kept the Bay Area in a prominent position on the map of culture.

But as culinary tastes widen and develop, the old lines of distinction are becoming blurred. Fewer Bay Area chefs are billing their cooking as strict California cuisine, opting instead to emphasize the Mediterranean latitude of California's climate and the Mediterranean attitude of its lifestyle. The 'warm goat cheese cliché' is still around (and still delicious), but chefs at restaurants like LuLu, Rose Pistola and 42 Degrees have upped the ante by incorporating flavors and techniques from Provence, Catalonia, the Italian Riviera, Greece and even North Africa into the blend. Bacalao is well on its way to becoming a household word for San Francisco diners.

Looking in the direction of our Pacific neighbors, East-West fusion cuisine is also evolving into a sort of international eclecticism. The Pacific Rim trend is far from being played out, but it's being tempered with inspiration from both the European tradition and the American heartland. Chefs like Larry Tse at House, Arnold Wong at Eos and Tod Kawachi at Brix in Napa are crossing culinary and national borders with a sense of adventure. They're less concerned with labeling their cooking than with experimenting with the Bay Area's many available raw materials, both local and imported.

So, with all this in mind, what's really cooking in San Francisco? Seafood, for one thing. Coastal cuisine is a theme that's at high ebb. Mark Franz and Pat Kuleto's phenomenal Farallon and Mark Lusardi's wonderful Yabbies have reinvigorated the city's piscine scene. Even some venerable Fisherman's Wharf seafooders have put in for extensive menu and decor drydocking during the past year. As expected, Aqua continues to enjoy a flood of praise.

Celebrity chef-watching is still a prime spectator sport for San Franciscans. Traci des Jardins (ex Rubicon) took the wraps off her namesake restaurant, Jardiniere, only days before press time. Viognier, the new San Mateo venture of Gary Danko (ex Ritz-Carlton Dining Room), also opened too late for inclusion on this year's *Survey*. Danko is relaxing into

6

a more rustic approach here, and the much-anticipated Mediterranean should shake out to be a boon for South Bay diners and a destination for San Franciscans as well.

In the Wine Country, reviewers have caught the scent of the feast that Daniel Patterson and Elizabeth Ramsey are cooking up at Babette's in historic Downtown Sonoma. And there's been more evolution than revolution in the East Bay, with Rivoli and Citron continuing to explore the territory blazed by their more famous Berkeley forebears.

Back in the city, Joseph Manzare's intimate and very happening Globe, with a small but brilliantly executed New American menu, is one of the most talked-about premieres of 1997. Let's hope its late-night hours are the beginning of a trend in restaurants of this high caliber.

The reawakening of the Civic Center after many years of post-earthquake trauma means changes for pre- and post-performance diners in the vicinity of the newly restored Opera House. Ivy's is gone as is Backstage, but in place of the latter we have the very promising Indigo. Just blocks away, German food gets a new lease on life at the youthful Suppenküche, and Max's ownership has transformed the former Act IV into the dramatic Ovation at the Opera.

With such a wide variety of dining experiences to choose from, it's no wonder that San Franciscans are stepping away from the stove and eating out more these days – an average of 3.5 times a week – even though it's not exactly inexpensive to do so. The average cost of a meal increased slightly to $26.13 in 1997 from $25.55 in 1996, and the tab at the 20 most expensive eateries rose to $53.52 from $49.17. But when you factor in the many best value restaurants (more than 150 are listed on pages 17–18), where the average cost of a meal is less than $13, it becomes clear that eating out in San Francisco can indeed be a good deal.

Sadly, a few favorite restaurants (both moderate and pricey) have gone out of business since our last *Survey*. Charles Solomon's highly rated The Heights was toppled by litigation over draconian handicap-access laws. Hyde Street Bistro, after changing hands, closed due to a tragic family loss. Michel Richard's high-profile Bistro M and Robert Reynolds' cozy Le Trou are likewise closed, but new restaurants have already opened in their places, proving that San Francisco continues to generate the highest level of excitement both for chefs and for the dining public.

San Francisco, CA   Anthony Dias Blue
November 17, 1997

Key to Ratings/Symbols

This sample entry identifies the various types of information contained in your Zagat Survey.

(1) Restaurant Name, Address & Phone Number

(2) Hours & Credit Cards

(3) ZAGAT Ratings

	F	D	S	C
Tim & Nina's ●ⓈⓂ≠	23	5	9	$19

4 Columbus Circle (8th Ave.), 212-977-6000

■ "What a dump!" – open 7 days a week, 24 hours a day, this successful "deep dive" started the "deli-tapas craze" (i.e., tidbits of pastrami, corned beef, etc. on cracker-size pieces of stale rye); though the place looks like a "none-too-clean garage" and T & N "never heard of credit cards or reservations", "dirt cheap" prices for "great eats" draw demented crowds.

(4) Surveyors' Commentary

The names of restaurants with the highest overall ratings, greatest popularity and importance are printed in **CAPITAL LETTERS**. Address and phone numbers are printed in *italics*.

(2) Hours & Credit Cards

After each restaurant name you will find the following courtesy information:

●	*serving after 11 PM*
Ⓛ	*open for lunch*
Ⓢ	*open on Sunday*
Ⓜ	*open on Monday*
≠	*no credit cards accepted*

(3) ZAGAT Ratings

Food, **Decor** and **Service** are each rated on a scale of **0** to **30**:

F	D	S	C

F	.... *Food*
D	.... *Decor*
S	.... *Service*
C	.... *Cost*

23	5	9	$19

0 - 9	.... *poor to fair*
10 - 15	.... *fair to good*
16 - 19	.... *good to very good*
20 - 25	.... *very good to excellent*
26 - 30	.... *extraordinary to perfection*

▽ 23	5	9	$19

▽ .... *Low number of votes/less reliable*

The **Cost (C)** column reflects the estimated price of a dinner with one drink and tip. Lunch usually costs 25% less.

A restaurant listed without ratings is either an important **newcomer** or a popular **write-in**. The estimated cost, with one drink and tip, is indicated by the following symbols.

−	−	−	VE

I	.... *$15 and below*
M	.... *$16 to $30*
E	.... *$31 to $50*
VE	.... *$51 or more*

(4) Surveyors' Commentary

Surveyors' comments are summarized, with literal comments shown in quotation marks. The following symbols indicate whether responses were mixed or uniform.

◪ .... *mixed*

▪ .... *uniform*

Bay Area's Favorites

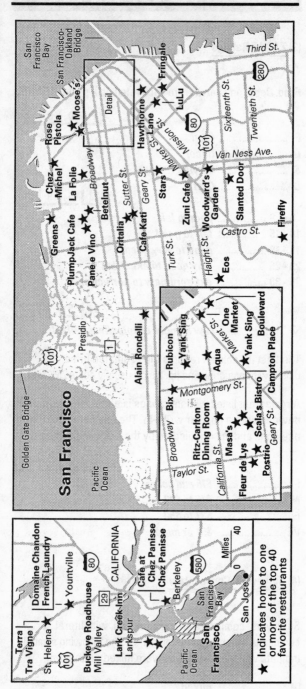

San Francisco

Golden Gate Bridge

Pacific Ocean

San Francisco Bay

San Francisco-Oakland Bridge

Third St.

Fringale

Moose's

Rose Pistola

Hawthorne

LuLu

Chez Michel

La Folie

Betelnut

Sutter St.

Geary St.

Stars

Zuni Cafe

Woodward's Garden

Van Ness Ave.

Slanted Door

Firefly

Greens

PlumpJack Cafe

Pane e Vino

Oritalia

Cafe Kati

Turk St.

Haight St.

Castro St.

Eos

Broadway

Detail

Market St.

Mission St.

Sixteenth St.

Twentieth St.

280

80

101

Presidio

1

101

Alain Rondelli

Detail:

Rubicon

Yank Sing

One Market

Yank Sing

Boulevard

Aqua

Campton Place

Montgomery St.

Market St.

Bix

Broadway

Ritz-Carlton Dining Room

Masa's

Scala's Bistro

Postrio

Fleur de Lys

California St.

Geary St.

Taylor St.

Lower map:

Terra

Tra Vigne

St. Helena

Domaine Chandon / French Laundry

Yountville

CALIFORNIA

80

29

101

Buckeye Roadhouse
Mill Valley

Lark Creek Inn
Larkspur

Cafe at Chez Panisse / Chez Panisse

Berkeley

San Francisco Bay

580

Miles
0   40

San Jose

San Francisco

Pacific Ocean

★ Indicates home to one or more of the top 40 favorite restaurants

10

Bay Area's Favorite Restaurants*

Each of our reviewers has been asked to name his or her five favorite restaurants. The 40 spots most frequently named, in order of their popularity, are:

1. Boulevard
2. Postrio
3. Hawthorne Lane
4. Fleur de Lys
5. Aqua
6. French Laundry/N
7. La Folie
8. Ritz-Carlton Din. Rm.
9. Fringale
10. Masa's
11. Chez Panisse/E
12. Alain Rondelli
13. Terra/N
14. Rose Pistola
15. PlumpJack Cafe
16. Cafe at Chez Panisse/E
17. LuLu
18. Tra Vigne/N
19. Zuni Cafe
20. Bix

21. Pane e Vino
22. Lark Creek Inn/N
23. Greens
24. Betelnut Pejiu Wu
25. Rubicon
26. Campton Place
27. Moose's
28. Cafe Kati
29. Domaine Chandon/N
30. Scala's Bistro
31. Firefly
32. Chez Michel
33. Slanted Door
34. Eos
35. Stars
36. Buckeye Roadhse./N
37. Oritalia
38. Woodward's Garden
39. One Market
40. Yank Sing

It's obvious that many of the restaurants on the above list are among the most expensive, but San Franciscans also love a bargain. Were popularity calibrated to price, we suspect that a number of other restaurants would join the above ranks. Thus, we have listed over 150 Best Buys on pages 17–18.

---

* All restaurants are in the City of San Francisco unless otherwise noted (E=East of San Francisco; N=North of San Francisco and S=South of San Francisco).

Top Ratings*

Top 40 Food Ranking

28 La Folie
   Ritz-Carlton Din. Rm.
   Erna's Elderberry/S
   French Laundry/N
   Masa's
27 Fleur de Lys
   Terra/N
   Chez Panisse/E
   Aqua
26 Sent Sovi/S
   Fringale
   Wente Vineyards/E
   Cafe at Chez Panisse/E
   Postrio
   Domaine Chandon/N
   Campton Place
   Roy's at Pebble Beach/S
   Pacific's Edge/S
   Woodward's Garden
   Thep Phanom

   Willowside Cafe/N
   Boulevard
   Swan Oyster Depot
25 Kyo-Ya
   Hawthorne Lane
   Fresh Cream/S
   Acquerello
   Alain Rondelli
   Ebisu
   231 Ellsworth/S
   Cafe Beaujolais/N
   Rivoli/E
   Charles Nob Hill
   Lalime's/E
   Silks
   Meetinghouse
   Meadowood Rest./N
   Babette's/N
   Auberge du Soleil/N
   Tommy Toy's

Top Spots by Cuisine

Top American (New)
28 French Laundry/N
26 Campton Place
   Pacific's Edge/S
   Woodward's Garden
   Willowside Cafe/N

Top American (Regional)
27 Terra/N
25 Auberge du Soleil/N
24 Catahoula/N
23 John Ash & Co./N
22 Rio Grill/S

Top American (Traditional)
25 Ritz-Carlton Terrace
23 JoAnn's Cafe/S
   Lark Creek Inn/N
22 Bix
   Roti

Top Breakfast**
24 Downtown Bakery/N
23 Universal Cafe
   JoAnn's Cafe/S
22 Ella's
21 Doidge's

Top Brunch
28 Erna's Elderberry/S
26 Wente Vineyards/E
23 Montrio/S
   Chapeau!
   Universal Cafe

Top Californian
28 Erna's Elderberry/S
27 Terra/N
   Chez Panisse/E
26 Cafe at Chez Panisse/E
   Postrio

---

* Excluding restaurants with low voting; all restaurants are in the City
  of San Francisco unless otherwise noted (E=East of San Francisco;
  N=North of San Francisco and S=South of San Francisco).
** Other than hotels.

Top Chinese
- 25 Tommy Toy's
- 24 Fook Yuen/S
- 23 Eliza's
  Ton Kiang
- 22 Hong Kong Flower/S

Top Continental
- 24 Kenwood/N
- 23 Dal Baffo/S
- 22 Cypress Club
- 21 Big Four
  Park Grill

Top Dim Sum
- 24 Fook Yuen/S
  Yank Sing
- 23 Ton Kiang
- 22 Hong Kong Flower/S
  Betelnut Pejiu Wu

Top Eclectic
- 25 Lalime's/E
  Oritalia
- 24 Firefly
- 23 2223 Rest. & Bar
  Wappo Bar Bistro/N

Top Family Dining
- 23 House of Prime Rib
- 22 Rio Grill/S
  Hunan
- 21 Olive's
- 20 Mescolanza

Top French Cafe/Bistro
- 26 Fringale
- 24 L'Amie Donia/S
- 23 Zax
  Chapeau!
  Plouf

Top French Classic
- 28 French Laundry/N
  Masa's
- 27 Terra/N
- 25 231 Ellsworth/S
- 24 Cafe Jacqueline

Top French (New)
- 28 La Folie
  Ritz-Carlton Din. Rm.
  Erna's Elderberry/S
  Masa's
- 27 Fleur de Lys

Top Hotel Dining
- 28 Ritz-Carlton Din. Rm.
  Masa's/Vintage Court
- 26 Postrio/Prescott
  Campton Place
  Roy's/Inn at Spanish Bay/S

Top Indian
- 23 Ajanta/E
- 21 Maharani India
- 20 North India
  Indian Oven
- 18 Appam

Top Italian
- 27 Terra/N
- 25 Acquerello
- 24 Pane e Vino
  Tra Vigne/N
  Ristorante Milano

Top Japanese
- 25 Kyo-Ya
  Ebisu
- 24 Kabuto Sushi
- 23 Kirala/E
- 22 O Chame/E

Top Late Night
- 25 Ebisu
- 24 Helmand
  Eos
- 23 French Room
  Scala's Bistro

Top Mediterranean
- 26 Postrio
  Willowside Cafe/N
- 25 Rivoli/E
  Lalime's/E
  PlumpJack

Top Mexican/Tex-Mex
- 23 La Taqueria
- 21 Pancho Villa
- 20 La Cumbre
  Casa Aguila
  Roosevelt Tamale

Top Newcomers/Rated
- 25 Babette's/N
- 24 Insalata's/N
- 23 Chapeau!
  Yabbies Coastal Kit.
  Wappo Bar Bistro/N

13

Top Newcomers/Unrated
Farallon
Globe
Indigo
Jardiniere
Viognier/S

Top Offbeat
24 Helmand
Flying Saucer
23 Plouf
Pauline's
22 Betelnut Pejiu Wu

Top Pacific Rim
26 Roy's at Pebble Beach/S
24 House
Eos
23 Brix/N
22 Bridges/E

Top People-Watching
27 Chez Panisse/E
26 Postrio
24 Rubicon
23 Zuni Cafe
22 Buckeye Roadhse./N

Top Pizza
24 Zachary's/E
23 Pauline's
22 Tommaso's
Olive's
21 Vicolo

Top Seafood
27 Aqua
26 Swan Oyster Depot
23 Plouf
Yabbies Coastal Kit.
Hayes Street Grill

Top Spanish
22 Zarzuela
21 Iberia/S
20 Timo's
18 Esperpento
Bolero/N

Top Steakhouses
23 Harris'
House of Prime Rib
Morton's of Chicago
21 Alfred's
20 Izzy's

Top Tapas
22 Zarzuela
20 Cha Cha Cha
Timo's
18 Esperento
17 Babaloo Tapas

Top Thai
26 Thep Phanom
24 Marnee Thai
22 Manora's
Royal Thai/N
Khan Toke

Top Vegetarian
27 Fleur de Lys
22 Greens
Flea St. Cafe/S
21 Val 21
20 Millennium

Top Vietnamese
24 Slanted Door
22 Tu Lan
Le Soleil
La Vie
21 Emerald Garden

Top Wild Cards
24 Cafe Jacqueline/Soufflés
Helmand/Afghan
22 Ti Couz/Crêpes
21 Straits Cafe/Singaporean
20 Angkor Wat/Cambodian

Top Worth a Drive
28 Erna's Elderberry/S
Oakhurst
French Laundry/N
Yountville
27 Terra/N
St. Helena
Chez Panisse/E
Berkeley
26 Sent Sovi/S
Saratoga

Top 40 Decor Ranking

28 Auberge du Soleil/N
Garden Court
Ritz-Carlton Din. Rm.
27 Pacific's Edge/S
Fleur de Lys
Erna's Elderberry/S
French Laundry/N
26 Domaine Chandon/N
French Room
Postrio
Tra Vigne/N
Cypress Club
Grand Cafe
Bolero/N
Aqua
Carnelian Room
Campton Place
Bix
Roy's at Pebble Beach/S
Chateau Souverain/N

Wente Vineyards/E
Boulevard
25 Terra/N
Hawthorne Lane
Tourelle/E
Tommy Toy's
El Paseo/N
Big Four
Julius' Castle
Bridges/E
Silks
Lark Creek Inn/N
Tonga
Masa's
Ritz-Carlton Terrace
Bella Vista/S
24 Napa Valley Wine Train/N
Vertigo
Meadowood Rest./N
Mecca

Top Outdoor

Bay Wolf/E
Chez Renee/S
Domaine Chandon/N
Erna's Elderberry/S
French Laundry/N
Insalata's/N

Kenwood/N
Le Mouton Noir/S
Roy's at Pebble Beach/S
Sent Sovi/S
Tra Vigne/N
Trilogy/N

Top Romantic

Acquerello
Casanova/S
Cassis Bistro
Chez Michel
Chez Renee/S
Erna's Elderberry/S
Fleur de Lys

Globe
Jardiniere
Julius' Castle
Pacific's Edge/S
Sierra Mar/S
Terra/N
Venticello

Top Rooms

Aqua
Big Four
Boulevard
Campton Place
Cypress Club
Farallon
Fleur de Lys
Fournou's Ovens
French Laundry/N

Garden Court
Grand Cafe
Jardiniere
Lark Creek Inn/N
Madrona Manor/N
Meadowood Rest./N
Postrio
Ritz-Carlton Din. Rm.
Ritz-Carlton Terrace

Top Views

Alta Mira/N
Auberge du Soleil/N
Caprice/N
Carnelian Room
Cliff House
dalla Torre
Domaine Chandon/N
Gaylord India
Greens
Harbor Village

Horizons/N
Julius' Castle
Mandarin
McCormick & Kuleto's
Meadowood Rest./N
Mikayla/N
Pacific's Edge/S
Sam's Anchor Cafe/N
Splendido
Waterfront

Top 40 Service Ranking

28 Ritz-Carlton Din. Rm.
Erna's Elderberry/S
27 Masa's
French Laundry/N
Fleur de Lys
26 Terra/N
La Folie
Campton Place
Domaine Chandon/N
Chez Panisse/E
25 French Room
Acquerello
Meetinghouse
Ritz-Carlton Terrace
El Paseo/N
24 Silks
Sent Sovi/S
Alain Rondelli
Willowside Cafe/N
Roy's at Pebble Beach/S

Fresh Cream/S
Wente Vineyards/E
Albona Ristorante
Tommy Toy's
231 Ellsworth/S
Postrio
Chez Michel
Aqua
Boulevard
23 Babette's/N
Pacific's Edge/S
Big Four
Chateau Souverain/N
Auberge du Soleil/N
Hawthorne Lane
Lalime's/E
Ristorante Milano
Kenwood/N
Cafe at Chez Panisse/E
Rivoli/E

Top 80 Bangs For The Buck

This list reflects the best dining values in our *Survey*. It is produced by dividing the cost of a meal into the combined ratings for food, decor and service.

1. La Taqueria
2. Caffè Greco
3. Downtown Bakery/N
4. Pancho Villa
5. La Cumbre Taqueria
6. Mo's Burgers
7. Pluto's
8. JoAnn's Cafe/S
9. World Wrapps
10. Mario's
11. Dottie's True Blue
12. Bette's Oceanview/E
13. Kate's Kitchen
14. Pasta Pomodoro
15. Bill's Place
16. Roosevelt Tamale
17. Sweet Heat
18. Wa-Ha-Ka
19. Cafe Fanny/E
20. Tu Lan
21. Zachary's/E
22. Miss Millie's
23. Mel's Drive-In
24. Fat Apple's/E
25. Ti Couz
26. Eliza's
27. Blue Nile/E
28. La Mediterranee
29. Mifune
30. Cheers Cafe
31. La Rondalla
32. Marnee Thai
33. Hamburger Mary's
34. Doidge's
35. Cha Am Thai
36. Hahn's Hibachi
37. Cafe Flore
38. Tommy's Joynt
39. Campo Santo
40. Pauline's
41. Angkor Wat
42. Eric's
43. Thep Phanom
44. Ajanta/E
45. Michelangelo Cafe
46. Ella's
47. Khan Toke
48. Swan Oyster Depot
49. Manora's
50. La Vie
51. Aux Delices
52. Hayes & Vine
53. Max's Diner
54. Pyramid Alehouse/E
55. Hunan
56. Ton Kiang
57. Tortola
58. Plearn Thai/E
59. Brother's Deli/S
60. Casa Aguila
61. Vicolo
62. Curbside Cafe
63. Olive's
64. Long Life Vegi Hse./E
65. Sears Fine Food
66. Tommaso's
67. Town's End
68. Saul's Rest. & Deli/E
69. Bubba's Diner/N
70. Armani Cafe
71. Yank Sing
72. Mom is Cooking
73. House of Nanking
74. Brandy Ho's
75. California Pizza Kit.
76. Delancey St.
77. Bocce Café
78. Le Soleil
79. U.S. Rest.
80. Jasmine House

---

* All restaurants are in the City of San Francisco unless otherwise noted (E=East of San Francisco; N=North of San Francisco and S=South of San Francisco).

Additional Good Values
(A bit more expensive, but worth every penny)

Alegrias Food From Spain
Amber India/S
Aperto
Appam
Avenue 9
Baker Street Bistro
Bistro Aix
Bistro Clovis
Bucci's/E
Cafe Akimbo
Cafe For All Seasons
Cafe Marimba
Café Riggio
Cafe Tiramisu
Caffe Centro
Caffe Delle Stelle
Caffè Macaroni
California Cafe/N
Cassis Bistro
Cha Cha Cha
Chef Chu's/S
Duarte's Tavern/S
E'Angelo
Ebisu
Emerald Garden
Enrico's Sidewalk Cafe
Ernesto's
Esperpento
Fook Yuen/S
Fountain Court
Gira Polli
Golden Turtle
Harbor Village
Hong Kong Flower/S
Hong Kong Villa
I Fratelli
Indian Oven
Katia's
Kirala/E
Little City Antipasti

L'Osteria del Forno
Maharani India
Mandalay
Mangiafuoco
Marin Joe's/N
Mayflower
Mescolanza
Millennium
Narai
Nob Hill Cafe
North India
O Chame/E
Osome
Pacific Cafe
Parma
Pasta Moon/S
Pasta Prego/N
Piazza D'Angelo/N
Picante Cocina/E
PJ's Oyster Bed
Rendezvous du Monde
Rick's Rest. & Bar
Rooster
Royal Thai/N
Slanted Door
Slow Club
Soizic/E
Straits Cafe
Suppenküche
Timo's
Trattoria Contadina
Valentine's Cafe
Val 21
Venezia/E
Yaya Cuisine
Yoshi's/E
Yuet Lee
Zazie
Zinzino
Zza's Trattoria/E

Alphabetical Directory of Restaurants

San Francisco

ACQUERELLO
| 25 | 23 | 25 | $51 |

1722 Sacramento St. (bet. Polk St. & Van Ness Ave.),
415-567-5432

■ "The host is the most" at Giancarlo Paterlini's "romantic", "refined" Van Ness/Polk "nouvelle" Northern Italian with "beautiful surroundings", "complex" and "intense" flavors and "gracious service"; a few quibble over small portions, but most call it a "memorable" experience that "lingers on."

ALAIN RONDELLI S
| 25 | 21 | 24 | $52 |

126 Clement St. (bet. 2nd & 3rd Aves.), 415-387-0408

☑ Chef "Alain-is-God" Rondelli "pushes the envelope" at his "sophisticated", "cosmopolitan" and "expensive" Richmond District New French; naysayers find it "a touch pretentious" ("duck with sorbet – weird") and think it's not just the famous "cotton candy gimmick" that's "a lot of fluff", but devotees brave the "parking hassle" to indulge in "amazing" cuisine from "a genius with a unique vision."

Albona Ristorante Istriano
| 23 | 17 | 24 | $32 |

545 Francisco St. (Taylor & Mason Sts.), 415-441-1040

■ "Bruno makes everyone welcome" at his moderately priced North Beach Istrian-Italian where the "unusual cuisine" is served in a "warm, inviting atmosphere" that makes up for the "unfortunate location"; "get a history lesson" on Istria as you enjoy the "lovingly prepared food" including strudel, "delicious lamb" and "tasty rabbit."

Alegrias Food From Spain L S M
| ▽ 19 | 18 | 18 | $23 |

2018 Lombard St. (Webster St.), 415-929-8888

☑ An affordable Union Street Spaniard that's a "great place for sangria and tapas" while soaking up "authentic decor" that "feels like Spain"; some find it "good but nothing memorable", but throw in weekend flamenco guitar and, in a town short on Iberian fare, it makes for "a nice change."

Alfred's Steak House L S M
| 21 | 18 | 22 | $39 |

659 Merchant St. (bet. Montgomery & Kearny Sts.), 415-781-7058

■ This "red velvet relic" with "crusty waiters" recently moved to a new Downtown location with decor that's "even more bordello" than before, but it's still a "classic" steakhouse with an atmosphere "like a private club" where "a steak and a cocktail" keep carnivores happy; "grandpa loved this place" and even youngsters have "no beef with this beef."

Alioto's ⓁⓈⓂ
15 | 15 | 17 | $27
8 Fisherman's Wharf (Taylor St.), 415-673-0183

◨ While the majority calls this Southern Italian seafooder with a "pretty view" "mass produced" and only for "out-of-town visitors who must eat on the Wharf", a few find it a "pleasant surprise" and note that they're "working on improving" it.

Allegro ⓁⓈⓂ
19 | 18 | 20 | $31
1701 Jones St. (Broadway), 415-928-4002

◨ "There's more going on than just eating" at this "cozy and cute" North Beach Italian that's a magnet for local politicos ("if you're not a VIP, plan on being ignored"); but the "good fish dishes" and "divine gnocchi" make it worth the upscale price tag.

Angkor Wat ⓁⓈⓂ
20 | 16 | 21 | $20
4217 Geary Blvd. (6th Ave.), 415-221-7889

■ The "delicate" food sings and there are "charming" dancers (on weekends) at this "reasonable" Richmond District Cambodian; it's "a nice alternative to Chinese" even if the "damp", "dingy space needs dusting"; expect "unrelentingly good service" from Charlie the host, who will recommend his favorites.

Anjou Ⓛ
23 | 20 | 23 | $32
44 Campton Pl. (Stockon St.), 415-392-5373

■ It's so quiet "you can actually talk" at this pre-show, post-shopping Contemporary French "hideaway" near Union Square; "tight quarters" and "small tables" are the major complaints, but "bargain" prices, "reliable", "well-prepared" dishes and "warm", "personal" service mean it's too "charming" to ignore.

Antica Trattoria Ⓢ
22 | 18 | 21 | $29
2400 Polk St. (Union St.), 415-928-5797

◨ "Too bad everyone else found out" about this Van Ness/Polk Italian that's now a lot of people's "favorite new place"; the dark "char-burned interior" gets mixed reviews, but Ruggiero Gadaldi's "interesting variety" of "delicious food" and "great Italian wine list" make it "a real keeper."

Aperto ⓁⓈⓂ
20 | 15 | 17 | $24
1434 18th St. (Connecticut St.), 415-252-1625

■ With its "unpretentious servers", "generous portions" of "simple", "honest" Italian "peasant cuisine" ("whole plates of vegetables, like in Italy") and "homey, friendly ambiance", this "lively" Potrero Hill place is a "frequent haunt" for locals.

Appam Ⓢ Ⓜ
18 | 17 | 14 | $25
1261 Folsom St. (bet. 8th & 9th Sts.), 415-626-2798

◨ "Clueless waiters" mar the dining experience at this SOMA Indian where the "pleasant" decor and "nice outdoor setting" are "a contrast to the neighborhood"; traditionalists insist "nouveau Indian barely works", but others say it's "spicy", "inventive" and "delicious."

AQUA ⚁Ⓜ   27 | 26 | 24 | $51
252 California St. (bet. Battery & Front Sts.), 415-956-9662
◼ A deluge of praise floods in for this "grand scale" Downtown seafooder where "pretty people eat fish" and say "every bite's ambrosia"; the staff can be "austere", but "they put the napkin on your lap" and the "spectacular" flower-filled room might make it "the most beautiful restaurant in SF"; expect a big tab for "shrimpy portions", but for "event dining" it's "close to perfect."

Armani Cafe   18 | 20 | 16 | $20
1 Grant Ave. (O'Farrell St.), 415-677-9010
◪ "Can't afford the clothes, but the salads are great" is the consensus on this Downtown Italian cafe in the Giorgio Armani boutique ("strange to eat amongst the clothes"), an "extra hip" place "where the beautiful people lunch" on "the best margherita pizza west of New York"; it's all a lot of "pretentious fun" complete with "attitude-heavy service."

Aromi ⚁ⓈⓂ   20 | 17 | 19 | $28
1507 Polk St. (California St.), 415-775-5977
◼ The "aromas from the sidewalk entice" at this "casual" Van Ness/Polk trattoria that really "feels Italian"; overall, the "eclectic menu" is "surprisingly good considering the location" and the outdoor patio is a winner.

A. Sabella's ⚁ⓈⓂ   17 | 17 | 18 | $31
2766 Taylor St. (Jefferson St.), 415-771-6775
◪ Locals are wary of Fisherman's Wharf ("if you're not a tourist, why are you there?"), yet some report an "amazing improvement" in this "old San Francisco" Californian seafooder thanks to a "new menu and remodel"; even if prices are "a bit high", most agree it's "dependable."

Asimakopoulos Cafe ⚁ⓈⓂ   17 | 14 | 17 | $19
288 Connecticut St. (18th St.), 415-552-8789
◼ "What a view!" from this "popular", "casual" taverna high on Potrero Hill; it's known for "irresistible kebabs", "good mezethakia" and "got to try" waffles for Sunday brunch; the decor may be "spartan", but where else can you dine under "a bean painting of Aristotle Onassis"?

Aux Delices Ⓜ   20 | 11 | 18 | $18
2327 Polk St. (bet. Union & Green Sts.), 415-928-4977
◼ "Those bamboo shrimp roll things are the reason to go" to this Van Ness/Polk Vietnamese that's "surprisingly good for its ordinary looks"; there's also a "peaceful" ambiance that's a "charming exception to the noise and crush of most good Asian restaurants" and a "very inexpensive" tab; so "why is it always empty?"

Avenue 9 L S M　　21 16 18 $26
1243 Ninth Ave. (bet. Lincoln & Irving Aves.), 415-664-6999
☑ Surveyors say this new "cute" French-influenced New American bistro lends a little "class" to the Sunset; while not everyone's taken with the diner-like "retro" look and "lackluster" service, the food ("great duck confit", "potent garlic french fries") represents an "honest effort."

Babaloo Tapas L S M　　17 18 17 $21
2030 Lombard St. (Fillmore St.), 415-346-5474
☑ "Spunky", "loud", affordable Gen X Marina tapas hangout that's a lot of "fun" for a group; even though "there are better tapas" places, this one's a "good value" with "outrageous place settings" and a "cute" menu displayed in a cigar box; those who don't yet get the concept sniff "small portions."

Bahia Cabana L S M　　▽ 14 13 14 $23
1600 Market St. (Lily St.), 415-626-3306
☑ The "loud" but "good vibes" at this Civic Center Brazilian nightclub-cum-restaurant (live music Wednesday–Saturday) will "bring out the passion in you", but the "slow service" might make you lose your patience; though the feijoada and other "filling" offerings are only "decent" at best, it's still a "nice change of pace."

Baker Street Bistro L S　　20 15 21 $25
2953 Baker St. (bet. Lombard & Greenwich Sts.), 415-931-1475
■ The "sights, sounds and smells of Paris" emanate from this "adorable", "affordable" Union Street French bistro with the "best blanquette de veau around" and "unreal" rabbit in mustard sauce ("like grandmère would have cooked"); it's "cramped and noisy", but the "welcoming" maitre d' and "sincere waiters" leave fans saying "je t'aime, je t'aime."

Balboa Cafe L S M　　17 16 17 $23
3199 Fillmore St. (Greenwich St.), 415-921-3944
☑ Old-timers are still wondering "what happened" to this Marina "burger joint extraordinaire" "in the heart of yuppieville"; it's now a "poseur scene" filled with young singles who crowd the bar for "good booze"; P.S. "the cigar smoke is a little overwhelming."

Basta Pasta ◗ S M　　13 14 15 $20
1268 Grant Ave. (Vallejo St.), 415-434-2248
☑ "Tired" and "predictable" is the inside word on this moderately priced North Beach Italian, but the "great corner location" makes it "an out-of-towner's favorite" (cynics say "the tourists deserve it"); night owls like to gather for "a decent dinner after 10 PM", while early risers retort "basta, basta."

Bauhaus Art Club & Restaurant – | – | – | M
6139 Geary Blvd. (bet. 25th & 26th Aves.), 415-387-1151
Few reviewers have discovered this avant-garde Richmond
District Californian where the decor pays homage to the
German Bauhaus art movement of the 1920s; a young
clientele goes for the changing art exhibits, dancing and
live entertainment in the industrial space.

Beach Chalet Brewery L S M 14 | 23 | 15 | $24
1000 Great Hwy. (bet. Fulton St. & Lincoln Ave.), 415-386-8439
☑ Suddenly the Sunset District is "overrun with yuppies"
mobbing this "loud and chaotic" brasserie located in a
historic chalet on Ocean Beach; the "restoration of the
building is magnificent" and the house-brewed beers are
"great", but the food is "sketchy" and the "servers are
recruited from the movie *Clueless*"; nonetheless, it's "a
great alternative to the Cliff House" for a "view and brew."

Bella Trattoria S M ▽ 20 | 19 | 23 | $29
3854 Geary Blvd. (3rd Ave.), 415-221-0305
■ "Don't miss out" on this Richmond Italian newcomer run
by "nice people"; a few find it "too touchy-feely", but it
garners near unanimous praise for "delicious fish" and
"superb pasta and game" served by "handsome hunks."

Benihana L S M 15 | 16 | 18 | $26
1737 Post St. (bet. Webster & Laguna Sts.), 415-563-4844
☑ A "gimmicky", "commercialized" Japanese steakhouse
chain that's mainly for "kids, tourists" and groups, though
locals grudgingly admit that the chefs' precision knifework
can be "fun and entertaining"; P.S. "keep your fingers off
the table" just in case.

BETELNUT PEJIU WU L S M 22 | 22 | 19 | $28
*2030 Union St. (bet. Buchanan & Webster Sts.),
415-929-8855*
☑ Cecilia Chang's happening Union Street Chinese beer
house with Shanghai "opium den" decor is "so '90s it hurts",
but when you get beyond the hype you'll find "awesome"
Pan-Asian tapas such as "terrific" Szechuan string beans
and "world-class jumbo prawns"; N.B. pack your "DKNY
shades" because there's plenty of time to scope out the
"hip" crowd while you wait for a table.

Big Four L S M 21 | 25 | 23 | $41
*Huntington Hotel, 1075 California St. (Taylor St.),
415-771-1140*
☑ There's a "quiet, self-assured" ambiance at this blue-
chip Nob Hill Continental where the "old fogey set" gets
down to business while putting fork and knife to some
"excellent food"; a few feel it's "stuffy", but "one of the
best bars in town" keeps the conversation well oiled and
for many it's "a classic SF must."

Bill's Place L S M ≠ 15 | 10 | 15 | $11
2315 Clement St. (bet. 24th & 25th Aves.), 415-221-5262
◩ A "throwback" Richmond District "burgers in the fog" joint with a rep for whipping up "killer peanut butter milk shakes"; "they could fix the decor" and the "waitresses are crabby", but it's a sentimental favorite and a "model for all greasy spoons."

Biscuits & Blues S M ▽ 17 | 16 | 16 | $20
401 Mason St. (Geary St.), 415-292-2583
◩ "Dingy" Downtown Southern–Soul Fooder serving "spectacular fried chicken, "great shrimp Caesar" and "awesome mudslide pie" at reasonable prices; the live bands can be "in your face", but isn't that what you're paying for?; "just get up and dance!"

Bistro Aix S M 19 | 16 | 18 | $26
3340 Steiner St. (bet. Chestnut & Lombard Sts.), 415-202-0100
◩ Most of our respondents like this "sleek", "no hype" Marina French bistro with "secluded", less-noisy patio dining; the thin-crust pizza shines as does the "bargain" weekday prix fixe (before 8 PM).

Bistro Clovis L M 19 | 18 | 20 | $25
1596 Market St. (Franklin St.), 415-864-0231
■ "You'll get a "warm welcome" from the owner and the staff of this affordable Civic Center French bistro with a "charming", "very Left Bank feel"; the "good value" wine sampler helps wash down classics like "yummy lamb salad", "excellent beef burgundy" and tantalizing tarte Tatin; an "intensely French" experience; N.B. at press time, a renovation was in full swing.

BIX L S M 22 | 26 | 21 | $39
56 Gold St. (bet. Pacific & Jackson Sts.), 415-433-6300
■ "Wasn't that Jay Gatsby?" at the bar of this expensive, swanky, jazz-age supper club sporting live music and "high-octane martinis"; while you'll find "solid" American eats such as chicken hash, remember that "dressing up" and looking "glamorous" "takes precedence"; a few feel the staff is "snooty" but admit it's one "stunning", "stylish place" ("coolest room in the city"); N.B. cigar smoking no longer permitted.

Bizou L M 21 | 19 | 19 | $33
598 Fourth St. (Brannan St.), 415-543-2222
◩ "The chef cooks from the heart every time" at this "noisy" French on SOMA's bistro row; while some surveyors find the "creative combinations" "hit or miss" and "overly ambitious", more are won over by the signature beef cheek and other "fascinating tastes."

Blowfish Sushi To Die For 🄻🅂🄼
▽ 19 | 22 | 17 | $23

2170 Bryant St. (20th Ave.), 415-285-3848

◩ Moderate Mission District Japanese newcomer that despite the name doesn't serve authentic blowfish (yet); but you're not out of danger because too much exposure to the "tragically hip loft crowd" could prove fatal; the decor is "sparse" with the best accommodations in the house reserved for the "beautifully displayed" fish.

Blue Light 🄻🅂🄼
11 | 12 | 13 | $18

1979 Union St. (bet. Laguna & Buchanan Sts.), 415-922-5510

◪ An "annoying frat boy crowd" (a "guy pinched my butt") frequents this "dumpy" Union Street bar and cafe where if you have "no expectations" you won't be let down by the "ok" American grub; just "bring earplugs" and "stick to the calamari and burgers."

Blue Point 🅂🄼
▽ 20 | 19 | 21 | $23

2415 Clement St. (bet. 25th & 26th Sts.), 415-379-9726

◩ Our reviewers have had a year to size up this Outer Richmond "neighborhood" seafooder with Mediterranean and Californian touches; the verdict: "cozy", "friendly" and "reasonably priced" with "good, fresh" fish; those wanting more carp "dull", "not interesting enough."

Bocce Café 🄻🅂🄼
13 | 19 | 15 | $18

478 Green St. (Grant St.), 415-981-2044

◩ "Terrible food and lots of it" sums up this "cheap, cheap, cheap" Italian North Beach "fixture" that's "great for large parties"; sure the fun atmosphere in an "Italian villa setting" (with patio) is a plus, but many shake their heads: "inexpensive, but should be free."

Bonta 🅂
21 | 19 | 21 | $28

2223 Union St. (bet. Fillmore & Steiner Sts.), 415-929-0407

◪ A Union Street "sweet hideaway" Italian that "sooner or later is gonna get the recognition it deserves" for dishes such as "awesome sea bass ravioli" and "some of the best gnocchi in town"; there's "no pretense", "the waiters know their stuff" and the room is "acoustically challenged" but still "great for a first date."

BOULEVARD 🄻🅂🄼
26 | 26 | 24 | $44

1 Mission St. (Steuart St.), 415-543-6084

▩ Just "sitting at the counter" of this SOMA New American (SF's most popular restaurant) is "an experience", but try for a seat in the "can you say big" beaux arts dining room; either way, expect "culinary nirvana" from "soaringly imaginative dishes" and "unobtrusive" service from a "gracious" staff; a few find the hubbub and "long waits" discouraging, and as for reservations, "call waaayyy ahead."

Brandy Ho's on Broadway L S M   19 | 13 | 15 | $18
450 Broadway (Kearny St.), 415-362-6268
217 Columbus Ave. (bet. Broadway & Pacific Ave.),
415-788-7527
☑ "Lively", "tatty looking" North Beach Hunans with "abrasive service"; boosters call them "spicy fun" and pine for their specialty smoked dishes, while detractors would like to give the "heave Ho" to "overpowering hot chile sauces" that make "every dish taste the same."

Brasserie Chambord L S M   17 | 14 | 17 | $33
Hotel Galleria Park, 150 Kearny St. (Sutter St.),
415-434-3688
☑ A "reliable but not exceptional" Financial District French "standby" that's a "great deal" for lunch with a full repertoire of bistro standards; those expecting snobby service are pleasantly surprised by the "non-condescending French waiters."

Bruno's   22 | 21 | 17 | $31
2389 Mission St. (bet. 19th & 20th Sts.), 415-550-7455
☑ The "big red booths" and live jazz re-create the feel of the original '50s Bruno at this "retro-hip" supper club serving "surprisingly good" French-Mediterranean fare; it's "not in the nicest part of town" and the "space-case service" needs work, but many maintain it's "too much fun" to pass up.

Buca Giovanni L S M   21 | 18 | 20 | $31
800 Greenwich St. (Mason St.), 415-776-7766
☑ They "do wonders with rabbit" ("do they have anything else?") at this venerable grotto-like trattoria that, way back when, helped many a fledgling foodie discover Northern Italian cuisine; what some call "atmospheric" others call "dungeon dining", but for a "rustic" experience it's "a North Beach best."

Buchanan Grill L S M   14 | 15 | 17 | $22
3653 Buchanan St. (bet. Bay & Northpoint Sts.), 415-346-8727
☑ This "neighborhood" Marina New American has a "sports bar" and singles atmosphere that's great for "Green Bay Packers" fans and "swingin'", "middle-aged divorced" types; the "boring", "average" food is more tame than the ambiance, but at least it's a "good value."

Cadillac Bar & Restaurant L S M   14 | 13 | 14 | $19
1 Holland Ct. (bet. 4th & 5th Sts.), 415-543-8226
☑ If you can't make "spring break in Mazatlán", try this huge, "anarchic" SOMA Mexican, a Moscone-handy favorite for tequila slammers and Fleetwood-sized portions of "ok if you're hungry" eats; the "forced Tex-Mex environment" means "friends from San Jose like it", but many locals find it "obnoxious" and insist they're "too old for this."

Cafe Akimbo 🔳Ⓜ   20 | 18 | 21 | $26
116 Maiden Ln. (bet. Stockton & Grant Sts.),
415-433-2288

▪ A "lovely little sleeper" off Union Square that's a good
choice after shopping for reasonably priced Cal-Japanese
cuisine and "work of art" desserts; some say the decor
is "lackluster", but with a "nice crew" and "inventive
combinations", many claim it's "my secret."

Cafe Bastille 🔳Ⓜ   18 | 17 | 16 | $20
22 Belden Pl. (bet. Bush & Pine Sts.), 415-986-5673

☑ "If you miss Paris", come to Downtown SF's answer to
the Place de la Bastille; you'll find "sexy French waiters"
dishing out "great crêpes" and three seating options: an
"intimate" dining room with live jazz and blues, an "idyllic"
outdoor alley and a "Eurotrash bar" in the basement; N.B.
a few Francophiles find the fare "uninspiring."

Cafe Claude 🔳Ⓜ   17 | 18 | 15 | $20
7 Claude Ln. (bet. Grant & Kearny Sts.), 415-392-3515

☑ "Bring your Gitanes and beret" and join the Claude-
hoppers at this authentic Parisian ("I just go for the
accents") cafe brought over in pieces and reassembled in
a Downtown alley on SF's "Rive Gauche"; croque monsieurs,
cassoulet and "cool" service make it "too hip for words."

Cafe de Paris L'Entrecôte 🔳ⓈⓂ   18 | 16 | 17 | $32
2032 Union St. (Buchanan St.), 415-931-5006

☑ This Union Street French bistro with a "charming"
garden room plays to mixed reviews; some "only order
the entrecôte" because the rest can be "greasy", while
others say it's "ok for simple dishes"; it's reportedly "always
empty", bolstering critics who maintain "needs work."

Cafe Flore 🔳ⓈⓂ≠   11 | 16 | 11 | $13
2298 Market St. (Noe St.), 415-621-8579

▪ "Eye candy is the main menu selection" and the best dish
is rarely on the "paper plates" at this "amusing" "gay
fraternity party" at a busy Castro District intersection;
regulars implore you to skip the Cal cuisine ("who goes there
for the food?") and go for a latte and "people-watching."

Cafe For All Seasons 🔳ⓈⓂ   20 | 14 | 19 | $21
150 W. Portal Ave. (bet. 14th Ave. & Vicente St.),
415-665-0900

☑ "There's not much else in the neighborhood", so this
"homey" Sunset District cafe stands out for its "solid"
New American food doled out in "plain environs"; many
feel the "noise level is a problem", but the James Beard–
sized portions of yummy salads and soufflés at a good
price more than make up for it.

Cafe Jacqueline S
24 | 19 | 21 | $35
1454 Grant Ave. (bet. Green & Union Sts.), 415-981-5565
■ It's "cholesterol and romance" at this North Beach French where you can linger for hours over "soufflés like clouds" – the only items on the menu; a few deflators wonder about "shockingly high prices" for "smartly packaged air", but many more sigh "divine", "nothing like it."

CAFE KATI S
24 | 18 | 22 | $37
1963 Sutter St. (bet. Fillmore & Webster Sts.), 415-775-7313
■ A "sassy", "cozy" Pacific Heights New American that from a "shoebox kitchen" turns out "large portions" of "dramatic", "vertical" "art to eat" ("my salad looked like Lyle Lovett's hair") that's way up there on flavor too; the "personal service" also comes in for high praise; a minority finds the menu limited and the presentation "contrived."

Cafe Majestic S M
19 | 22 | 20 | $37
Majestic Hotel, 1500 Sutter St. (Gough St.), 415-776-6400
☑ This "elegant" cafe serving "inconsistent", "not daring" Cal cuisine amidst Victorian decor is a perennial romantic spot that's ideal for "escape dining" and "blue-rinse brunch."

Cafe Marimba L S M
19 | 19 | 15 | $22
2317 Chestnut St. (Scott St.), 415-776-1506
☑ "The buzz has faded" from this "colorful", "funky" Marina Mexican, but the "noisy yup crowd" hasn't; don't expect any smiles from the "cold", "airhead" servers, but with "authentic" Oaxacan fare and "great margarita and tequila tastings" most don't mind.

Café Mozart S
18 | 19 | 18 | $36
708 Bush St. (Powell St.), 415-391-8480
☑ Reviewers can't decide if this Downtown French has an "oppressive", "sterile" atmosphere and "food that could be better" or is a "cute", "romantic" "old favorite."

Café Riggio S M
18 | 16 | 17 | $25
4112 Geary Blvd. (bet. 5th & 6th Aves.), 415-221-2114
☑ "A holdover from the '70s", this "unpretentious", "kid-tolerant" Richmond District "neighborhood" Italian still draws crowds for its "hearty portions" of "standard" fare; "no reservations" means the "madhouse" waits can be long, but the "warm hostess and cordial staff" will help you cope.

Cafe Tiramisu L M
21 | 18 | 19 | $27
28 Belden Pl. (bet. Bush & Pine Sts.), 415-421-7044
■ A "Eurochic" Financial District Italian with a "friendly staff" attending to "power lunchers" nibbling on "rich", "authentic pastas"; to avoid the "cramped" main dining room, sit in the "interesting" basement wine cellar or opt for the "Romanesque" outdoor alley.

Cafe 222 **L S M**   ▽ 20 | 19 | 20 | $28 |

Hotel Nikko, 222 Mason St. (O'Farrell St.), 415-394-1111

◩ A "stylish" Downtown Japanese-American in the Hotel Nikko with "artistic fare" that'll get you psyched for your evening show; cynics who expected more lament "good for a hotel" and "fine but not special."

Caffe Centro **L M**   ▽ 19 | 16 | 16 | $19 |

102 South Park (bet. 2nd & 3rd Sts.), 415-882-1500

◪ "Perfect for panini" or focaccia or "outstanding baked goods", this hip South Park cafe draws a "typical SOMA crowd" from Multimedia Gulch; it's a "fun place for large groups" hanging out during breakfast or lunch.

Caffe Delle Stelle **L M**   19 | 16 | 18 | $23 |

395 Hayes St. (Gough St.), 415-252-1110

◩ Sink your dente into "toothsome pastas" at this "bustling" trattoria with "welcome to Italy" owners; the new, more spacious location is even closer to the Civic Center, making it one of the best in its genre for pre- or post-opera dining; service can be "slow", so leave enough time to get to your seat.

Caffè Greco ◑**L S M**⇪   18 | 18 | 16 | $12 |

423 Columbus Ave. (bet. Green & Vallejo Sts.), 415-397-6261

◩ An "atmospheric" North Beach cafe "complete with poets and writers" and a meager menu that's compensated for by "one of the best cups of coffee in SF"; if you can find a seat, it's "a fun place to people-watch" and sample desserts.

Caffè Macaroni **L M**⇪   21 | 16 | 20 | $24 |

59 Columbus Ave. (Jackson St.), 415-956-9737

◪ This "postage stamp" North Beach trattoria with "noodles on the ceiling" has an "enthusiastic" staff and an "impressive menu" of "authentic", "rich" pastas – two reasons why surveyors say it's "well worth the wait"; if you're "worried about poking your elbow in your neighbor's risotto", try the upstairs area.

Caffe Sport **L**⇪   17 | 15 | 11 | $27 |

574 Green St. (Columbus Ave.), 415-981-1251

◩ North Beach Sicilian "tourist trap" strikes out with its "lunatic asylum" atmosphere, "'50s rococo" decor, garlic-loaded pastas that "hit or miss" and "rude waiters" that are "part of the act"; although a minority finds it "lots of fun", more agree it "gets old" fast.

California Pizza Kitchen **L S M**   14 | 12 | 15 | $16 |

Hotel Diva, 438 Geary St. (bet. Mason & Taylor Sts.), 415-563-8911

◩ Although they might only admit it in the *Survey*, everyone in SF seems to have eaten at one of these "I wanna live in LA" chain pizzerias with "mirrored checker cab decor"; the large menu of "designer" pies with "funky toppings" is "just awful" or "just delicious" depending on how far south your taste buds go; all agree it's "definitely California."

Campo Santo 🅛🅢🅜 16 | 18 | 16 | $17
240 Columbus Ave. (Broadway), 415-433-9623
☒ The "Day of the Dead decor" at this graveyard-themed
Mexican can be as "unnerving" as the striptease joint
neighborhood, but it's a "zany, fun" place for "really cheap"
albeit "unexceptional food."

CAMPTON PLACE 🅛🅢🅜 26 | 26 | 26 | $49
*Campton Place Hotel, 340 Stockton St. (bet. Post & Sutter Sts.),
415-955-5555*
■ If you can't make the "great" breakfast in the "refined
power dining room" of this "quiet", "spacious", "classically
understated" New American, then try it for a "tryst and
lunch" or top-notch dinner; the "impeccable" servers
make you feel "royal" and chef Todd Humphries' "superb"
cuisine offers "an emotional experience" – bring your
own hanky, but "make sure someone else is paying."

Capp's Corner 🅛🅢🅜 15 | 14 | 18 | $19
1600 Powell St. (Green St.), 415-989-2589
☒ A "colorful", "noisy", family-run North Beach Italian
"institution" with "old-world" "NYC" servers, "goofy decor"
and "large portions" of "banal" red sauce–covered fare;
groups consider it a "must stop before Beach Blanket
Babylon"; besides "where else can you go for this price?"

Careme Room 🅛🅢🅜 19 | 16 | 18 | $27
*California Culinary Academy, 625 Polk St. (bet. Turk &
Eddy Sts.), 415-771-3536*
☒ While "they try hard" and it "can be superb", the New
American food is often as "inconsistent" as the students
cooking it at this Van Ness/Polk dining room of the CCA;
the glassed-in "operating theater" kitchen is worth watching,
but don't take your eyes off the waiter trainees or "you
might wear the food home"; N.B. the students also operate
an informal grill, Tavern on the Tenderloin, at the Academy.

Caribbean Zone 🅛🅜 15 | 22 | 16 | $22
55 Natoma St. (bet. 1st & 2nd Sts.), 415-541-9465
■ "Bring your passport" because this SOMA Caribbean with
"plane crash in the jungle" decor will "take you out of SF
for a few hours"; a "hip, young crowd" crashes here in the
fuselage of a downed DC-3; the food is merely the co-pilot,
but most embarkees think it's "a hoot."

CARNELIAN ROOM 🅢🅜 19 | 26 | 21 | $45
*Bank of America Ctr., 555 California St., 52nd fl. (bet.
Kearny & Montgomery Sts.), 415-433-7500*
☒ "On a clear night" the view's "unending" from this
"elegant" Downtown New American on the 52nd floor of the
Bank of America monolith and every night the bill can be
just as dizzying; while the food's "not up to the view", it's
"surprisingly good" and brought to table by career waiters in
a "do you have Grey Poupon?" atmosphere.

Carta 🅛🆂　　　　　20 | 15 | 18 | $28
1772 Market St. (bet. Gough & Octavia Sts.),
415-863-3516
🆕 As with the weather, some months are better than others
at this International restaurant in the Civic Center where
"you never know what you'll have" because the cuisine
changes every month; voters love the concept and say it
"succeeds more than it fails", though the "sterile" setting
(in a former candy store) is a drawback.

Casa Aguila 🅛🆂🅼　　　　20 | 14 | 16 | $19
1240 Noriega St. (bet. 19th & 20th Aves.), 415-661-5593
🔳 "Prices are low" and portions are "huge" at this "tiny",
"amazing" Sunset District Mexican "dive" with "funky",
"colorful" south of the border decor; it's crowded, but most
don't mind waiting because they throw in "free tamales."

Cassis Bistro ⊘　　　　21 | 18 | 23 | $27
2120 Greenwich St. (Fillmore St.), 415-292-0770
🔳 Patrons unanimously praise this "refreshing", "sweet",
très "charming" Union Street New French offering "superior
food" served by a "warm and friendly" staff; the tables are
tightly packed, yet most rave "this is what bistros are all
about"; N.B. no reservations.

Castagnola's 🅛🆂🅼　　　▽ 17 | 16 | 18 | $24
286 Jefferson St. (Fisherman's Wharf), 415-776-5015
🆕 "Fisherman's Wharf place" says enough for most locals,
and there may be "better seafood nearby", but in all fairness
you can get a "great water view of fishing boats" and even
some good cannelloni and crab melts at this "ok for tourists"
Italian; don't forget to "ask about Mike the Sea Lion."

Cha Am Thai 🅛🆂🅼　　　　20 | 14 | 17 | $17
701 Folsom St. (3rd St.), 415-546-9711
🆕 Opinions vary on these "good value" Thai twins, with
some calling the Moscone-convenient SOMA version
"pretty decent" but most favoring the "smaller", "cozier"
Berkeley locale; customers can't decide whether they're
"unchallenging" or "excellent", so you might just have to
try Am both to find out.

Cha Cha Cha 🅛🆂🅼　　　　20 | 19 | 14 | $21
1801 Haight St. (Shrader St.), 415-386-5758
🆕 A "loud", sangria-soaked Haight-Ashbury Caribbean-
Latin "party" madhouse where you'll have to "run, run,
run" to arrive before the crowds (no reservations); a zillion
"young", "hip", "people-watching" loyalists love the
"commotion" and think the "tasty tapas" and fab plantain
lasagna are "worth every trial"; detractors, on the other
hand, say it's "gone downhill."

Chapeau! S
23 | 17 | 21 | $31
1408 Clement St. (15th Ave.), 415-750-9787
■ Respondents take their hats off to this Richmond District "real find" for "comforting cassoulet" and dishes that "remind me of great meals in France"; the "warm and friendly owner" greets you as you enter and the "overeager" service "tries hard" even if the kitchen is "slow"; even with the kinks, however, surveyors say it's one of SF's "best new restaurants"; just be prepared to "cover your ears."

Charles Nob Hill S
25 | 24 | 23 | $65
1250 Jones St. (Clay St.), 415-771-5400
☑ "Understated", "private club"–like Nob Hill New French with "intimate little rooms" and "highbrow" service from lots of waiters; a few find it "a little too stuffy" and say you'll need oxygen when you see the tab, but executive chef Michael Mina has created "some truly remarkable dishes" and "with a little time", "this could become a real winner."

Cheers Cafe L S M
17 | 15 | 17 | $16
127 Clement St. (bet. 2nd & 3rd Aves.), 415-387-6966
☑ "Consistently good food at low prices" is the take on this kid-friendly Richmond District all-American cafe with a patio that's "relaxing on a nice day"; serious diners register only a "ho-hum" on the gustatory thermometer, but it gets some kudos for the "best omelets on the west side of town."

Chevys L S M
14 | 13 | 15 | $17
150 Fourth St. (Howard St.), 415-543-8060
3251 20th Ave. (Winston St.), 415-665-8705
2 Embarcadero Ctr. (Sacramento St.), 415-391-2323
Additional locations throughout the Bay Area.
☑ "Seen one, seen 'em all" Tex-Mex chain links proffering "plentiful margaritas" and "birthday sombreros"; a few amigos assert that "kids love it and if you order carefully you can enjoy it too", but most locals think it's "mass produced" and say in a town like SF "why not go authentic?"

Chez Michel S
25 | 23 | 24 | $51
804 North Point St. (Hyde St.), 415-775-7036
☑ A new chef has critics concerned that this Fisherman's Wharf–area New French won't be able to maintain its high standards, but one thing that hasn't changed is the "superattentive" staff and "sparkling touch" of host-owner Michel Elkaim who "knows how to work the tables"; dissenters call the whole experience "pretentious."

Chow
– | – | – | M
215 Church St. (Market St.), 415-552-2469
"New, trendy, cheap" Castro/Noe pasta and salad place at a busy public transit connection point; it's a good value for a "bite and beer" and the cute found-object decor makes up for the staff that is sometimes busy watching *Oprah* reruns.

City of Paris 🇱 🆂 🅼   18 | 17 | 17 | $25
101 Shannon Alley (bet. Taylor & Jones Sts.), 415-441-4442
◪ The "pre-theater" crowd favors this "steady" Downtown French for grilled chicken and fries and other "plain bistro fare"; "very reasonable" prices and a "convenient location" ensure that it will survive even though more demanding diners "wouldn't rush back."

Clement Street Bar & Grill 🇱 🆂   18 | 15 | 18 | $22
708 Clement St. (8th Ave.), 415-386-2200
■ You "don't have to dress up" at this "underestimated" Richmond District pub-grub grill that "fits the neighborhood like a glove"; it's no destination, but the fireplace is homey and veggie options make it "terrific for what it tries to be."

Cliff House 🇱 🆂 🅼   14 | 20 | 15 | $27
1090 Point Lobos (Great Hwy.), 415-386-3330
◪ Most "come to gaze, not to graze" at this "tourist-infested" American "where you take your aunt from Illinois" for a "nice" champagne brunch; there's "'60s rec room decor", "indifferent service" but a "zillion-dollar location" high above scenic Ocean Beach; "even peanut butter and jam would be fine with a window seat."

Coconut Grove Supper Club 🆂   17 | 22 | 17 | $38
1415 Van Ness Ave. (bet. Pine & Bush Sts.), 415-776-1616
◪ A Van Ness/Polk Continental supper club with "'40s throwback decor" and "mobster-like" clientele; it's currently "going through a transition" (new management) and early reports are that it's best as a "fun place to go out and dance with friends"; otherwise it's "too pricey for what it is."

Columbus Ristorante 🆂 🅼   – | – | – | M
3347 Fillmore St. (Chestnut St.), 415-474-4180
May Ditano moved her longtime North Beach restaurant to the Marina in early 1997 and discovered a whole new continent of fans; the cuisine is Italian 'family food' and chef Ditano runs both the kitchen and the front of the house with a gruff but lovable touch; pastas and risottos excel.

Cordon Bleu Vietnamese 🇱 🆂 ⊄▽ 19 | 6 | 15 | $14
1574 California St. (Polk St.), 415-673-5637
■ "Absolutely no frills" Polk/Van Ness Vietnamese "dive" with a meat-only menu so small you could print it on a won ton skin; it's "not exactly a heart-smart meal", but for "five-spice chicken on a stool" it's as good as it gets; "I've eaten here every Saturday for 20 years – enough said!"

Correnti's 🆂 🅼   – | – | – | M
1630 Powell St. (bet. Union & Green Sts.), 415-392-2738
Italian newcomer in North Beach promising romantic decor with oil paintings of Golden Gate Park and big portions of hearty, traditional Italian and Sicilian cuisine; private parties are accommodated in the cozy upstairs dining room with views of Coit Tower.

Courtyard Bar & Grill L S M   15 | 15 | 17 | $21
2436 Clement St. (bet. 25th & 26th Sts.), 415-387-7616
◪ Relaxed and retro "palm and fern" American in the
Richmond District that "needs perking up"; service runs
the gamut from "friendly" to "grumpy", but you can get "a
properly done Caesar with two whole anchovies for $7"
and with portions so sizable "your entree is also a takeout."

Crustacean L S M   22 | 16 | 18 | $34
Chelsea Plaza, 1475 Polk St. (California St.), 415-776-2722
◼ Van Ness/Polk Asian seafooder that means two things
to our surveyors – "sensational" roast crab and "must have"
garlic noodles; there are long waits and a "difficult upstairs
location", but it's worth the stairway to "heaven"; while
your eyes are on the "beautiful blown-glass creatures
overhead", don't forget to "watch the prices."

Curbside Cafe L S M   18 | 12 | 16 | $17
2417 California St. (Fillmore St.), 415-929-9030
◼ There's "good people-watching" from the sidewalk seats
of this Pacific Heights Californian hole-in-the-wall popular
for "lunch and brunch"; prices are "very reasonable", so
"expect to wait", especially at peak hours.

CYPRESS CLUB S M   22 | 26 | 21 | $45
*500 Jackson St. (bet. Montgomery & Columbus Sts.),
415-296-8555*
◪ The light fixtures resemble . . . hmmm . . . "bosoms" at
John Cunin's pricey and udderly sophisticated North Beach
supper club with "Dalí meets Warhol" decor so exotic-
erotic "you may not remember the food"; too bad because
it can be "delicious" with "attention to tiny details"; some
think the place "works too hard at being fun" and has a
staff that's "disaffected" and "harried", but most find it a
"seductive" scene; N.B. at press time, a new chef was
scheduled to take over the stoves.

dalla Torre S M   ▽ 19 | 24 | 19 | $37
1349 Montgomery St. (Union St.), 415-296-1111
◪ This year's location, location, location restaurant is a
North Beach hideaway Italian beneath Coit Tower; "reserve
upstairs" for "fabulous views" across the skyline and the
Bay; the food gets a fritto misto of comments, from "really
good" to just "ok", but most agree it's "a great date place"
that "with some help could be worthy of its setting."

dame L S   – | – | – | M
1815 Market St. (bet. Valencia & Guerrero Sts.), 415-255-8818
"Friendly husband and wife chefs" run this small, modestly
priced Civic Center New American bistro; "slow service"
and "too few wines" on the list detract, but this dame
sizzles with "delicious, creative cuisine", "amazing baked
goods" and some of the "best homemade ice cream"
around; by the way, "you've got to see the bathrooms!"

Delancey Street 🇱🇸　　18 | 18 | 21 | $22
600 Embarcadero (Brannan St.), 415-512-5179
◨ Blackened catfish yes, but "blackened meat loaf"? – oh
well, it's "mediocre food for a good cause" at this "feel
good" South Beach American "with a story" (run by ex-cons
on the mend); a "politically correct brunch" on the sunny
patio and "heartfelt enthusiasm" from the staff make some
respondents almost farklemt: "just love the cause."

Doidge's 🇱🇸🇲　　21 | 14 | 17 | $17
2217 Union St. (bet. Fillmore & Steiner Sts.), 415-921-2149
◼ This "homey" Union Street American has been an AM
"standby for 20 years" and the "wait to get in" can be
about that long too; staff "grumpiness is part of the
experience" and some "fail to see why" it's popular, but
the answer may lie in the "supreme corned beef hash"
and "best hollandaise", and because "I feel like I'm back
in Vermont when I eat here."

Dottie's True Blue Cafe 🇱🇸🇲　　20 | 13 | 17 | $13
522 Jones St. (bet. Geary & O'Farrell Sts.), 415-885-2767
◼ This tiny Downtown cafe in a "seedy neighborhood" in
the Tenderloin offers "one of the best breakfasts in SF"
amongst an "interesting mix of people"; the "blue plate
specials" at lunch are also a big draw because you get
"a lot of food at reasonable prices."

Dusit Thai 🇱🇸🇲　　▽ 22 | 14 | 20 | $18
3221 Mission St. (Valencia St.), 415-826-4639
◼ "Nobody does it like Dusit", an "off the beaten path",
"dimly lit", "friendly" Mission District Thai that gets high
ratings for its "excellent balance of flavors" resulting in
"delicious, delicate" dishes; the "broad menu of family
recipes" assures there's something for everyone.

E'Angelo 🇸⌀　　19 | 11 | 19 | $20
2234 Chestnut St. (bet. Pierce & Scott Sts.), 415-567-6164
◨ A "comfortable old shoe" Marina Italian that "kinda
looks like a dump inside" but is "always a bargain" for
"gnocchi to die for" and "excellent veal" from a "mom
and pop menu"; reactions to the service are sharply
divided between those who say "one of the friendliest
staffs in the city" and others who claim the waiters "rush
you out" and are "sometimes boorish."

EBISU 🇱🇸🇲　　25 | 14 | 19 | $27
1283 Ninth Ave. (Irving St.), 415-566-1770
◼ Everyone has a favorite among the "many novel choices"
at this "superb" Sunset District Japanese; popular choices
include the caterpillar roll, "49er roll" ("a touchdown"),
"swamp thing" and "pink Cadillac" (scallops wrapped
with salmon); the no-reservations wait is "a real ordeal"
("I could've watched *Ran*"), but everyone still shouts "go!"

Eddie Rickenbacker's **L M**   15 | 17 | 15 | $20
133 Second St. (Minna St.), 415-543-3498

☑ "Marginal" SOMA American watering hole with toy train sets for decor and motorcycles hanging over the bar; it's "good for a burger" and the "pub atmosphere" makes it a classic after-work hang and "a great place to be a regular."

El Balazo **L S M**⊅   ▽ 19 | 18 | 15 | $8
1654 Haight St. (bet. Clayton & Cole Sts.), 415-864-8608

■ Serving the only burrito with "saffron rice" and the "best chile relleno" version, this "cheap" taqueria in the Upper Haight is "muy bien" according to our voters; there's a huge menu of hot and spicy dishes and the large portions mean "you'll have leftovers to share with the panhandlers."

Eleven Ristorante & Bar **M**   17 | 20 | 16 | $27
374 11th St. (Harrison St.), 415-431-3337

☑ A "trendy" "models" and "brown-lipstick crowd" hangs at this moderately priced but oh-so-SOMA Italian in a "chic", "modern", "industrial" warehouse; "dine and go deaf" on "blah food" and good live "loft jazz" while the "overworked, overwhelmed staff does its best" to cope; many agree it's fun as "an atmosphere experience" ("if you can stand the cigar smoke") but wish they would "sort out the menu."

Elite Cafe **S**   20 | 19 | 17 | $28
2049 Fillmore St. (California St.), 415-346-8668

☑ A "crowded" Pacific Heights Cajun-Creole "yuppatorium" with a "top-notch oyster bar" and winning jambalaya and blackened catfish; reviewers love the "classic", "intimate" booths but could do without the "occasionally snooty" staff (after a few Sazeracs you won't even notice); is 10 years too soon to call it "a SF institution"?

Eliza's **L M**   23 | 20 | 18 | $19
205 Gough St. (Oak St.), 415-621-4819
1457 18th St. (Connecticut St.), 415-648-9999 **S**

■ "Well-spiced, swell-priced" Chinese from these try-hard twins makes them favorites with the "yuppie" crowd; even the "cute Matisse decor" (Civic Center) and the glass artwork (Potrero Hill) are "refreshing"; maybe "portions could be bigger", but the food is "beautiful" and most say you "can't lose" here.

Ella's **L S M**   22 | 15 | 18 | $19
500 Presidio Ave. (California St.), 415-441-5669

☑ "Look at the lines!" for breakfast at this Pacific Heights American where "attitude is part of the charm" and "fantastic scramble" describes both the food and the scene; still, regulars swear it's worth the wait and some have even "moved to New York and dreamed every day about that chicken hash."

Elroy's 🅛🅢🅜 | 14 | 22 | 14 | $27 |
300 Beale St. (Folsom St.), 415-882-7989
◪ Elroy's got "growing pains" at this "loud", *Jetsons*-themed Southwestern with "poor", "not very interesting" vittles and "horrendous" service; yet everyone agrees the "eye-catching" decor is "out of this world" and it's a "cool", "yuppie" "scene", so just slip into a "big strong margarita" and press "cruise."

Emerald Garden 🅛🅢🅜 | 21 | 17 | 20 | $24 |
1550 California St. (bet. Polk & Larkin Sts.), 415-673-1155
◼ "Garden green" French-Vietnamese jewel tucked into a narrow Van Ness/Polk alleyway between two buildings still manages to be "romantic and atmospheric"; a few think the Emerald needs polish, but most call the "great value" food "outstanding" and the service "excellent"; "hard to find, but find it!"

Empress of China 🅛🅢🅜 | 17 | 17 | 15 | $27 |
838 Grant Ave. (bet. Washington & Clay Sts.), 415-434-1345
◪ "Great Coit Tower views" and "very good service" aside, this Chinatown Chinese is seen by surveyors as an "aging dowager" that's "definitely living in the past"; "the view's wasted on poorly prepared food", though the "very elegant" setting makes it a good place to Empress out-of-towners.

Enrico's Sidewalk Cafe ❶🅛🅢🅜 | 20 | 21 | 17 | $26 |
504 Broadway (Kearny St.), 415-982-6223
◼ This Mediterranean sidewalk cafe is a great place to watch life's "passing parade" and brings back "fond memories of Enrico and his violin" and the old North Beach of yore; there's "interesting tapas" (late-night menu until 1 AM), "much improved service" and "great vibes" from "good live jazz" every night.

Eos Restaurant & Wine Bar 🅢🅜 | 24 | 19 | 21 | $35 |
901 Cole St. (Carl St.), 415-566-3065
◼ A "splashy" Cole Valley Euro-Asian bistro and wine bar with "enter and feel cool" ambiance, "one of the best wine lists in the Bay Area" and "awesome architectural" food that "pushes the fusion envelope" (but "can I eat this garnish?"); the noise level is high and "prices have climbed", but chef Arnold Eric Wong "continues to challenge himself" nightly with "a fabulous melding of East and West."

Eric's 🅛🅢🅜 | 21 | 16 | 16 | $18 |
1500 Church St. (27th St.), 415-282-0919
◼ "Who cares about the name?" – "the crowd tells the story" at this California-style Chinese in Noe Valley; the service is "too fast-paced" ("they should stop pushing people out of their way"), but "fine" dishes like chicken with seaweed and pine nuts are adequate compensation.

Ernesto's S
19 | 12 | 17 | $21
2311 Clement St. (bet. 24th & 25th Aves.), 415-386-1446
☑ "Garlic reigns supreme" at this Richmond District Italian proffering "generous portions" of "simple", "heavy" food that sometimes "swims in too much sauce"; some say "uninspiring", but many more consider it a "straight-ahead solid" place where "you get your money's worth."

Esperpento L S M⊞
18 | 17 | 15 | $20
3295 22nd St. (Valencia St.), 415-282-8867
☑ A "lively, cramped" Mission tapas place with "quirky decor", "forgetful service" and a "strong smell from the kitchen" (mostly garlic) – maybe that's why it "reminds us of Barcelona"; some critics complain that the dishes are "greasy", but that's what the "sangria wash-down" is for; P.S. "watch out for serenades" from mariachi minstrels.

Essex Supper Club ◑
18 | 21 | 17 | $41
847 Montgomery St. (bet. Jackson & Pacific Sts.), 415-397-5969
☑ Expensive North Beach nightclub (on the site of the former Ernie's) with an "awesome layout" and "doormen with too much attitude"; it's "cellular phone city" inside and there's a "*Miami Vice* vibe" in the cigar-smoky air; the "mediocre" California-French fare barely gets mentioned, but then again it's really "not a dining experience"; serious foodies implore "please bring back Ernie's."

Farallon L S M
– | – | – | VE
450 Post St. (bet. Mason & Powell Sts.), 415-956-6969
Pat Kuleto has outdone himself at this year's newest darling, creating an exquisite undersea setting complemented by Mark Franz's (ex Stars) glorious seafood that manages to retain both focus and flavor; service can be erratic, but it's friendly and has a great wine list; reserve well in advance.

Faz L S M
18 | 19 | 17 | $26
Crocker Galleria, 161 Sutter St. (Montgomery St.), 415-362-0404
☑ Downtown, Pleasanton, Sunnyvale, Danville – Faz is everywhere and he's "anxious to please"; the Union Square location is a "lunch oasis" with a "sort of '80s" ambiance and "dependable" Mediterranean cuisine, but quality elsewhere "ranges from excellent to poor" as does the service; the consensus: "adequate, not exciting."

Fior d'Italia L S M
17 | 17 | 18 | $31
601 Union St. (Stockton St.), 415-986-1886
☑ "Even the grease is tired" at this Italian "museum of fine dining" featuring "plush red booths" and a room named after the man who left his heart in San Francisco; the nostalgic call it "quintessential North Beach" and insist it still puts out a "lunch full of memories"; "this is how SF ate in 1960", but "Tony and Frankie would love it."

Firefly S M　　　24　20　21　$30
4288 24th St. (Douglass St.), 415-821-7652
■ This adorable Noe Valley Eclectic–New American Firefly's "got a buzz" with "scrumptious", "imaginatively prepared food, a "sexy", "incredibly helpful" staff and "funky" decor; the "young, cute" crowd claims "it feels like everyone is happy" here – probably because it's a "perfect neighborhood restaurant."

Fizz Supper Club ◑ L M　　▽　17　17　15　$32
471 Pine St. (bet. Kearny & Montgomery Sts.), 415-421-3499
◪ Italian supper club newcomer (operated by the owners of Cafe Tiramisu around the corner) that "needs work" but "shows traces of potential"; "check out the large courtyard" for lunch or stop in during late-night hours for some "delicious appetizers", "tender seafood" and live jazz.

FLEUR DE LYS M　　　27　27　27　$72
777 Sutter St. (bet. Jones & Taylor Sts.), 415-673-7779
■ "Big bucks are needed" for this Downtown New French where "all the parts come together"; expect "spectacular" "fabric orgy" decor, "unmatched service" and Hubert Keller's "stunning" cuisine including a "fabulous vegetarian tasting menu"; even the reluctant ("the wife talked me into it") admit "it's class all the way"; of course, reservations are "harder to get than tee-off times at Pebble Beach."

Flying Saucer　　　24　18　17　$36
1000 Guerrero St. (22nd St.), 415-641-9955
◪ The "chef is clearly alien" at Albert Tjordjman's "goofy", "zany" Mission New American serving "hard to describe cuisine" that's "too cool to eat" ("my salmon was served at a 90-degree angle"); some see it as a case of "form over function" and think the service "the slowest, rudest ever", but most beam up for the "wild ride" and say "it's all about food and good humor."

Fly Trap L M　　　20　18　18　$30
606 Folsom St. (2nd St.), 415-243-0580
◪ "The name isn't appetizing, but the food is" at this SOMA American with a low-key ("good for an interview") atmosphere; the "glorified bar food" menu featuring classic concoctions like celery Victor and Hangtown fry makes thrill-seekers "yawn", but there's an "old SF feel" to the place and it's one trap that's "consistently good."

Fog City Diner L S M　　　19　20　17　$27
1300 Battery St. (bet. Greenwich & Lombard Sts.), 415-982-2000
◪ "Boomers and tourists and yuppies . . . oh my"; this "crowded", stylish, chrome-clad Downtown American diner made famous in a VISA commercial ("all waiters must have an agent" now) has become a bit "expensive for what you get", but some swear there's still "no better comfort food in town" ("what about those pork chops!").

42 Degrees ◐ⓁⓈⓂ | 21 | 22 | 19 | $33 |
Esprit Outlet, 235 16th St. (3rd St.), 415-777-2938

☑ Everyone has something to say about this cavernous "industrial" Mediterranean in a "built to last" warehouse behind the Esprit Outlet – "the chairs were great", "tall hostesses", "hated the napkins", "I love any place that can be this snobby"; but don't let the "cool as a cuke" ambiance deter you from sampling the "great cross section of Med favorites"; live jazz and a bar that's "hip to the nth degree" add up to "chic urban fun."

Fountain Court ⓁⓈⓂ | 20 | 15 | 16 | $20 |
354 Clement St. (5th Ave.), 415-668-1100

☑ The "iron plates and firepots are worth the parking hunt" at this Richmond District Shanghai-Szechuan; "great caramelized eggplant" and other "new tastes for Western palates" make many think it's "one of the best Chinese in SF", with a dim sum lunch that's a "bargain" . . . but "darling, get a decorator!"

Fournou's Ovens ⓁⓈⓂ | 22 | 21 | 22 | $44 |
Renaissance Stanford Court Hotel, 905 California St. (Powell St.), 415-989-1910

☑ "The lamb is capable of great things" at this "elegant and pricey" Mediterranean in Nob Hill's "old-world" Stanford Court; it might be a little "stodgy", but the something-from-the-oven menu and "splendid cellar" make it "great for holiday dinners" or when the folks are in town.

Frascati ⓈⓂ | – | – | – | M |
1901 Hyde St. (Green St.), 415-928-1406

This midrange Van Ness/Polk ex-Italian has been "refined" and refocused by "young, energetic working owners" and gets write-in kudos for its "fresh, ever-changing American menu"; there's "quiche to die for", but you might want to stick around to sample the "best pasta I've had yet."

FRENCH ROOM ⓈⓂ | 23 | 26 | 25 | $49 |
Clift Hotel, 495 Geary St. (Taylor St.), 415-775-4700

■ New Clift Hotel owner Ian Schrager is spiffing up this already "warm and sophisticated" French-Eclectic and there's talk about combining it with the distinguished bar next door (The Redwood Room); and while the "food doesn't match" the "palatial elegance" of the decor", with a few improvements, it could prove to be as superb as it deserves to be.

FRINGALE ⓁⓂ | 26 | 20 | 22 | $37 |
570 Fourth St. (bet. Bryant & Brannan Sts.), 415-543-0573

■ "Masterpieces" for moderate moolah make this SOMA French the "best bistro" by far; surveyors put up with "long waits", "tables too close together" and sometimes "snobby servers" for "spectacular", "superbly satisfying" lamb, steak and pork dishes; "too bad it's impossible to get in for dinner."

GARDEN COURT 🇱🇸🇲 | 19 | 28 | 20 | $38 |

Sheraton Palace Hotel, 2 New Montgomery St. (Market St.),
415-546-5010

◪ A "glorious", palm-lined, belle epoque room provides a "majestic" backdrop for high tea, brunch or special occasions at this Downtown American in the Sheraton Palace Hotel; the food is "variable", but it's "a piece of SF history" ("Warren Harding thought it was to die for, so he did") and "the best indoor view" in town means it's booked well in advance; call now for Mother's Day 2010.

Garibaldi's on Presidio 🇱🇸🇲 | 22 | 20 | 20 | $30 |

347 Presidio Ave. (bet. Sacramento & Clay Sts.),
415-563-8841

▨ "I love it more each time I go" rave reviewers of this Pacific Heights neighborhood Cal-Med favorite with a "metropolitan feel" and "accommodating staff"; the "upscale" bar with infused vodkas whets appetites for signature lamb dishes and other "honest preparations"; now that "it's been discovered", the only question is "can they squeeze another table in?"

Gaylord India Restaurant 🇱🇸🇲 | 17 | 16 | 16 | $27 |

Ghirardelli Sq., 900 North Point (bet. Beach & Larkin Sts.),
415-771-8822
1 Embarcadero Ctr. (bet. Sacramento & Battery Sts.),
415-397-7775

◪ Opinions on these tandoori triplets are as varied as their curries; all agree that the Ghirardelli Square location has a "great view", the Menlo Park locale a "cheap lunch buffet" and that they're all "a little pricey" for dinner; when it comes to taste, however, some think they're "ok", even "solid", while many others find them "greasy", "bland" and "for the Midwesterner looking for the exotic."

Gira Polli 🇸🇲 | 21 | 14 | 18 | $21 |

659 Union St. (bet. Columbus & Powell Sts.), 415-434-4472

▦ "Why cook" when you can get "mouthwatering" takeout and sides at these on-the-cheap North Beach and Marin chicken rotisseries?; a minority shrugs over the limited menu, but "if you love chicken with an Italian accent" you might find yourself in the chorus singing "may they multiply."

Globe 🌑🇱🇲 | – | – | – | E |

290 Pacific Ave. (bet. Front & Battery Sts.), 415-391-4132

This hot Downtown New American write-in with a "New York" feel just might be the "best new restaurant in the Bay Area"; it's a "very exciting place" with late-night hours, an interesting wine list and a small but "quality" menu courtesy of chef-owner Joe Manzare, "a star" with "great credentials" (Spago, Postrio); it's been "crowded" since day one and the many enthusiastic fans "wish them success."

Godzilla Sushi 🅢🅜
– | – | – | M

1800 Divisadero (Bush St.), 415-931-1773

Mothra, beware: "sushi in a hip environment" at this "cheap, good" Japanese in lower Pacific Heights where a "fun crowd" munches maguro "while jamming to the Dead"; the impending cinematic return of everyone's favorite movie monster might mean this place will be even more "packed."

Golden Turtle 🅢
21 | 17 | 19 | $23

2211 Van Ness Ave. (bet. Broadway & Vallejo St.), 415-441-4419

■ "Terrific", long-standing Van Ness/Polk Vietnamese serving "classics done well and served sweetly", though it pays to "take someone from Vietnam" to help with the menu; a handful of critics cry "tired" and "highly average", but "unusual decor" and moderate prices put this turtle in the race for "favorite Asian restaurant."

Gordon Biersch Brewing 🅛🅢🅜
16 | 17 | 15 | $22

2 Harrison St. (Embarcadero), 415-243-8246
See review in South of San Francisco Directory.

Gracie's ◐🅛🅢🅜
▽ 14 | 19 | 13 | $34

Maxwell Hotel, 398 Geary St. (Mason St.), 415-646-8600

☑ "Disappointing" is the early 4-1-1 on this Downtown American "glorified coffee shop" with "no theme yet"; "very unpolished service" is another kvetch, although some think " it will settle down in time"; "convenience to the theater" seems to be its saving grace so far.

GRAND CAFE 🅛🅢🅜
20 | 26 | 20 | $33

Hotel Monaco, 501 Geary St. (Taylor St.), 415-292-0101

☑ "Go for the glitz" at this '30s "movie set" Downtown New French in the Hotel Monaco boasting a "fabulous" dining room filled with "funny bunny sculptures"; throw in awesome "people-watching" and you see why it's a "grand experience" despite "spotty" service and only "respectable" food that "doesn't live up to the lure of the location."

Great Eastern ◐🅛🅢🅜
▽ 20 | 12 | 13 | $19

649 Jackson St. (bet. Grant & Kearny Sts.), 415-986-2500

☑ "Stick with seafood" and "be sure to try something alive" is the best advice about this "reliable" Chinatown Chinese "favored by many locals"; service is as "rushed" as a Shanghai subway and the decor is "authentic" – "wow, those are some bright fluorescent lights!"

GREENS 🅛🅢🅜
22 | 23 | 20 | $30

Ft. Mason Ctr. Bldg. A (bet. Buchanan St. & Marina Blvd.), 415-771-6222

☑ This Marina Vegetarian has something to please or annoy everyone; lettuce-heads call it the "best vegetarian in town" with a menu of "innovative", "impeccably prepared "dishes that will "convert carnivores", while detractors declare it's for "tourists", "left me hungry and penniless" and needs a "revamp"; in any case, it's "uniquely San Francisco."

Hahn's Hibachi 🇱🇸🇲   17 | 10 | 15 | $14
1305 Castro St. (24th St.), 415-642-8151
3318 Steiner St. (bet. Chestnut & Lombard Sts.),
415-931-6284
1710 Polk St. (Clay St.), 415-776-1095
▪ Korean "bulk up" barbecue joints where a "colorful clientele" gobbles "huge portions" of cheap food, oblivious to the "terrible" decor; if you "can't stand the smoke" stay out of the hibachi, but if you "like kimchi" head on in.

Hamano Sushi 🇸🇲   – | – | – | M
1332 Castro St. (bet. 24th & Jersey Sts.), 415-826-0825
"A serious new contender" appears on the sushi scene with this Noe Valley Japanese known for "good service" (but "prepare to wait for a table"); "big pieces" of "excellent, fresh" sushi are capped off with "free green tea ice cream."

Hamburger Mary's ❶🇱🇸🇲   16 | 17 | 14 | $16
1582 Folsom St. (12th St.), 415-626-5767
▨ "Too '60s" SOMA burger-bar institution where the "counter culture", "wild late-night world" from Folsom Street (and maybe Chelsea Clinton on a weekend furlough from Stanford) meets for "killer hamburgers" and "great fries"; the "wall of paraphernalia" gives it that "kinky SF ambiance"; hey Chelsea, "pass the grease."

Harbor Village 🇱🇸🇲   22 | 20 | 17 | $26
4 Embarcadero Ctr. (bet. Drumm & Clay Sts.), 415-781-8833
▨ Downtown Chinese with "dim sumptuous" dim sum and a "gorgeous" view from a "large, impersonal", "zoo"-like room equipped with managers bearing walkie-talkies; respondents suggest that you "take a Cantonese speaker" with you because you may have difficulty communicating with the less-than-warm staff; believers boast "the communists have Hong Kong, but SF has Harbor Village."

Hard Rock Cafe 🇱🇸🇲   12 | 18 | 14 | $19
1699 Van Ness Ave. (Sacramento St.), 415-885-1699
▪ They're still "milkin' it" at the Van Ness/Polk link in this concept chain with a memorabilia-themed atmosphere "like a rock fest" gone retail ("I have enough T-shirts"); it's "not a bad burger", but given the tourist quotient, most locals "can't imagine why" anyone would bother; "only the young could be this conned."

Harris' 🇸🇲   23 | 22 | 22 | $43
2100 Van Ness Ave. (Pacific Ave.), 415-673-1888
▪ "They never steer you wrong" at this pricey Van Ness/Polk steakhouse with an "old and stuffy" ambiance ("where's Lawrence Welk?"); service is unflappable "even during a blackout" and the steaks, lobster and martinis are "consistently excellent"; "here's the beef", now "bring me the defibrillator."

Harry Denton's 🔲🆂🅼   17 | 19 | 18 | $30

Harbor Court Hotel, 161 Steuart St. (bet. Howard & Mission Sts.), 415-882-1333

☑ "White guys in midlife crisis hang out" with "women with big hair" at this lively SOMA "pickup" bar and grill with a great view (the one outside); the "standard American" food is largely "a bust" and the staff is "invisible", but "the pot roast is good" for a "happening party scene."

Harry Denton's Starlight   15 | 24 | 17 | $34
Room ◗🆂🅼

Sir Francis Drake Hotel, 450 Powell St. (bet. Sutter & Post Sts.), 415-395-8595

☑ A beautiful Downtown bar atop the Sir Francis Drake Hotel offering "breathtaking views" and dancing to live orchestras (like "a perfect prom experience" with "obnoxious young business types" or "the high school in-crowd" 20 years later); "food? who knows?", but for "champagne, caviar and romance" it's "head and shoulders above" the rest.

HAWTHORNE LANE 🔲🆂🅼   25 | 25 | 23 | $49

22 Hawthorne St. (Howard St.), 415-777-9779

☑ Expect "celebrities to the ceiling" (and a check through the roof) at this "stellar" SOMA New American that's "California cuisine personified"; "the wood tones gleam softly" in the "cavernous" room as the kitchen turns out "daring food" that's "a taste fantasy with each bite" (especially the desserts); naysayers call it a "triumph of PR" with "small portions" and "slow service."

Hayes & Vine Wine Bar ◗🅼   18 | 23 | 20 | $22

377 Hayes St. (bet. Franklin & Gough Sts.), 415-626-5301

■ "Sophisticated" Civic Center wine bar where it's "great to unwind after work" or sample a post-symphony Syrah; an "impressive range" of wines awaits you, although they "could use more menu choices" and what there is "seems prepared and brought" in from elsewhere; the owners may be "aloof", but no one knocks the "sexy" "Philippe Starck knockoff" decor.

Hayes Street Grill 🔲🆂🅼   23 | 18 | 21 | $34

320 Hayes St. (bet. Franklin & Gough Sts.), 415-863-5545

■ It's "not cutting edge anymore", but this Civic Center American grill with the "traditional" white linen look is "still the best at what it does", which is "uncomplicated" and "straightforward" seafood; a few carp that it's "unimaginative", but supporters rave about "the best grilled fish anywhere" and the "fabulous crème brûlée"; sure it requires greenback bait, but angling admirers say it's an "excellent" catch.

Helmand ⑤Ⓜ   24 | 18 | 21 | $28
430 Broadway (bet. Montgomery & Kearny Sts.), 415-362-0641
■ "If you're tired of typical", try this "exotic" North Beach Afghan with "delectable" lamb dishes, "incredible" veggie specialties like pumpkin ravioli and even a "decent wine list"; the "honky tonk" strip of Broadway "isn't inviting", but "surprising decor" and an "excellent staff" make San Franciscans "love this place" anyway; go early to find parking at this "unique and extraordinary" find.

Hong Kong Flower Lounge Ⓛ⑤Ⓜ 22 | 17 | 16 | $25
5322 Geary Blvd. (bet. 17th & 18th Aves.), 415-668-8998
See review in South of San Francisco Directory.

Hong Kong Villa Ⓛ⑤Ⓜ   ∇ 20 | 12 | 14 | $22
2332 Clement St. (25th Ave.), 415-752-8833
■ Service is "a little surly" and there's "only one restroom per sex" (quick, how many does that add up to in SF?), but that doesn't dissuade our shrug-it-off surveyors from enjoying "outstanding lobster", "good Peking duck" and "great sauces" at this Richmond District Chinese; "the food is beautiful to look at" and many say it's "just like Hong Kong – only cheaper."

House, The Ⓛ⑤   24 | 19 | 22 | $29
1230 Grant Ave. (bet. Columbus Ave. & Vallejo St.), 415-986-8612
1269 Ninth Ave. (bet. Irving St. & Lincoln Way), 415-682-3898
■ This "youthful spirit" North Beach original and its Sunset District offshoot are "reasonably priced" Cal-Asians where the decor is "crooked windows", but the "killer Chilean sea bass" and other "innovative" dishes are right on the level; they're "too noisy" for some, but most report an "outstanding" experience and call these Houses home.

House of Nanking Ⓛ⑤Ⓜ⊅   21 | 6 | 10 | $14
919 Kearny St. (bet. Jackson St. & Columbus Ave.), 415-421-1429
☑ Long lines are proof for some that this North Beach "dive" has "hands down the best Chinese in town" and "they almost give it away"; but even fans warn "the decor is so bad it's distinctive" and since the "cruelty of the service is legendary", "let the waiter order" (he will anyway) and "don't be surprised if your Coke is tossed to you"; others dismiss it as "touristy" ("have you ever seen any Chinese eating here?") and "same sauce" city.

House of Prime Rib ⑤Ⓜ   23 | 18 | 20 | $33
1906 Van Ness Ave. (bet. Washington & Jackson Sts.),
415-885-4605
■ "Forty years and still slicing" at this "masculine" Van Ness/Polk American "time warp" where the "succulent" prime rib is "done to perfection" and waitresses still toss salads at the table; reviewers report long waits even with reservations, so have a "superb martini" and remind yourself if you like meat "you gotta love this place."

Hunan ⑤Ⓜ　　　　22｜10｜15｜$17
1016 Bryant St. (8th St.), 415-861-5808
924 Sansome St. (Broadway), 415-956-7727
674 Sacramento St. (bet. Montgomery & Kearny Sts.),
415-788-2234

■ These "tried and true", "reasonably priced" but "no ambiance" Hunans are "consistent winners" since the fare is "fiery and good" and "you never have to wait"; only a few call them "food factories" and say the service is "indifferent."

Hungarian Sausage Factory &　▽ 16｜15｜15｜$16
Bistro Ⓛ⑤
419 Cortland Ave. (bet. Bennington & Wool Sts.), 415-648-2847

☑ "Is this that place on Bernal Heights?" – yep, and it's a "cute, homey neighborhood" Hungarian full of goulash and "garlic sausage" with "entertainment every night" from a gypsy violinist; while fans call it "a favorite everyday spot", foes find it "limited in selection" and only "fun once."

I Fratelli ⑤Ⓜ　　　　19｜18｜18｜$24
1896 Hyde St. (Green St.), 415-474-8240

☑ "Get your garlic fix for a month" at this "cornerstone" Van Ness/Polk Italian; maybe it's "kinda tired now", but that doesn't stop the "fun and lively" neighborhood crowds from fraternizing over "basic Italian" (although the bruschetta rates an "unbelievable" on some scorecards); its location on the Hyde Street cable car route makes it "ideal for taking out-of-towners."

Il Fornaio Ⓛ⑤Ⓜ　　　20｜21｜19｜$29
1265 Battery St. (bet. Union & Greenwich Sts.), 415-986-0100

☑ The roamin' empire of high-style "cookie cutter" Italians is "all concept", but it's "a formula that works"; "wonderfully open space" is a trademark at this "when all else fails place"; to some the "reliable" food "tastes like something I can cook", but a largely business clientele counters "they never fail to please"; N.B. the famous French toast makes for great "power breakfasts."

Imperial Palace Ⓛ⑤Ⓜ　　▽ 19｜18｜18｜$26
919 Grant Ave. (bet. Jackson & Washington Sts.), 415-982-8889

☑ Boosters say for "lots of lobster and shrimp dim sum" it might be "one of the better" Chinatown Chinese, especially "if you ask for the Hong Kong specialties", but others advise "for better Chinese and less worn decor, go elsewhere."

Incontro Ⓛ⑤Ⓜ　　　▽ 16｜14｜19｜$21
41 Franklin St. (bet. Market & Oak Sts.), 415-436-9355

☑ "Neighborhood grub of the Italian persuasion" can be had at this modestly priced and "very welcoming" Civic Center haunt with "great service"; "rabbit is a specialty" according to admirers who also say "don't miss the seafood risotto"; even naysayers who find the food "on the bland side" admit "they try harder."

Indian Oven 🅂🅼   20 | 14 | 16 | $21

233 Fillmore St. (bet. Haight & Waller Sts.), 415-626-1628
■ Some participants rate it "the best Indian in the city" and "savor every morsel" ("excellent naan and samosas"), although fiery tandoori and curries mean it's "hot in that Oven"; the "decor is hip" and "the owners couldn't be nicer" at this "bargain", but if you don't have a purple Mohawk you might find the neighborhood "scary."

Indigo 🅂🅼   – | – | – | M

687 McAllister St. (Gough St.), 415-673-9353
The hosts "pay attention to detail" at this Civic Center New American featuring "fabulous service" from a "friendly staff" and "inventive dishes" from an "up and coming new chef" (John Gilbert); the setting is (what else?) deeply blue and the "upscale feel" makes the entire experience "very cool."

Infusion Bar and   16 | 17 | 15 | $27
Restaurant 🅻🅂🅼

555 Second St. (bet. Bryant & Brannan Sts.), 415-543-2282
◪ "Young, trendy and free" – well, at least affordable – that's how surveyors sum up this "good vibes" SOMA New American where "25-year-old multimedia start-ups" download infused-vodka martinis to sound bytes from live bands; some say the food "needs help", but a few of our more candid critics get downright "orgasmic" over the mashed sweet potatoes.

Iroha 🅻🅂🅼   ▽ 14 | 10 | 10 | $17

1728 Buchanan St. (bet. Sutter & Post Sts.), 415-922-0321
◪ "Noncommittal service" but "cheap prices" mark (or mar) this "cozy", "classic, old" Japantown noodle house; while a few think it's a "good place for lunch", others call the ramen "gooey and unflavorful"; at least it's "a bargain."

Iron Horse 🅻🅂🅼   17 | 15 | 17 | $28

19 Maiden Ln. (bet. Post & Geary Sts.), 415-362-8133
◪ "Dark" Downtown Italian with a "high-end funky" ambiance that's "straight out of 1972"; there's "excellent ravioli" and the bar offers a "great happy hour", but most maintain this horse has "seen better days" and now trots in the "middle of the road."

Irrawaddy Burmese   ▽ 19 | 16 | 18 | $21
Cuisine 🅂🅼

1769 Lombard St. (bet. Laguna & Octavia Sts.),
415-931-2830
■ The "best find" of the year might be this affordable Marina Burmese with "creative cuisine" in "unusual combinations" including "great curries"; the "very accommodating staff" makes it "a pleasant surprise" even if they "aren't shy about talking politics", leading customers to conclude "we need more Burmese like this."

Isobune Sushi **L S M**   16 15 15 $22
1737 Post St. (Webster St.), 415-563-1030

▣ The sushi keeps going and going around the bar on a "corny flotilla" of toy boats at these "clever" but "dizzying" Japanese concept stops; sometimes the fish may have "been around the block too many times" and can "log more miles than a frequent flier", but it's "novel for the neophyte" and "my eight-year-old's favorite" – is this "sushi for Californians" or what?

Izzy's Steaks & Chops **S M**   20 17 17 $31
3345 Steiner St. (bet. Chestnut & Lombard Sts.), 415-563-0488

▣ There's "big food for big people" at this Marina "carnivore's landmark" with its "great place for a fight" ambiance and "ketchup collection" decor; "veteran servers" bring on the beef and back it up with "must-have potatoes and creamed spinach"; a few detractors call it "mediocre" and "routine", so you'll have to decide Izzy or Izzy not the "best steak in town"?

Jackson Fillmore Trattoria **S M**   20 14 17 $28
2506 Fillmore St. (Jackson St.), 415-346-5288

▣ "Yuppies on garlic" jam this "overcrowded" Pacific Heights Southern Italian for "old country" dishes like the "best bruschetta" in town; the "dumpy" decor may resemble "a Laundromat", but it can't remove the traces of "the best sauce on this continent" from reviewers' napkins; while there's no reservations for duos and it's "hell to get into", making more than a few ask "why be tortured?", most think it offers "tasty fare at great prices."

Jakarta **S**   – – – I
615 Balboa St. (7th Ave.), 415-387-5225

There's surprisingly varied fare at this hidden-away, exotic and tasty Sunset Indonesian; eager and willing service and rock-bottom prices are additional pluses.

Jardiniere   – – – E
300 Grove St. (Franklin St.), 415-861-5555

Press time finds Traci des Jardins (ex Rubicon) teaming up with design-and-conquer restaurant mogul Pat Kuleto to open the Civic Center's hottest new Cal-French destination on the much-revamped site of the former Kimball's; if you care about food, plan on planting yourself here 'cuz most likely it will be one high-class garden of eatin'.

Jasmine House **L S M**   19 12 19 $19
2301 Clement St. (24th St.), 415-668-3382

▣ "The garlic noodles and crab lead", but the "catfish is also yummy" and the "eggplant in coconut curry is divine" at this Richmond "genuine" Vietnamese where "cheap" prices and "service with a smile" make up for "weird interior design"; others caution that "it's not as good as it once was" and a lower food score supports that point of view.

Jessie's 🅛🅢🅜   ▽ 16 | 16 | 16 | $27
1256 Folsom St. (bet. 8th & 9th Sts.), 415-437-2481

☑ Opinion on this "nice small place for a date" SOMA Cajun-Creole is divided along a culinary Mason-Dixon line: supporters say the signature alligator and other "rich and flavorful" dishes add up to the "best Southern cooking in SF", but detractors think the "unremarkable" food "gives gators a bad name."

Johnny Love's 🅛🅢🅜   8 | 10 | 9 | $20
1500 Broadway (bet. Van Ness Ave. & Polk St.), 415-931-8021

■ "Relive the '70s" at these "loud and touchy" singles bars where "the only good service is the bouncer"; reaction to the California fare runs the gamut from "people eat here?" to "are you kidding?", but if you want a "bridge and tunnel" drinks and dancing experience, you might Love Johnny's.

Juban 🅛🅢🅜   – | – | – | M
Japan Ctr., 1581 Webster St. (Post St.), 415-776-5822
See review in South of San Francisco Directory.

Julie's Supper Club 🅛🅜   17 | 18 | 16 | $25
1123 Folsom St. (7th St.), 415-861-0707

☑ The "cyber crowd" sups and yups at this hip and "very retro" SOMA Californian dinner club "hangout"; it's a "high maintenance" experience with difficult parking, hard-to-snag reservations and a "noisy as hell" Technicolor dining room; the food may be "generic", but the "great ambiance" makes for a "fun place to drink and dance."

Julius' Castle 🅢🅜   18 | 25 | 20 | $46
1541 Montgomery St. (Union St.), 415-392-2222

☑ The "unsurpassed view" and "superb service" make this "way too expensive" New American tucked away on the flank of Telegraph Hill a "romantic must"; a number of surveyors say the "food has improved" since last year and a rise in ratings echoes that opinion; N.B. there's also an outstanding wine list.

Kabuto Sushi   24 | 11 | 17 | $32
5116 Geary Blvd. (bet. 15th & 16th Aves.), 415-752-5652

■ No matter how they slice it, this highly rated but pricey Richmond District Japanese has "superb sushi"; the "hard-working" staff makes up for the "close your eyes" decor, while behind the bar the "maniacal" Sachio Kojima inspires Zen-like devotion – "he's my master!" – from the hamachi hungry who chant "who needs Nobu? we have Kabuto!"

Kansai 🅛🅜   ▽ 15 | 11 | 14 | $25
325 Sacramento St. (bet. Front & Battery Sts.), 415-392-2648

☑ A few claim that "terrific noodles" and "quick service" make this Downtown Japanese "good for a business lunch", but the only thing critics Kansai is the food is "passable", servers get the "orders mixed up" and "it's a bit high-priced for dingy" decor.

Kate's Kitchen █ ⑤ Ⓜ   21 | 13 | 17 | $14
471 Haight St. (Fillmore St.), 415-626-3984
█ "Good grub, but good grief" you've got to wait and wait for a breakfast seating at this "funky" Traditional American in the "grimy" Lower Haight; but "great down-home cooking", an "eclectic crowd" of "out of this world patrons" and a "friendly, funny" staff make it all bearable; P.S. "nothing beats a hangover like the banana pancakes" here.

Katia's Russian Tea Room █ ⑤   20 | 17 | 19 | $22
600 Fifth Ave. (Balboa St.), 415-668-9292
█ They "need a vodka license", but the "bargain" blinis and the "best borscht" in a near-borschtless town make this Richmond District Russian "worth a try"; the atmosphere is largely balalaikas ringing out in a homey "no frills setting"; the friendly staff "tries to please" but is sometimes "slow": now what page of *War and Peace* was I on?

Kelly's on Trinity █ Ⓜ   ▽ 19 | 13 | 16 | $14
333 Bush St. (Sutter St.), 415-362-4454
☒ This "great for catering" Downtown American also offers "good lunches" and a "nice assortment of salads", though a number complain that "service is slow" and the "space cadets behind the counter" "need to get organized."

Khan Toke Thai House █ ⑤ Ⓜ   22 | 24 | 19 | $23
5937 Geary Blvd. (bet. 23rd & 24th Aves.), 415-668-6654
█ It's "a little dark", but this "must try" Richmond Thai with "happy servers" is a SF favorite; hosiery salespeople love the "take your shoes off" requirement and the low sunken tables make for "novel" decor; the food is "always delicious" and can be fiery as well, so "bring on the ice water."

Kim's of Saigon █ ⑤ Ⓜ   ▽ 19 | 15 | 22 | $16
508 Presidio Ave. (bet. California & Pine Sts.), 415-923-1500
█ The lucky few who've discovered this "charming", "good value" Pacific Heights Vietnamese call it "a treasure" with "tasty, authentic" fare, "friendly family service", a "lovely owner" and "beautiful orchids everywhere."

Kirin █ ⑤ Ⓜ   ▽ 17 | 10 | 17 | $18
6135 Geary Blvd. (bet. 25th & 26th Aves.), 415-752-2412
☒ Patrons praise the "fun food in a Formica atmosphere", particularly the "great grilled items", at this Richmond Chinese; but others rate it "run of the mill", concluding they have "seen better, been to worse" in a neighborhood with more Chinese restaurants than parking places.

Kiss █ ⑤ Ⓜ   19 | 16 | 18 | $27
680 Eighth St. (bet. Brannan & Townsend Sts.), 415-552-8757
█ "When the showrooms wear you down", retreat to this Contemporary French "sleeper", which some say is "the only good place" to eat in the interior design district; the menu is "creative", the food is "beautifully presented" and the "desserts are fantastic"; too bad it's only open for lunch.

Korea House 🅛🅢   ▽ 20 | 13 | 14 | $22
1640 Post St. (Laguna St.), 415-563-1388

☑ "Cook it yourself is fun once in a while" at this "hot, hot, hot" Japantown Korean BBQ; there's lots of "authentic" food for the money and "courteous" but "slow" service.

Kuleto's 🅛🅢🅜   20 | 21 | 19 | $31
Villa Florence Hotel, 221 Powell St. (bet. Geary & O'Farrell Sts.), 415-397-7720

☑ "It's packed", but there are "no bad seats" at this "classy" Downtown "over the top" Northern Italian with "the Kuleto touch"; they "always have tantalizing selections", although a few may find them "oily" and service can be "savvy" or "sorry" depending on your draw, but with "big bottles of Chianti everywhere" and "great people-watching" most call it "cool-eatos."

KYO-YA 🅛   25 | 23 | 22 | $49
Sheraton Palace Hotel, 2 New Montgomery St. (Market St.), 415-546-5090

☑ Numbers-wise this "superfancy" Downtown "designer Japanese" in the Sheraton Palace Hotel edged out closest competitor Ebisu (by a sashimi's width) for Top Japanese this year, even though it doesn't seem to inspire the same fanatical devotion; although the "absolutely beautiful presentation" and "wonderfully gracious service" draw praise, they come at "prices of the gods" and a few think it "should be better for this much money."

La Belle Saison 🅢   ▽ 17 | 12 | 17 | $27
200 23rd Ave. (California St.), 415-751-7066

☑ A "tiny" New French menu pleases most at this "welcoming" Richmond District spot with "gushing service" and an atmosphere that "feels like someone's living room"; some say it "needs help" and wonder "what's French about this place" (how about "classic French onion soup"?); seasoned fans say it's a "friendly surprise."

La Bergerie 🅢🅜   ▽ 19 | 14 | 22 | $23
4221 Geary Blvd. (bet. 6th & 7th Aves.), 415-387-3573

☑ The "menu from the '50s" never seems to change at this Richmond District French with "lime green vinyl banquettes" ("good thing it's dark" in there); some rate it "comme ci, comme ça", but for "a complete dinner at bargain prices" it's "almost unbeatable."

La Cumbre Taqueria   20 | 8 | 13 | $9
515 Valencia St. (bet. 16th & 17th Sts.), 415-863-8205

■ "Good tongue" is available at these "awesome, authentic" taquerias and the carne asada burritos are "outstanding" too; the Mission District location can be "a little too close to the action" ("and we're from New York"), but "in the face of nouvelle burritos" this duo "puts other taquerias to shame"; three words: "quick, cheap, good."

La Felce L S M ▽ 22 16 19 $26
1570 Stockton St. (Union St.), 415-392-8321

■ "Old North Beach lives" at this storefront with "dingy decor", a "friendly owner" and "great old-fashioned Northern Italian fare"; "not many tourists" comes as good news for the "mostly local" clientele that considers it a "very good value" and "the kind of restaurant that made SF great" long before tortellini went trendy.

LA FOLIE M 28 22 26 $63
2316 Polk St. (bet. Union & Green Sts.), 415-776-5577

■ Roland Passot's "extravagant" yet "unpretentious" Van Ness/Polk New French earns the No. 1 food rating in our *Survey;* his "superb skill" in the kitchen and "smooth professional service" in the freshly fluffed theatrical dining room means there's "never a disappointing course"; these "labor-intensive preparations" "can cost as much as a French vacation" and an "outrageous corkage fee" has some popping their tops, but "there's no substitute" for "true genius" or for this "divine" madness.

Laghi S 23 16 21 $28
1801 Clement St. (19th St.), 415-386-6266

■ The "tables are right on top of each other" at Gino Laghi's Richmond District storefront Northern Italian and so are the raves such as "best comfort food", "intense flavors" and "pure pleasure"; some say they "need a bigger location", but the small menu of "different regional dishes" with house-cranked pastas and other "homey Italian food" has most surveyors shouting "bring it on, Laghi!"; P.S. go early to deal with "impossible parking."

La Mediterranee L M 20 14 19 $17
2210 Fillmore St. (bet. Sacramento & Clay Sts.), 415-921-2956
288 Noe St. (Market St.), 415-431-7210 S

■ Even carnivores "love the hummus" (as well as the "don't-miss dolmas", "great phyllo thingies" and other "good but not inventive" eats) at these "bargain basement" Middle Eastern–Mediterranean "sardine cans" where "hearty servings", a "homey local atmosphere" and "chummy" service add up to a "no-stress meal."

La Rondalla ◑ L S M ⊭ 14 17 15 $16
901 Valencia St. (20th St.), 415-647-7474

◪ This "late-night", "cheap high" Mission Mexican is "my kind of dive"; blinking lights for decor means it's "Christmas all year long" and with a "kitschy" scene like this and "the kind of margaritas that make you ache the next day", "who cares about the food?"; it may or may not be "the most fun restaurant in SF", but "lots of writers hang out there" so it can't be all bad.

La Scene ●SM
20 | 20 | 20 | $29

Warwick Regis Hotel, 490 Geary St. (Taylor St.), 415-292-6430

■ An "elegant setting" with a piano bar and a "great prix fixe" makes for "good value" pre-curtain dining at this Downtown Californian in the Warwick Regis Hotel; it's a "romantic" "little find" with a "reasonable wine list" and a "tasty" new menu from Natalie Sellers (ex Stars); even those not given to drama consider it "charming."

La Taqueria LSM⇄
23 | 11 | 15 | $10

2889 Mission St. (25th St.), 415-285-7117

■ "World-class burritos"? – you'd better believe it; this "muy bueno" Mission District "favorite" has "melt in your mouth tacos" and "out-of-sight agua frescas" (fruit drinks) too, and it all costs a lot less than the parking ticket you might get while waiting on line; devotees "don't mind the nonexistent decor" and "cafeteria-style service": "fresh" ingredients and "cheap" prices make it "heaven."

La Traviata S
▽ 20 | 20 | 22 | $26

2854 Mission St. (bet. 24th & 25th Sts.), 415-282-0500

◪ The "love of opera is a part of everything" at this "amusing", "underappreciated" Italian with "comfy-cozy" ambiance and Pavarotti's rec room decor; a few say the "rough" Mission District location "doesn't appeal at night", but with "friendly" service, "generous servings" of "old-time" pastas and Callas taking high Cs on the sound system, it's worth a season subscription.

La Vie LSM
22 | 13 | 20 | $19

5830 Geary Blvd. (bet. 22nd & 23rd Sts.), 415-668-8080

■ This "high-caliber" Richmond District Vietnamese newcomer gets high marks for its "refined" dishes and "personable staff"; if you can live with "sparse decor" you'll enjoy "first-rate" seafood dishes like steamed sea bass and catfish in a clay pot; "this place is just fabulous" – "too bad it's been discovered!"

Le Central LM
21 | 19 | 20 | $32

453 Bush St. (bet. Grant Ave. & Kearny St.), 415-391-2233

■ If you can't have "dinner in the fifth arrondissement", you might settle for this "habit-forming", "see and be seen" Downtown French bistro where "everything comes with sausage" and the "cassoulet is terrific"; "it's a special place" even if some cynics say it "needs jazzing up."

Le Charm LM
23 | 16 | 20 | $28

315 Fifth St. (bet. Folsom & Harrison Sts.), 415-546-6128

■ For "gourmet dining at '70s prices" ($20 prix fixe), try this "unassuming" but "superb" SOMA French bistro with a "swell menu" of "très simple, très bon" cuisine prepared with "great attention to ingredients"; the whole experience is "what dining out should be but rarely is"; N.B. the tarte Tartin alone will turn you upside down.

Le Cyrano ⑤ | 21 | 18 | 20 | $28 |
4134 Geary Blvd. (bet. 5th & 6th Aves.), 415-387-1090
☑ "Many pleasant old memories" linger in the air – along with the scent of "great rack of lamb" – at this "proper" Richmond District French; it's "definitely not a hot spot" ("we were the only people there under 70") and youngsters might find it "depressing", but where else can you "order frogs' legs" and still find the tab "an unbeatable value"?

Left at Albuquerque 🄻⑤Ⓜ | 17 | 18 | 15 | $20 |
2140 Union St. (bet. Fillmore & Webster Sts.), 415-749-6700
See review in South of San Francisco Directory.

Lehr Brothers Bistro 🄻⑤Ⓜ   ▽ 17 | 18 | 17 | $33 |
740 Sutter St. (bet. Taylor & Jones Sts.), 415-474-6478
☑ Those who remember the greenhouse ambiance of this Downtown steak-oriented American "miss" the old decor and ask "why did they change?" because "now there's nothing left but average food" (and a new cigar room); others disagree and say the new chef's steak "may get them back on track."

Le Soleil 🄻⑤Ⓜ | 22 | 15 | 18 | $21 |
133 Clement St. (bet. 2nd & 3rd Aves.), 415-668-4848
▨ Surveyors say this Soleil is on the rise thanks to "fresh, light, delicious" Vietnamese fare at "enormous bargain" prices; the "friendly" (if "hurried") service and "sunny", "clean, bright" atmosphere help make it "one of the best Vietnamese places in the city."

Leticia's 🄻⑤Ⓜ | 13 | 15 | 16 | $22 |
2247 Market St. (bet. 16th & Sanchez Sts.), 415-621-0442
☑ A Mexican Castro/Noe "gay hangout" that's "a scene" with its "fun clientele" and "great mango margaritas"; in the food department, however, it's "still tired after all these years" and "has nothing on a $6 Mission dinner."

Lhasa Moon 🄻   ▽ 15 | 14 | 17 | $21 |
2420 Lombard St. (Scott St.), 415-674-9898
☑ This Union Street Tibetan "may not suit all palates"; some think the "moderately priced" "exotic food" is "very interesting", while others find it "the culinary equivalent of fingernails on a blackboard"; both camps agree it's "a real original" with an "accommodating, personable staff."

Liberty Cafe 🄻⑤ | 23 | 17 | 19 | $29 |
410 Cortland Ave. (bet. Bennington & Wool Sts.), 415-695-8777
☑ "Noteworthy Caesar" and "awesome banana cream pie" are some of the cries that go up for this "consistently delicious", affordable and "so cute" American in "dreary" Bernal Heights; the staff has "gotten a bit big for their britches", but maybe that's from dealing with the "hassle" of an unfortunate "no reservations" policy.

Lichee Garden ⬛🅛🅢🅜 ▽ | 18 | 11 | 12 | $21 |
1416 Powell St. (bet. Broadway & Vallejo St.), 415-397-2290
◪ "If many happy Asian-American families are any sign", this "basic" Chinatown Chinese can be "recommended"; customers just wish they'd "get the floors cleaned" and spiff up the "dismal" decor, but there's "good dim sum" and it's thankfully "undiscovered by tourists."

Little City Antipasti Bar 🅛🅢🅜 | 18 | 17 | 17 | $24 |
673 Union St. (bet. Powell & Columbus Sts.), 415-434-2900
⬛ "Bustling" and "fun" North Beach Mediterranean grazing bar off Washington Square where many first "learned how to roast garlic"; "appetizers galore" means there's "something for everyone" including the must-order brie and garlic; it's a "nice stop" for a long leisurely meal.

Little Henry's 🅛🅢🅜⇗ ▽ | 13 | 8 | 15 | $15 |
955 Larkin St. (Post St.), 415-776-1757
◪ "No decor, bad location" but "a ton of" "cheap" food are the hallmarks of this Van Ness/Polk Italian; "the sauces need more work" and gourmets be-Little it as "nothing", but "when you're really hungry", "it's pretty good."

Little Italy Ristorante 🅢🅜 | 18 | 16 | 17 | $29 |
4109 24th St. (bet. Castro & Diamond Sts.), 415-821-1515
◪ There's "lots of garlic" at this Noe Valley Italian offering "outstanding stuffed artichokes" and "amazing cioppino"; while it's "not fine dining" and "needs painting", "nice people" work there and it has a "homey" neighborhood feel.

Little Joe's 🅛🅢🅜 | 15 | 11 | 15 | $19 |
523 Broadway (bet. Kearny St. & Columbus Ave.), 415-433-4343
◪ North Beach locale serving "heavy", "uneventful" Italian; while many think it's "slipped", it's still a "great spot for out-of-town guests who've maxed out on California cuisine"; "watch the cooks" at the open kitchen, then "mangia."

L'Olivier 🅛🅜 | 21 | 21 | 23 | $39 |
465 Davis Ct. (Jackson St.), 415-981-7824
⬛ Hipsters "can't get excited" about this "old-world" Downtown Classic French and claim it "could be livened up" a bit, but the over-50 crowd treasures it as an oasis of "quiet elegance" and "polished service" with a kitchen that "can do fine things"; prices are high, but the bouillabaisse (Friday–Saturday nights) "is worth the tariff."

London Wine Bar 🅛🅜 | 15 | 15 | 17 | $21 |
415 Sansome St. (bet. Sacramento & Clay Sts.), 415-788-4811
⬛ While the "cheese plate goes well" with the "excellent selection of wines" by the glass, the American-Californian menu is "secondary" at this "crowded" Downtown wine bar popular for "post-work socializing"; the "knowledgeable, generous bartender" makes up for the fact that some people haven't realized that "fine wine and a smoky bar don't mix."

Long Life Noodle Co. L S M ▽ 13 | 14 | 14 | $18
139 Steuart St. (bet. Mission & Howard Sts.),
415-281-3818
☑ If this "downscale" Downtown Asian Betelnut spin-off
is going to have a long life, then the "bland" jook (rice
porridge), "scatterbrained service" and "bad noodle trip"
decor are "kinks" that need to be worked out; meanwhile,
the jook's on you.

L'Osteria del Forno L S M ≠ 21 | 15 | 18 | $22
519 Columbus Ave. (Green St.), 415-982-1124
■ The "pleasant", "considerate" staff "tries hard and it
shows" at this "easygoing", "unpretentious", "crowded"
North Beach Italian "dive" with "amazing" food like salmon
carpaccio; throw in budget-conscious prices and it's no
wonder "there's always a line."

LULU ● S M 22 | 21 | 18 | $32
816 Folsom St. (bet. 4th & 5th Sts.), , 415-495-5775
☑ "Beautiful people" chow down on original takes on
Provençal classics (pan-roasted mussels, "wonderful"
rotisserie) at this "noisy" SOMA hot spot with a "big
warehouse feel"; most consider it "fun" and "perfect for
big noisy parties", but those who find it less of a lulu say
it's "annoyingly hip" with irritating family-style presentation
and poor service ("rudest front door in SF").

MacArthur Park L S M 18 | 18 | 18 | $27
607 Front St. (Jackson St.), 415-398-5700
☑ A longtime "not thrilling but never bad" Downtown
American grill popular at lunch and after work with suits
who go for the "good babyback ribs", Cobb salad, shoestring
potatoes and "pretty ladies"; despite the "pickup joint" bar
scene, it's still "family friendly" and a "reliable" choice for
food of the "solid" sort.

Maharani India L S M 21 | 18 | 15 | $25
1122 Post St. (bet. Van Ness Ave. & Polk St.),
415-775-1988
☑ The neighborhood isn't too hot, but the curries are at this
Van Ness/Polk Indian with traditional decor (including
"fantasy" booths) that strikes some as "beautiful" and
others as just plain "hokey" and "weird"; the reason
customers "keep coming back" is it's still one of the better
Indian restaurants in town.

Mai's L M ▽ 19 | 10 | 17 | $18
316 Clement St. (bet. 4th & 5th Aves.), 415-221-3046
☑ Fans "forgive the decor" ("zilch") at this "friendly",
"inexpensive" Richmond District Vietnamese because
"the imperial rolls rule" and it offers one of "the best hot
and sour soups in the city"; others advise that on densely
packed Clement Street, there may be "several better
restaurants within a two-block radius."

Maki ⓁＬ   ▽ 22 | 18 | 21 | $26
1825 Post St. (Webster St.), 415-921-5215
■ This "big as a shoebox" Japantown spot is "the smallest restaurant around", but it serves "lovely, delicate, authentic" Japanese dishes and is "the only place you can get wappa meshi" (steamed rice preparations); most consider it a "serene oasis" with "fine service" and "great sake."

Mama's Girl ⓁⓈ≠   ▽ 22 | 14 | 15 | $14
1701 Stockton St. (Filbert St.), 415-362-6421
■ "If you don't mind the wait to get in", this North Beach American serves the "best breakfast in town" including winning French toast and "fabulous" omelets and fries; it's an "excellent way to start a Sunday", though the wheatgrass drink has its detractors.

Mandalay ⓁⓈⓂ   19 | 11 | 16 | $19
4348 California St. (6th Ave.), 415-386-3895
■ When you need a "nice change of pace from Chinese", take the road to Mandalay where the mango and ginger salads "make up for zero atmosphere", service is "gracious" without being unctuous and there's "never a wait"; a minority maintains the Burmese duo is "too greasy" and "has gone downhill", but more observe that the "pictures of food on the menu do not compare to the great meals."

Mandarin ⓁⓈⓂ   20 | 22 | 19 | $36
Ghirardelli Sq., 900 North Point St. (Polk St.), 415-673-8812
☑ "Classy" Ghirardelli Square Chinese veteran with a view that makes it "worth the tourist setting"; a few protesters proclaim "oh, how the mighty have fallen" and suggest "stick to the classics", but those who've gone recently say it's "returned to the glory of the past" thanks to a new menu; N.B. if money isn't an issue, order the beggar's chicken.

Mangiafuoco ⓈⓂ   21 | 18 | 19 | $27
1001 Guerrero St. (22nd St.), 415-206-9881
☑ "Funky", "happening", "always crowded" Mission storefront Italian offering "yummy gnocchi", "lovely lobster ravioli" and other "pasta so light it floats to your mouth"; it can be "hard to park" and service can be "rushed", but what can you say except "love this spicy food."

Manora's Thai Cuisine ⓁⓈⓂ   22 | 16 | 19 | $20
1600 Folsom St. (12th St.), 415-861-6224
■ "Some of the best Thai seafood dishes" in the city are prepared at this very popular, "inexpensive" SOMA locale with an "efficient" kitchen that turns out "consistent quality"; admirers also give two thumbs up to the "friendly", "gracious" staff that makes you "always want to come back with more friends."

Marina Central ⬛🅛🅢🅜   15 | 17 | 17 | $28
2001 Chestnut St. (Fillmore St.), 415-673-2222
◼ Veteran Bay Area restaurateur Doyle Moon is "trying very hard" at this "comfortable", "lively" Marina newcomer that's ideal for drinks at the "yuppie bar"; but the Italian-overtoned "San Francisco menu" is still in the "has potential" phase.

Mario's Bohemian Cigar   18 | 19 | 17 | $14
Store Cafe 🌙🅛🅢🅜
566 Columbus Ave. (Union St.), 415-362-0536 ⊟
2209 Polk St. (bet. Vallejo & Green Sts.), 415-776-8226
◼ "The kitchen is a toaster oven", yet this "cheap" North Beach coffeehouse with a "cool" vibe is great for a "sublime focaccia sandwich and beer"; the Van Ness/Polk location is a chip off the old North Beach "landmark" and has a "locals-only feel that keeps it from turning into a Marina slumming post"; "bring a book" from City Lights and you too can feel "real SF."

Marnee Thai 🅛🅢🅜   24 | 14 | 17 | $18
2225 Irving St. (bet. 23rd & 24th Aves.), 415-665-9500
◼ "The chef's wife is in your face" (yep, that would be Marnee) telling you what to order at this top-rated Sunset District Thai, but her choices never disappoint; prepare your palate for "an incredible mix of spices" in food "worth fighting over" such as spicy angel wings, pad Thai and yellow curry prawns; it's an "intense scene" that plays itself out in a "virtual hut" setting that's "tight for comfort", but "people still flock to this place."

Marrakech 🅢🅜   ▽ 21 | 22 | 20 | $37
419 O'Farrell St. (bet. Jones & Taylor Sts.), 415-776-6717
◼ Go for the couscous, "stay for the belly dancers" at this Downtown Moroccan that's great for "large groups", "out-of-towners" or "if the company is paying"; some say dining to gyrating navels is "not my style" and complain that you get "too little for too much", but believers call the fare "euphoria inducing" and recommend ordering the seven-course sampler menu.

MASA'S   28 | 25 | 27 | $83
Vintage Court Hotel, 648 Bush St. (bet. Powell & Stockton Sts.), 415-989-7154
◼ Spectacular ratings and uniformly glowing comments ("world class", "unforgettable", "maybe the best meal in the USA") indicate this "dauntingly" expensive Downtown French is "still on top" and remains the SF "dining room against which all others are measured"; expect an "intimate" but "formal" atmosphere and "impeccable" service to round out the impressive picture.

Massawa L S　　　▽ 18 | 9 | 16 | $15
1538 Haight St. (Ashbury St.), 415-621-4129

☑ The "hospitable" staff is full of "explanatory" help about the "finger fantasy" Ethiopian food at this Haight-Ashbury haunt where you'll "definitely need a beer to quench the spice"; there can be "long waits" due to the slow kitchen, but culinary adventurers generally consider it "tasty and innovative" and "wish more people would try it."

Ma Tante Sumi S M　　　▽ 21 | 18 | 20 | $29
4243 18th St. (Diamond St.), 415-626-7864

■ An "absolutely lovely" place that delivers an "exquisite mix of French and Japanese" – what a "surprising find" in this "oh so gay" Castro/Noe neighborhood; a few feel it's "overpriced", but the prix fixe option is "a great value" and sometimes "they pass out free hors d'oeuvres"; everyone agrees it's a "cool amalgam" – "fusion works here."

Matsuya M　　　▽ 18 | 11 | 16 | $22
3856 24th St. (Church St.), 415-282-7989

☑ This Castro/Noe Japanese is "fun for the atmosphere and the proprietor's personality" ("that lady's a riot"), but the sushi is a mixed bag; from the dwindling responses we're inclined to conclude "it's really not so special."

Matterhorn Swiss Restaurant S　　19 | 19 | 19 | $29
2323 Van Ness Ave. (bet. Green & Vallejo Sts.), 415-885-6116

☑ "Yodel for your supper" at this "so '70s" Van Ness/Polk Swiss with "wonderfully kind owners"; the "excellent fondues" are "gaining in popularity", though they might be "the only thing worth getting" (how about those "regional Swiss wines"?); the "stark Alpine interior" is "kitschy", but most think the dipping and twirling is "actually fun."

Maxfield's ◐ L S M　　　▽ 18 | 23 | 20 | $28
Sheraton Palace Hotel, 2 New Montgomery St. (Market St.), 415-546-5020

☑ Featuring a Maxfield Parrish mural and "Florentine mosaic floors", this New American in the Sheraton Palace Hotel is "one of the warmest, prettiest rooms in town"; too bad the food is only "ordinary" ("shame, shame"); still, "superb service" and "relaxing" ambiance make it "great for drinks" or a business lunch or simply adding "a touch of luxury to your day."

Max's Diner L S M　　　17 | 15 | 16 | $18
311 Third St. (Folsom St.), 415-546-6297

☑ "Fun waiters", "happy surroundings" and "gluttony" are the hallmarks of this "big, brassy" SOMA deli serving "oversized sandwiches", "bigger than life onion rings" and "softball-sized muffins"; while no one leaves hungry, detractors insist the "matzo ball soup's not like mama's" and the fare's "greasy"; P.S. if you can believe it, some suggest "leave room for dessert.

Max's Opera Cafe L S M | 17 | 15 | 16 | $20 |
601 Van Ness Ave. (Golden Gate Ave.), 415-771-7300

☑ "Mile-high sandwiches with all the fixings" and the "world's biggest desserts" ("three of us couldn't finish one") are de rigueur at these deli/cafes with a "goofy singing staff" floor show; those who find the performance lacking implore "forget the size, improve the taste"; so "it's not NYC" – west of the Hudson it's still "a classic Jewish nosh."

Maye's Oyster House L M | 16 | 14 | 16 | $25 |
1233 Polk St. (Bush St.), 415-474-7674

☑ Van Ness/Polk seafooder that's an "old-time hangout" for political mussel-men from nearby city hall; the local powers that be claim it's "consistent" for a "pleasant meal", but the average Joe says it's "lost its charm" and whatever it was "it's not what it used to be."

Mayflower L S M | 21 | 12 | 16 | $20 |
6255 Geary Blvd. (27th Ave.), 415-387-8338

▉ A gem of a restaurant off the beaten tourist path, this "always packed", "nongreasy" Richmond Cantonese gives you "dim sum served with a smile" and standout dishes such as salt and pepper prawns, and crab and corn soup; despite a few grumblings ("chef must have moved"), the food rating has held up since our last *Survey*.

McCormick & Kuleto's L S M | 18 | 23 | 18 | $33 |
Ghirardelli Sq., 900 North Point St. (bet. Beach & Larkin Sts.), 415-929-1730

☑ "If you could eat the view" at this "elegant" Pat Kuleto–designed seafooder it might rate higher, but it still makes a "great spot for champagne and oysters" and has a room that ranks high on locals' "perfect for visiting relatives" list; while it "feels like a factory", there's no denying it's the "nicest-looking tourist trap on Fisherman's Wharf."

Mecca ◗ S M | 20 | 24 | 19 | $36 |
2029 Market St. (bet. Dolores & 14th Sts.), 415-621-7000

☑ "Noisy" Castro/Noe locale serving New American–Mediterranean fare in a "hard-edged", "blinding stainless steel", "wild post-modern nightclub setting" complete with "floor-to-ceiling chocolate velvet curtains"; it's become an ultra "hip" straight/gay scene that's "great for clothes, people-watching, live jazz and cocktails"; those who've noticed the food say it's "tasty" as well.

Meetinghouse, The S | 25 | 23 | 25 | $34 |
1701 Octavia St. (Bush St.), 415-922-6733

▉ "They get all the details right" at this Pacific Heights New American with a "refreshingly simple" Shaker-like setting, "flawless service" and "homespun cooking taken to a higher level"; nearly everyone thinks it's one of the "best new restaurants in town"; P.S. Joanna Karlinsky whips up "luscious fruit desserts" and "great biscuits."

Mel's Drive-In ◖🄻🅂🄼⊭   14 | 16 | 15 | $14
3355 Geary Blvd. (bet. Parker & Stanyan Sts.), 415-387-2255
2165 Lombard St. (Steiner St.), 415-921-2867
☑ Wits can quip "nostalgia is not what it used to be", but these "hokey, caloric" American diners give it a good try (remember "vanilla Coke"?); the "'50s-redux" setting is "a kick" and a "nice crew" serves up late-night burgers, curly fries and "milk shakes to die for" to those jonesing for "great greasy grub"; but "beware: adolescent date location."

Mescolanza 🅂🄼   20 | 15 | 19 | $22
2221 Clement St. (bet. 23rd & 24th Aves.), 415-668-2221
■ "Informal, homemade, consistent" sums up this "unassuming" Richmond District Italian with a "bright, cheerful dining room", "friendly staff" and much raved about thin-crust pizza; while "not a destination", it's a "great standby" that locals call "a well-kept secret."

Michelangelo Cafe 🄻🅂🄼   20 | 18 | 17 | $20
579 Columbus Ave. (Union St.), 415-986-4058
■ The "red sauce and red wine" flow freely at this North Beach Italian "goodie" with an "entertaining mishmash of art on the walls"; reviewers report "great food for the money" including a "seafood pasta special that wins my vote" and the "best gnocchi in SF – I've tried them all"; the "line around the corner" "looks longer than it is", but it's still "not a place for a leisurely meal."

Mifune 🄻🅂🄼   19 | 12 | 13 | $14
1737 Post St. (bet. Webster & Buchanan Sts.), 415-922-0337
☑ A "bare-bones", "cheap" and "yummy" Japantown noodle house; the interior's "run-down" and "the customer is never right" or "easily forgotten", but slurp some "warming" soba or udon on a foggy day and you'll know why customers call it "excellent" "comfort food."

Milano Pizzeria ◖🄻🅂🄼⊭   ▽ 19 | 12 | 18 | $15
1330 Ninth Ave. (bet. Judah & Irving Sts.), 415-665-3773
☑ Get your pizza "to go" at this Inner Sunset Italian because the "plain", "downright depressing" dining room is "a good place to have a fight with your honey"; while the pies have their supporters ("great crust", "great pizza"), others opine "nothing new here"; but at least it's "cheap."

Millennium 🅂🄼   20 | 19 | 21 | $27
Abigail Hotel, 246 McAllister (bet. Hyde & Larkin Sts.),
415-487-9800
☑ "Hard-core militant eco-vegans", your millennium has arrived; this Civic Center Vegetarian "with class" has a "fantastic menu" featuring an "exciting treatment of nonproteins"; some carnivores concede it's "innovative" and "novel", but others find it "a challenge" ("maybe I just haven't been this hungry yet") and rely on the "witty waiters" to add some meat to the experience.

Miss Millie's 🅛🅢　　　20 | 19 | 18 | $16 |
4123 24th St. (bet. Castro & Diamond Sts.), 415-285-5598
✉ Lemon ricotta pancakes and "fantastic" cinnamon rolls make for a winning brunch at this "cute", "homey" Noe Traditional American–Vegetarian that's "like eating at Aunt Bea's" but with "hang on it's coming" waits; it's now open for dinner Wednesday–Saturday.

Moa Room 🅢🅜　　　– | – | – | M |
1007 Guerrero St. (22nd St.), 415-282-1007
"Everything is organic" at this moderate Mission newcomer on the site for the former Le Trou; "unusual and refreshing decor" and "amazing" Pacific-inspired Eclectic cuisine make it one to watch; this room "promises to be a star of the neighborhood."

Mom is Cooking 🅛🅢🅜⊅　　19 | 9 | 14 | $16 |
1166 Geneva Ave. (bet. Edinburgh & Naples Sts.),
415-586-7000
✉ "Totally funky", out-of-the-way Mission District "dive" with "weird Astroturf seats" and a large "loose-leaf binder menu" of "authentic" moles and "tamales straight from Mexico"; the service isn't stellar and many detractors think it's an "overrated cult restaurant", but Mom's devotees herald "some of the best cheap eats in SF."

MOOSE'S 🅛🅢🅜　　　22 | 22 | 21 | $37 |
1652 Stockton St. (bet. Filbert & Union Sts.), 415-989-7800
■ A "convivial", "stylish", "quintessential" North Beach Cal-Med bar and grill that hosts a major "power scene"; patrons say Ed Moose "understands hospitality" and his "gracious" staff knows how to accommodate both "sweats and suits"; while many go for the "people-watching", there's "surprisingly good" food and an "excellent wine list."

Morton's of Chicago 🅢🅜　　23 | 19 | 21 | $50 |
Union Sq., 400 Post St. (bet. Powell & Mason Sts.),
415-986-5830
✉ "Robot waiters" go through a "routine" menu presentation with shrink-wrapped food at this Downtown "overpriced steak and cigar club" that "reeks of testosterone"; they serve a "great T-bone" and other "oversized food", but "the total quickly adds up" ("is the water à la carte too?") and many locals find it just "too formulaic."

Mo's Burgers 🅛🅢🅜　　　22 | 12 | 17 | $12 |
1322 Grant Ave. (bet. Green & Vallejo Sts.), 415-788-3779
■ An "awesome", "huge" burger ("the best in North Beach"), "lots of" shoestring fries and a "great raspberry chocolate shake" are what to order at this patty palace where "they'll still cook it rare" if you want; the only whisper of criticism is from those who deviated ("stick with the burger").

Moxie Bar & Restaurant S   ▽ 20 | 19 | 17 | $29
2742 17th St. (Florida St.), 415-863-4177
◪ Jewish-Mediterranean bistro in an industrial Mission neighborhood serving cuisine like a "Jewish mom with a twist"; boosters call it an "excellent newcomer" and say mazel tov for "delicious brisket and lamb" and "matzo ball to die for", while detractors kvetch it's "uneven" with "slow" service and observe that "if this is Jewish food, Woody Allen's the pope."

Mozzarella Di Bufala L S M   15 | 10 | 13 | $15
2114 Fillmore St. (California St.), 415-346-9928
1529 Fillmore St. (bet. Geary & O'Farrell Sts.), 415-346-9888
69 West Portal Ave. (Vicente St.), 415-661-8900
◪ This "crowded" Italian pizzeria chainlet has a following for its "great cornmeal crust" pies and convenient takeout and delivery; mystified naysayers claim the pies "left no impression" but add "pizza is like sex – no matter how bad, it really isn't that bad."

Murasaki ●S M   ▽ 23 | 8 | 15 | $30
211 Clement St. (bet. 3rd & 4th Aves.), 415-668-7317
■ A small but vocal group of unagi fanatics thinks "Toshi Sasaki is the best sushi maker around" and deem this Richmond District Japanese a "gem" that's "impossible to get into 'cuz of the size"; too bad the staff has a "bad attitude" ... "speak Japanese for better service."

Narai L S   ▽ 19 | 13 | 18 | $21
2229 Clement St. (bet. 23rd & 24th Aves.), 415-751-6363
◪ While for some it may be true that "we never had a bad dish in 10 years", other patrons of this Richmond District Thai-Chinese sniff "used to be better"; nonetheless, you can still get "good penang beef curry", hot and sour soup and other "interesting combinations of flavors."

Neecha Thai Cuisine L S M   21 | 15 | 20 | $17
2100 Sutter St. (Steiner St.), 415-922-9419
■ Surveyors say "there's lots to like" about this "always tasty", "inexpensive" Van Ness/Polk Thai that recently underwent a remodeling and now has "huge new windows", "which may herald its discovery by yuppies"; there's also an "outstanding vegetarian menu" and a "friendly" much-praised staff; Neecha know more?

New Joe's L S M   ▽ 18 | 14 | 17 | $24
Handlery Hotel, 347 Geary St. (Powell St.), 415-397-9999
◪ "Sit at the counter" "before or after the theater" at this "consistently good" if unexciting ("nothing new here") Downtown Italian with large portions of pastas and well-prepared steaks and chops; you won't hit a culinary home run, but it's an "all-around great value" and there's an "excellent bar" as well.

Nightshade ⑤Ⓜ | – | – | – | M |
2101 Sutter St. (Steiner St.), 415-541-0795
"Charming owner" Dan Rubinstein (formerly of now-defunct Ruby's) is behind this Pacific Heights "up and comer" Italian highlighted by a signature cornmeal-crust "gourmet pizza" and 24 wines by the glass; the service needs work, so "be patient" and enjoy the "inventive decor."

Nippon Sushi ⓁⓂ⇄   ▽ | 19 | 11 | 15 | $12 |
314 Church St. (15th St.), no telephone
■ "Better known as No Name Sushi" (no sign, no phone, no credit cards, no reservations), this "funky", "hole-in-the-wall" Japanese is a long-standing Castro/Noe "insider's treat"; for "value, quality and quantity", fans call it the "best and cheapest in SF"; no wonder there's "usually a wait."

Nob Hill Cafe Ⓛ⑤Ⓜ | 19 | 15 | 18 | $23 |
1152 Taylor St. (bet. Sacramento & Clay Sts.),
415-776-6500
■ A "comfortable" Italian "hangout" on Nob Hill serving a "small menu" of "tasty", "uncomplicated food" brought to table by a "friendly", "gracious" staff that "tries hard to please"; now if only "we could make reservations."

North Beach ●Ⓛ⑤Ⓜ | 20 | 19 | 19 | $30 |
1512 Stockton St. (bet. Green & Union Sts.), 415-392-1700
☑ "Beautiful renovations" to this "touristy", "true North Beach" Italian mean it's "not as homey as the original", but a rise in ratings supports those who say "the remodeling seems to have improved the food"; try the pizzas, "delicious" veal dishes and a fine bottle from the "great wine list."

North India Ⓛ⑤Ⓜ | 20 | 15 | 17 | $27 |
3131 Webster St. (bet. Lombard & Greenwich Sts.),
415-931-1556
☑ While some avoid a discussion of SF Indian food by hopping on BART to Berkeley, others have strong opinions on this Union Street location; partisans point to "great" curry and tandoori dishes, "incredible" breads, "gracious" service and "authentic" atmosphere, while detractors fulminate against food that "could be better", a "slow" kitchen and a staff that should "try being a little bit friendly"; no complaints, though, about the "lovely fluffy naan."

Occidental Grill ⓁⓂ | 18 | 18 | 18 | $28 |
453 Pine St. (bet. Montgomery & Kearny Sts.), 415-834-0484
☑ The "very manly" bar at this "clubby" American caters to "loud, obnoxious stockbrokers" taking advantage of the "great selection of cigars"; some savor the "pleasant silky scent", others say it's just "too smoky" and head to the dining room – if they know it exists ("do people eat here?"); if you're on a tight schedule, they're "good at reservations."

Ocean L S M ▽ 21 | 9 | 13 | $19
726 Clement St. (bet. 8th & 9th Aves.), 415-668-8896
☒ The live tank of fish and specials written in Chinese suggest you're in for a good meal (once you figure out what to order) at this Richmond District restaurant where the "waiters are nicer if you speak Chinese"; if that's too much to ask, order takeout and stick to fish.

Old Swiss House L S M ▽ 15 | 22 | 19 | $29
Pier 39 (Fisherman's Wharf), 415-434-0432
☒ This Swiss-Continental may be "one of the better choices on Pier 39" thanks to its "lovely old-world charm", "cozy" fireplace and "nice view" of the "boats and seals", but it's still a "tourist trap"; locals "don't bother" unless requested by "relatives from out of town."

Olive's Gourmet Pizza L S M 21 | 12 | 14 | $18
3249 Scott St. (bet. Lombard & Chestnut Sts.), 415-567-4488
■ In the SF pizza wars, this "upscale" and proportionately "pricey" Marina pie palace scores high with its "chichi toppings" and "awesome cornmeal crust that's worth driving across the city for" (but "open another branch, please!"); "limited seating" and decor mean many "only do takeout"; P.S. there are "fresh salads" and "decent pasta dishes" too.

One Market L M 21 | 21 | 20 | $38
1 Market St. (Steuart St.), 415-777-5577
☒ Chef George Morrone has brought "dazzling new food on the cutting edge" to Bradley Ogden's Downtown New American with a seafood slant, making it "better than ever", and a recent redo has "added warmth" to the previously "stark" interior; but some things remain the same – the "immense" room is "too big to be intimate" and "service can be snobby" and "snail-paced", while on the plus side, "dining at the chef's table in the kitchen" is "extraordinary."

O'Reilly's L S M ▽ 18 | 23 | 19 | $20
622 Green St. (bet. Columbus Ave. & Powell St.), 415-989-6222
☒ The "authentic atmosphere" at this "Irish pub in the middle of North Beach" comes complete with "great morale, Guinness stew and, of course, Guinness!"; some say "the food needs time", but everyone agrees it can be "fun" as long as you avoid St. Patrick's Day – "not a good day to fairly judge an Irish place."

Original Joe's ◑ L S M 18 | 13 | 17 | $21
144 Taylor St. (Turk St.), 415-775-4877
☒ "Bad neighborhood, ok food, good toothpicks" is the take on this "unchanged" Tenderloin vet proffering "mammoth servings" of "no-nonsense" Italian food and "cuts of meat that could choke a hog"; it's the kind of place where you can "ask for extra garlic" and the waiters in "tattered tuxedoes" will know exactly what you mean.

Original Old Clam House 🅛🅢🅜　　16　14　14　$21
299 Bayshore Blvd. (Oakdale St.), 415-826-4880
☑ This Mission District seafood "roadhouse" is a "longtime blue-collar hangout"; it "looks like a dump", but inside there's an "old-fashioned atmosphere" that reminds some diners of the "family-style restaurants" of their youth; the food is "honest stuff" – "catfish in huge portions", crab omelets, "good steamers."

Oritalia 🅢🅜　　　　　25　20　21　$37
1915 Fillmore St. (Wilmot St.), 415-346-1333
☑ The "innovative fusion food" of Bruce Hill has been the trademark of this Pacific Heights Eclectic, but a press-time chef shake-up (Hill is moving to The Waterfront) leaves the future somewhat uncertain; more than one surveyor has encountered "attitude up the ahi" here, though there's a "happening" atmosphere and quality has always been "way up there"; respondents hope it remains a "perfect marriage of Italy and the Orient."

Osome 🅛🅢🅜　　　　　19　15　17　$25
3145 Fillmore St. (bet. Greenwich & Filbert Sts.), 415-931-8898
☑ Perhaps "there are much better ones in the city", but this "simple" (translation: "decor needs to be redone") Union Street Japanese has fans who feel it's "one of the best deals in town" with "good food at great prices", "well-meaning service" and a "charming sushi chef"; N.B. the Pacific Heights location has reopened as Osaka.

Osteria 🅢🅜　　　　　　–　–　–　M
3277 Sacramento St. (Presidio St.), 415-771-5030
"Dependably good" dishes and excellent service mark this "cozy, old-fashioned" Pacific Heights Italian; it's sometimes "too loud" with "tables too close together", but you can't beat the "consistent, delicious" food (including some of the "best veal scallopine" in town) and "friendly" service.

Ovation at the Opera 🅛🅢🅜　　–　–　–　E
333 Fulton St. (bet. Franklin & Gough Sts.), 415-553-8100
Flagship remake of the former Act IV by Max's owner Dennis Berkowitz is now more than ever one of the most romantic rooms in town with a menu of American classics prepared with Continental flair; look forward to a round of applause for this plush Civic Center showpiece.

Pacific ◐🅛🅢🅜　　　▽　26　21　24　$42
Pan Pacific Hotel, 500 Post St. (Mason St.), 415-929-2087
◼ "Why doesn't everyone go here?" reviewers wonder about this "undiscovered and underrated" Downtown Californian presenting "fabulous food" (including "fantastic fish and excellent desserts") and "wonderful service" in a "roomy and elegant" space; its third-floor location in the Pan Pacific Hotel keeps it "a wonderful secret" much to the delight of devotees.

Pacific Cafe 🅂🅼   21 | 15 | 20 | $24
7000 Geary Blvd. (34th Ave.), 415-387-7091

■ "I would sail around the world for their crab" speaks oceans about this "comfortable" fish house in Outer Richmond serving "great local seafood" and "free wine" during the "inevitable" "long wait"; some find both the "'70s decor" and menu "unimaginative", but fin fanciers swear "you can't beat it for basic fish" at "unpretentious prices."

Palio d'Asti 🅻🅼   21 | 20 | 20 | $31
640 Sacramento St. (bet. Montgomery & Kearny Sts.), 415-395-9800

■ A "classic SF paninoteca" that more than one surveyor says has "a special place in my heart" for its "great panini", "dreamy pastas", "out of this world risottos" and other more "exotic" Northern Italian specialties served in a "fun, lighthearted atmosphere"; it may be Downtown's "best lunch spot", but "why don't they serve dinner?"

Palomino Euro Bistro 🌓🅻🅂🅼   20 | 24 | 21 | $32
345 Spear St. (bet. Folsom & Steuart Sts), 415-512-7400

■ This "very hot and hip" SOMA Mediterranean with "sparkling glass sculpture decor" is a hit with reviewers; it's corporate-owned and some "hesitate to approve", but most insist it's not only a "great outdoor lunch spot" but "fabu in the evening" as well, with "friendly staff" and an "interesting menu" of pizzas and appetizers that are "better than the main courses"; "love the energy here."

Pancho Villa Taqueria 🌓🅻🅂🅼   21 | 11 | 15 | $11
3071 16th St. (Valencia St.), 415-864-8840

■ It's the "absolute best" Mission taqueria according to amigos who herald "cheap and fast" "terrific options" like "great grilled Mexican shrimp", BBQ pork and the "best horchata north of Mexico"; "ordering can be stressful", with lines out the door in an iffy neighborhood, but for "a real burrito experience" try this Pancho on.

PANE E VINO 🅻🅂🅼   24 | 20 | 20 | $31
3011 Steiner St. (Union St.), 415-346-2111

■ "Too loud, too brash and too tasty to stay away" from, this "terrific" Union Street trattoria is a jam-packed SF favorite; even if they "don't manage reservations well" and the staff "could be friendlier", the "great antipasti", "outstanding risottos" and "best pastas" all "prepared with pizazz" keep customers coming.

Paragon Bar & Grill 🅂🅼   16 | 13 | 13 | $24
3251 Scott St. (Chestnut St.), 415-922-2456

■ This Marina American is a "cool" "yuppie" "scene" with a new chef and a menu that's reportedly "surprisingly good"; however, you won't be able to discuss the food until after you leave because "it's so loud you have to shout"; they've remodeled the interior, but scores suggest no one's noticed.

Park Grill L S M   21 | 22 | 22 | $43
Park Hyatt Hotel, 333 Battery St. (Clay St.), 415-392-1234
■ "Power lunching at its best" is the stock in trade of this
Downtown Continental that also serves as a "sleeper for
dinner"; "tastefully prepared dishes", a "stylish but sedate
environment" and service that "caters to individual needs"
make it "exactly what you want a hotel restaurant to be";
it's the "best place you never thought of going."

Parma L S M   22 | 17 | 20 | $25
3314 Steiner St. (bet. Lombard & Chestnut Sts.), 415-567-0500
■ "Bravo, owner Pietro is a pleasure" and his "outrageously
friendly staff" will take good care of you at this modest
Marina Italian where every dish is "made with amore"; look
forward to "wonderful" pastas served "nostra famiglia style"
in a "quaint atmosphere"; it's "fine neighborhood fare."

Pasta Pomodoro L S M⇔   18 | 12 | 16 | $13
2304 Market St. (16th St.), 415-558-8123
2027 Chestnut St. (bet. Lombard & Steiner Sts.), 415-474-3400
655 Union St. (Columbus Ave.), 415-399-0300
816 Irving St. (bet. 9th & 10th Aves.), 415-566-0900
■ "What a concept" – "excellent pasta", "phenomenally
low prices" and decidedly "'90s decor" make for long
lines ("hunky help" can't hurt either) at this "cheap and
cheerful" pasta chain; from mid-morning to midnight
respondents are "amazed at how consistently good it is"
and the countertop consensus is "adoro Pomodoro."

Pastis L M   23 | 21 | 21 | $36
1015 Battery St. (bet. Union & Green Sts.), 415-391-2555
■ "Gerald Hirigoyen's got another great bistro" in this
"smart" Downtown French; while it's "not quite up to" its
crosstown sister, Fringale, it's "less noisy" and crowded,
"easier to get a table" and has a "can't go wrong" menu
of "sumptuous entrees and desserts"; plenty of "parking
in front", so don't Pastis one by.

Pauline's S   23 | 14 | 16 | $18
260 Valencia St. (bet. 14th & Duboce Sts.), 415-552-2050
■ "Fresh ingredients combined in new ways" make for
"organic pizza with panache" at this Mission District pie
emporium with a garden and "romantic" chandeliered
restroom; the "icky neighborhood" is the peril of Pauline's
and it might well be "the most expensive pizza you've ever
eaten", but most rave she "has no equal."

Pauli's Cafe L S M   17 | 14 | 17 | $21
2500 Washington St. (Fillmore St.), 415-921-5159
☑ They let the sun shine in ("lots of windows") at this
"comfy" Pacific Heights New American that respondents
report is "a good brunch spot" but otherwise "easy to
forget"; with such reasonable prices, this place "could do
better", but at least it "always has tables" available.

Perry's L M
| 15 | 16 | 16 | $22 |

1944 Union St. (bet. Laguna & Buchanan Sts.),
415-922-9022 ● S
185 Sutter St. (bet. Kearny & Montgomery Sts.), 415-989-6895
☑ Even though some ask "haven't we outgrown this
concept?", there's still a lot of "clubby charm" at this "old
single yuppies hangout" on Union Street and its newer
Downtown clone; the chopped salads and burgers are
"still first-rate", but the rest of the American menu suffers
from "kitchen indifference"; surveyors say it's the "same
as ever – for better or for worse."

Picaro L S M ⇗
∇ | 20 | 17 | 16 | $21 |

3120 16th St. (bet. Valencia & Guerrero Sts.), 415-431-4089
☑ Some call it "Americanized Spanish", but others say
there's a "good variety of yummy tapas" at this Mission
District cafe; surrealist decor and "fun" atmosphere keep
a picaresque clientele happy; there may be "better
options available", but at least "the price is right."

Pickled Ginger L S M
| – | – | – | M |

100 Brannan St. (Embarcadero), 415-977-1230
New South Beach write-in offering Asian-Californian fare
("the vegetable side dishes are outstanding"); the open
kitchen and comfy booths make for a contemporary feel;
look for lots of gingery dishes on the "sophisticated menu."

Pier 23 Cafe
| 14 | 17 | 13 | $20 |

Embarcadero (Greenwich St.), 415-362-5125
☑ The "outdoor deck" is the saving grace of this "funky"
Downtown "afternoon beer in the sun" place where
reviewers "kick back" with a drink or dance to live jazz
and reggae; while there's an unimpressive menu of
burgers, salads and fries that suits the mostly "20-year-
old crowd" just fine, the real reason people come here is
to enjoy the "Embarcadero with a soul."

PJ's Oyster Bed L S M
| 21 | 15 | 18 | $26 |

737 Irving St. (bet. 8th & 9th Aves.), 415-566-7766
☑ A "high energy", "hustle and bustle" Inner Sunset
seafooder with a "noisy and wild" "frathouse atmosphere"
that's perfect for a group; supporters say the huge, freshly
shucked shellfish platter from the adjacent seafood market
is a winner as are the Cajun-Creole nights; overall, it's
a great "value" that's "worth the crush" and "wait."

Planet Hollywood ● L S M
| 9 | 18 | 12 | $21 |

2 Stockton St. (bet. Market & O'Farrell Sts.), 415-421-7827
☑ Tough critics contend this movie memorabilia–filled
"magnet for camera-toting teenage tourists" represents
the "triumph of hype over gastronomic sensibility", serving
"bad", "overpriced" Traditional American grub; those
who went once say "no rerun" or are waiting to return when
the star investors show up – "I've never seen Demi here."

Plouf 🇱🇲　　　　23 | 20 | 20 | $29
40 Belden Pl. (bet. Kearny & Bush Sts.), 415-986-6491
■ A French seafood bistro with "charming European atmosphere" and, hands down, the "best mussels in town" (prepared seven different ways) along with other "terrific" oceanic inventions like rock shrimp on couscous; the "I just got here from Paris service" is sometimes "lacking" but "flirtatious" enough to keep the clientele amused; "so many mussels, so little time."

PLUMPJACK CAFE 🇱🇲　　　25 | 22 | 23 | $40
3127 Fillmore St. (bet. Greenwich & Filbert Sts.), 415-563-4755
■ The "in-crowd" squeezes into "elbow-to-elbow quarters" amidst "painstaking decor" at this Union Street Mediterranean co-owned by members of the Getty family; expect "consistently excellent", "sophisticated, savory" food from chef Maria Helm, an "outstanding" wine list at "bargain" prices and "ultraprofessional" service; now "if you can get a table, you've got it made."

Pluto's 🇱🇸🇲　　　　19 | 14 | 14 | $12
627 Irving St. (bet. 7th & 8th Aves.), 415-753-8867
3258 Scott St. (bet. Lombard & Chestnut Sts.), 415-775-8867
■ "It's Thanksgiving year around" at these "yuppeterias" offering "galactic portions" of "cheap, delicious, healthy, homestyle food" including "awesome salads", "fantastic flank steak" and roasted turkey with potatoes; some find the ordering system "infuriating" and the lines are long, but at these prices "why ever cook at home again?"

POSTRIO 🇱🇸🇲　　　　26 | 26 | 24 | $49
Prescott Hotel, 545 Post St. (bet. Mason & Taylor Sts.), 415-776-7825
■ When they say "only Wolfgang could do this", they don't just mean putting caviar on pizza; his "rich food/rich people" Downtown Cal-Med is still "flying high" complete with a "frenzy" of "hobnobbing" in the "dramatic" Pat Kuleto–designed room and a staff that will "even bone sand dabs at the table"; a few pout "Puck peaked a while ago", but most rate the Rosenthal brothers' cuisine "spectacular."

Prego Ristorante ⬤🇱🇸🇲　　18 | 18 | 18 | $29
2000 Union St. (Buchanan St.), 415-563-3305
☑ The "young crowd" that calls this Union Street trattoria home advises "wear black and bring a cell phone"; the Italian fare is "solid", though some complain of "aloof waiters" and "small portions" and say it's "wearing thin."

Primo Patio Cafe 🇱🇲⇄　　▽ 17 | 14 | 15 | $18
214 Townsend St. (bet. 3rd & 4th Sts.), 415-957-1129
■ A "funky brunch" of "tasty jerk chicken" can be had on the patio of this SOMA Caribbean-Cuban; there's a "very friendly" staff and at these prices it's "the perfect cheap thrill"; N.B. limited hours, so call ahead.

Puccini & Pinetti L S M
17 | 18 | 18 | $27

Monticello Inn, 129 Ellis St. (bet. Mason & Powell Sts.), 415-392-5500

◪ You can get a "reasonable pre-theater meal" at this "loud and raucous" Downtown Italian run by the Kimpton Group; expect "intriguing decor", a "fun crowd" and a kitchen that "can produce very tasty dishes"; but some think "it will have to be better to survive in this city."

Radicchio Trattoria S
▽ 19 | 18 | 20 | $26

1809 Union St. (Octavia St.), 415-346-7373

◪ "Quaint and comfortable" Union Street trattoria that's a good value even though "the food lacks variety and style"; the "pleasant staff" makes it a "friendly neighborhood place", but in this Italian-saturated part of town some rate it "decidedly ok" at best.

Rasselas Ethiopian S M
▽ 17 | 18 | 18 | $22

2801 California St. (Divisadero St.), 415-567-5010

◪ "The jazz really sets the mood" at this affordable Pacific Heights Ethiopian where most say you can "skip" the "spicy finger food"; before the live music comes on, you might find yourself "eating Ethiopian with Motown music blaring."

Raw Living Foods L S M
▽ 15 | 14 | 13 | $21

1224 Ninth Ave. (Lincoln Way), 415-665-6519

◪ No, it's not "a *Saturday Night Live* skit", but "it's an experience" swear visitors to this Inner Sunset Vegetarian with "odd garden furniture" decor; all the organic foods are served raw and, apparently, not always successfully ("the pizza was sawdust on plywood"); but all that counts is that "the veg people love it."

Rendezvous du Monde L M
20 | 18 | 20 | $24

431 Bush St. (bet. Grant & Kearny Sts.), 415-392-3332

■ "I'll have a rendezvous here any day" declare devotees of this "cozy" Downtown French-Mediterranean budget bistro with "Parisian alley" ambiance and a "hardworking", "gracious" staff; it's a "great shopping stop" for sandwiches, salads and "devastatingly good desserts."

Rick's Restaurant & Bar S M
▽ 19 | 19 | 19 | $25

1940 Taraval St. (30th Ave.), 415-731-8900

◪ The "beautiful" mahogany bar gets busy early at this Sunset District venue that locals feel is a "best-kept secret"; look for strictly "classic" American "home-cooked" food every day of the month except the first Monday, when it also serves "interesting Hawaiian dishes."

Ristorante Bacco S M
22 | 20 | 21 | $28

737 Diamond St. (bet. 24th & Elizabeth Sts.), 415-282-4969

■ There's "fancy", "absolutely blissful pasta" and "real Italian waiters" at this Noe Valley trattoria; it's "not that expensive" and for a neighborhood place it "can't be topped"; "what a nice place to have around the corner!"

Ristorante Ecco L M   21 | 22 | 20 | $37 |
101 South Park (bet. 2nd & 3rd Sts.), 415-495-3291
■ "I always feel special" at this "classy" and expensive Italian in a "beautiful", "sleek", "modern" "oasis of serenity" in South Park; the "surprisingly diverse menu" might include rabbit and features some of the "best risotto" in town; it's a "nice alternative to ever-popular loud and trendy restaurants" and there's a "great wine list."

Ristorante Ideale S   21 | 18 | 21 | $29 |
1309 Grant Ave. (bet. Vallejo & Green Sts.), 415-391-4129
■ "Friendly guys from Rome" serve "simply prepared and robust" Italian at this "overlooked" North Beach paesani post; admirers add that it has the most "authentic" feel of all the so-called Italians in the area.

Ristorante Milano S   24 | 17 | 23 | $30 |
1448 Pacific Ave. (bet. Hyde & Larkin Sts.), 415-673-2961
■ The hospitable owners are "very into it" at this "small and stylish" Italian on Nob Hill; outside the parking spaces are few and far between and inside the space is "cramped" and the "bustling servers" are sometimes "overwhelmed", but for "great dishes" like the gnocchi, risotto and tiramisu, some call it the "best Northern Italian cooking in SF."

RITZ-CARLTON DINING ROOM M   28 | 28 | 28 | $63 |
Ritz-Carlton Hotel, 600 Stockton St. (bet. California & Pine Sts.), 415-296-7465
■ "NY's loss, SF's gain" boast those who say that chef Sylvain Portay (ex NY's Le Cirque) "didn't miss a beat" in taking over the stoves at this "sterling" and top-rated Downtown New French; "phenomenal food" plus "accurate, polished service" in a serene, "buttoned-down atmosphere" assure a suitably ritzy experience that's "worth every dollar from beginning to end"; try as you may, "you just can't get a bad meal here."

Ritz-Carlton Terrace L S M   25 | 25 | 25 | $43 |
Ritz-Carlton Hotel, 600 Stockton St. (bet. California & Pine Sts.), 415-296-7465
■ You'll find "Ritz-Carlton style" at "affordable prices" at this "relaxing" Nob Hill American; "the English club theme is a little overdone", but there are no complaints about the "hovering service" and "very creative food"; there's also "lovely afternoon tea with excellent goodies" and the "best and most expensive Sunday brunch in SF."

Rocco's Seafood Grill S M   ▽ 21 | 18 | 19 | $28 |
2080 Van Ness Ave. (Pacific Ave.), 415-567-7600
☑ Sam Duvall's (Izzy's) Van Ness seafooder is an "art deco wonderland" proffering "plentiful" portions of "very good quality" seafood including some SF-style classics like cioppino and sauteed sand dabs; some find the service shaky, but most think it's "doing well for a newcomer."

Roosevelt Tamale Parlor ⓁⓈ⌀　　20 | 10 | 15 | $12
2817 24th St. (bet. Bryant & York Sts.), 415-550-9213
▨ This ageless ("better than 10 years ago") Mission Mexican in a "too scary" neighborhood is a "colorful" "icon" serving some of the "best mole in town" and "large portions" of "authentic tamales" at "low prices"; the decor is "no frills", but most don't mind because they just "love this old dump."

Rooster, The ⓈⓂ　　19 | 20 | 19 | $27
1101 Valencia St. (22nd St.), 415-824-1222
▨ The "20s crowd" claims it's "hard to get a reservation" at this "friendly" Mission International decorated with "rich eclectic colors" and electric lights; phobes think it's "all ambiance" and "needs less bark and more bite", but fans crow about the "hearty homestyle" food from Europe and Asia: "my stomach is always happy after eating here."

ROSE PISTOLA ⓁⓈⓂ　　22 | 21 | 19 | $36
532 Columbus Ave. (bet. Union & Green Sts.), 415-399-0499
▨ This "pretty" but "noisy" and "hectic" North Beach Italian from superchef Reed Hearon features a large menu of smashing, "inspiring" Ligurian seafood served family style; it's "great for groups" or to "sit at the counter watching the cooks", however we hear a lot of complaints about "icy" staff with "way too much attitude."

Rose's Cafe ⓁⓈⓂ　　– | – | – | M
2298 Union St. (Steiner St.), 415-775-2200
New upscale breakfast, lunch and dinner cafe on Union Street from Reed Hearon (Rose Pistola) featuring counter service for simple Italian and Mediterranean fare; the early word is the thin-crust pizzas are molto bene.

Rosti ⓁⓈⓂ　　15 | 13 | 15 | $20
2060 Chestnut St. (bet. Fillmore & Steiner Sts.),
415-929-9300
▨ "Monster portions" of "rich and alluring" grilled chicken is the main reason to stop at the Marina branch of this LA-based Tuscan chain; while the atmosphere is "informal", some still find the place "too assembly line–like" and think there are "better choices around"; nevertheless, it's "ok in a pinch" and a "solid value."

Roti ⓁⓈⓂ　　22 | 21 | 20 | $34
Hotel Griffon, 155 Steuart St. (bet. Mission & Howard Sts.),
415-495-6500
▨ Expect "elegance, style and flavor" – and a view of the Bay Bridge – at this "comfortable and cozy" SOMA American in the Hotel Griffon; "well-executed" rotisserie items head up the menu, with "doting" follow-through from a "four-star friendly" staff; while "not too exciting", at least "you know what to expect."

Rotunda 🅛🆂🅜 | 20 | 23 | 20 | $32 |
Neiman Marcus, 150 Stockton St. (Geary Blvd.),
415-362-4777
■ A "spectacular" Tiffany-like dome and view of Union
Square are the highlights of this "very civil" Downtown
American in Neiman Marcus; the "ladies lunch" crowd
calls it perfect for popovers and tea after a rough day of
looking for a new coat ("shopping for ermine can be so
tiring"); the new chef seems to be holding up well.

Royal Thai 🅛🆂🅜 | 22 | 15 | 18 | $21 |
951 Clement St. (11th Ave.), 415-386-1795
See review in North of San Francisco Directory.

RUBICON 🅛🅜 | 24 | 21 | 22 | $46 |
558 Sacramento St. (bet. Sansome & Montgomery Sts.),
415-434-4100
☑ This "very New York", "club-style" Downtown New
French is part of Manhattan restaurateur Drew Nieporent's
expanding empire; while many "miss Traci" des Jardins,
current chef Scott Newman's "elegant" fare is "hanging
on well" as is the superb wine list from Larry Stone, who
many consider "the best sommelier in town"; the disaffected
say the service can be inconsistent and think the wine more
of an event than the food.

Rumpus 🅛🆂🅜 | 20 | 19 | 20 | $34 |
1 Tillman Pl. (bet. Post & Sutter Sts.), 415-421-2300
☑ The name is no accident: it's "too damn noisy" at this
"artsy" Downtown Cal-French bistro hidden in an alley off
Union Square; a staff of "good people" creates a "fun and
friendly" ambiance and the casual food can be "wonderful",
with risotto and chocolate brioche singled out for kudos.

Sally's 🅛🆂🅜   ▽ | 18 | 10 | 13 | $12 |
300 De Haro St. (16th St.), 415-626-6006
■ "Stellar bakery goods" remain the main attraction at this
Potrero Hill "breakfast hangout" that also doles out killer
home fries; it's sometimes "too busy at lunch", but those
who view it as a "pickup spot" claim it's "worth the wait."

Sam's Grill & Seafood | 21 | 17 | 17 | $29 |
Restaurant 🅛🅜
374 Bush St. (bet. Kearny & Montgomery Sts.),
415-421-0594
■ "Bring a trench coat and fedora" to this "blast from the
past" Downtown seafood grill with private booths that
"promote conspiracy"; "everything dates from the year
one", including the "gruff" waiters who "never smile", but
the chef "cooks fish simply and well"; classic petrale,
"wonderful sand dabs" or the "best swordfish" – "no matter
what you get, order the creamed spinach."

Samui Thai Cuisine ⚫L⚫S⚫M ▽ | 19 | 12 | 17 | $19 |
2414 Lombard St. (Scott St.), 415-563-4405

🔳 Try the "excellent bean cakes", "awesome" duck curry and other "great southern Thai food" at this reasonable Union Street eatery; the ambiance is "unpretentious" and repeat visits (including takeout) by neighborhood fans mean "they get much of our money."

San Francisco BBQ ⚫L⚫S🔳 ▽ | 16 | 9 | 13 | $14 |
1328 18th St. (bet. Missouri & Texas Sts.), 415-431-8956

🔳 "Very reasonably priced" seems to be the operative phrase for this Thai barbecue on Potrero Hill; if you "don't mind the wait" you can get "freshly grilled foods" or "good duck or chicken with noodles"; P.S. "it's great for takeout."

Sanppo ⚫L⚫S⚫M ▽ | 19 | 15 | 16 | $18 |
1702 Post St. (Buchanan St.), 415-346-3486

🔳 The few reviewers who've discovered this "casual", "immaculate" Japantown Japanese insist it's "almost an institution" and a "family favorite" for chirashi and other "cheap and plentiful food."

Sanraku Four Seasons ⚫L⚫S⚫M ▽ | 26 | 18 | 21 | $30 |
704 Sutter St. (Taylor St.), 415-771-0803

🔳 It's "hard to choose" from the large selection of sakes at this "stylish" Downtown "sleeper" that's "definitely not your father's Japanese restaurant"; there are two dining rooms, one more formal than the other, and the handful who've tried either insist the fare's "exquisite" and a "great value as well."

Savor ⚫L⚫M | – | – | – | M |
3913 24th St. (Sanchez St.), 415-282-0344

Midscale, wallet-friendly Eclectic "local fun spot" in Noe Valley gets write-in votes for its fresh-baked goods, orange-ginger pancakes and "good crêpes"; the abobe-style ambiance includes a "delightful courtyard" where you can enjoy a "yuppie brunch"; surveyors say "you'll savor every bite."

SCALA'S BISTRO ⊘⚫L⚫S⚫M | 23 | 24 | 21 | $35 |
Sir Francis Drake Hotel, 432 Powell St. (bet. Post & Sutter Sts.), 415-395-8555

🔳 "Outstanding" Union Square French-Italian that just "gets better and better"; a "splendid high ceiling" and bold decor statements make it "a wow of a place" with "lots of energy" and "fascinating clientele"; the "excellent" bistro fare has "an earthy quality" and "professional" service from the "very special staff" will ensure that you make your theater curtain.

Schroeder's Cafe 🅛 Ⓜ   15 | 16 | 18 | $23
204 Front St. (California St.), 415-421-4778
☑ A "wonderfully cranky and abrupt staff" right out of "central casting" awaits you at this "dark, depressing" Downtown German that's a "flashback to another era"; while the food rating has risen since our last *Survey*, and a few holdouts insist they've gotten the "best sauerbraten" and "shoestring fries" here, a lot of respondents report that it remains in "a major decline."

Scoma's 🅛 Ⓢ Ⓜ   17 | 17 | 16 | $30
Pier 47, Fisherman's Wharf (bet. Jones & Jefferson Sts.), 415-771-4383
☑ "Totally touristy", "high-volume" Fisherman's Wharf and Sausalito seafooders whose customers "should be mooing because they're herded in and out"; most peg the food as "bland" and "overpriced", but since the Wharf branch is "one of the best" restaurants in the area and there's an "unforgettable view of the city" from the Sausalito spot, they're convenient "when visitors are in town."

Scott's Seafood Grill & Bar 🅛 Ⓢ Ⓜ   18 | 17 | 18 | $29
3 Embarcadero Ctr. (Drumm & Sacramento Sts.), 415-981-0622
2400 Lombard St. (Scott St.), 415-563-8988
☑ The original SF Scott's is operated independently, but other locations of this "sterile" seafood chain have become largely "formulaic"; some say there's still "surprisingly decent seafood" to be found among the "well-worn items" on the menu, but many find it "not terribly imaginative" and think it "needs to move into the '90s."

Sears Fine Food 🅛 Ⓢ Ⓜ⌿   17 | 12 | 16 | $17
Union Sq., 439 Powell St. (bet. Post & Sutter Sts.), 415-986-1160
☑ Before the invention of attitude there were simply "surly waitresses" and you can still find them (complete with pink uniforms) at this Downtown breakfast spot; the "retro" decor "seems authentic" because it is, and tourists and locals alike flock here for real "pre-WWII cuisine"; a few "don't understand the appeal", but supporters say it has something to do with those "wonderful little" pancakes.

Seoul Garden 🅛 Ⓢ Ⓜ   ▽ 22 | 15 | 15 | $24
Japan Ctr., 22 Peace Plaza (bet. Laguna & Webster Sts.), 415-563-7664
■ Attention kimchi addicts: this Japantown Korean with cook-it-yourself grills is an authentic sleeper; few responses from reviewers indicate you may have the "inviting decor" and deferential service to yourself, but with "delicious, traditional" fare you might want to keep it that way.

Silks ⬛🅂🅼　　25　25　24　$52
Mandarin Oriental Hotel, 222 Sansome St. (California St.),
415-986-2020
☑ "You're never rushed" at this "quiet", "understated",
"elegant" Downtown Cal-Asian that affords "privacy
within a roomful of others"; it's a "top-notch business
dinner place", though many say it "never seems to be
crowded" and are "amazed a restaurant of this caliber
remains undiscovered"; the less impressed sniff "tired" and
"used to be better", but solid scores tell a different tale.

Sinead's Irish Bar and　　–　–　–　M
Restaurant 🅂🅼
3565 Geary Blvd. (Arguello), 415-386-2000
This Richmond District Irish bar/restaurant on the site of
the former Orocco Supper Club proves that the cuisine
can go upscale; the largish venue features Irish specialties
along with live entertainment nightly.

Slanted Door ⬛🅂　　24　19　20　$25
584 Valencia St. (bet. 16th & 17th St.), 415-861-8032
◼ This Mission hot spot may have "down-market decor",
but there's an "inventive and varied menu" of "mind-
blowing" Vietnamese food that puts a whole new slant on
the cuisine, enhanced by an "excellently matched wine list";
the "scintillating" flavors and "well-informed staff" make
it a "scene-o-rama", so reserve early and "start salivating
two weeks in advance"; "watch this place – it's a winner."

Slow Club ⬛🅼　　21　19　16　$24
2501 Mariposa St. (Hampshire St.), 415-241-9390
◼ "Oh no, the secret's out!" – a young crowd zips in for "hip
cuisine" at this "dark" Potrero Hill American with "steel
mill" decor; Mediterranean influences on the menu mean
"great tapas" and "hearty portions of beautifully prepared
food"; the waiters "need to work on their attitude", but how
else would we know "this place is cool"?

Socca 🅂　　23　19　22　$34
5800 Geary Blvd. (22nd Ave.), 415-379-6720
◼ A popular Provençal street snack provides the name for
this "lively, cozy" Richmond "sensual Mediterranean"
with "sophisticated yet rustic" ambiance; service is "not
always professional", but the owners are "charming" and
the reasonably priced and "highly inventive" menu from
chef John Caputo has voters chanting "Socca to me!"

Sol y Luna ⬛🅼　　17　18　16　$26
475 Sacramento St. (bet. Battery & Sansome Sts.), 415-296-8696
☑ A "sizzling night scene is the draw" at this Downtown
"Latin dance and dine" where live flamenco shows and
salsa dancing take precedence over "average yuppie
tapas", though some report that the paella can be "terrific";
"go with your dancing shoes on" and bring a "large group."

South Park Cafe 🅛 🅜　　21｜19｜20｜$29｜
108 South Park (bet. 2nd & 3rd Sts.), 415-495-7275
■ "It's just like Paris, but they speak English" at this "boisterous" but "cozy as they come" SOMA French where the ambiance is "extra-extra romantic" and "you feel taken care of" by the attentive staff; "hugely satisfying" bistro fare has our Rive Gauche respondents raving that it's simply "magnifique."

Splendido 🅛 🅢 🅜　　21｜22｜20｜$32｜
4 Embarcadero Ctr. (bet. Drumm & Clay Sts.), 415-986-3222
■ Get a "live cooking lesson" from the open kitchen while enjoying "excellent Tuscan-style food" from new chef Giovanni Perticone at this Downtown Italian with Pat Kuleto's "subterranean Mediterranean" decor and "awesome stained glass"; while the "slow service" gets less than splendido reviews, the food is "always tasty" and "don't even think of sharing the warm chocolate cake."

Spuntino 🅛 🅢 🅜　　16｜15｜14｜$19｜
524 Van Ness Ave. (bet. McAllister & Golden Gate Sts.), 415-861-7772
☑ "Italian fast food at its finest" makes for a "quick but forgettable" pre-symphony fix at this affordable "cafeteria with an attitude" handy to Davies Hall and the Opera House; it's "too noisy" and as the place can be "crazed" before curtain, off hours are your best bet.

Stars 🅛 🅜　　21｜22｜20｜$48｜
150 Redwood Alley (Van Ness Ave.), 415-861-7827
☑ For some, Jeremiah Tower's "swanky", "high-energy" Civic Center New American is a SF "classic" with "good" California cuisine and maybe "the greatest bar in town"; but an increasing number of surveyors say it's "overrated", "vastly overpriced" and "losing its glimmer"; still, with a Who's Who clientele busy "celebrating themselves", the Stars-gazing is still unsurpassed; N.B. in December '97, Tower will reclaim the Stars Cafe name and open a new starlet smack next door to the mother ship.

Stars Cafe 🅛 🅢 🅜　　–｜–｜–｜M｜
500 Van Ness Ave. (McAllister St.), 415-861-4344
This offshoot of Stars around the corner from the original will get a new moniker and menu in December '97 when the name reverts back to owner Jeremiah Tower and he uses it for his new cafe, which will rise up next door to Stars.

Stelline 🅛 🅢 🅜　　–｜–｜–｜M｜
429 Gough St. (bet. Ivy & Hayes Sts.), 415-626-4292
Locals would "like to keep it a secret" but have to admit that this "bistro-like" Civic Center Italian write-in (run by the owners of nearby Caffe Delle Stelle) "can't be beat"; "great Italian food" and "great service" are a stellar combination and make this one shine.

Stinking Rose L S M   14 16 15 $24
325 Columbus Ave. (bet. Broadway & Vallejo St.),
415-781-7673
☒ "They season their garlic with too much food" at this
North Beach concept Italian where "everything's stinking,
including the service"; vampires hate it, tourists love it
and locals think it's "not even for relatives you don't like";
maybe it's just "too much of a good thing" since there's
even "garlic ice cream."

Storyville Classic Jazz Club   ▽ 15 21 17 $25
1751 Fulton St. (Masonic Ave.), 415-441-1751
■ "Music's the thing" at this Haight-Ashbury New American
where the "'50s jazz club" ambiance hits some high notes,
but the food is "sketchy" and in need of fine tuning.

Straits Cafe L S M   21 17 18 $24
3300 Geary Blvd. (Parker St.), 415-668-1783
■ "Don't hesitate to try something new" ("the leaf-wrapped
salmon is heavenly") at this "exceptional" Richmond
District Singaporean where chef-owner Chris Yeo's "flavors
dance in your mouth" and the "funky" "movie set" design
re-creates an Asian backstreet; it's "a favorite place
for adventure", so "if you love spicy, go to town!"

Sukhothai L S M   ▽ 18 12 17 $17
1319 Ninth Ave. (Irving St.), 415-564-7722
☒ "Straightforward" sums up this reasonable Sunset
Thai; some advise "remember the Rolaids" and turn their
noses up at "standard fare", but service is "very friendly"
so just ask and you might find a treasure or two among
the items not listed on the menu.

Suppenküche S M   22 18 19 $25
601 Hayes St. (Laguna St.), 415-252-9289
■ "Straight out of Bavaria" comes this Civic Center German
"wunderkind" with a "monastic beer hall" ambiance,
sauerbraten and schnitzel that are "as good as German
food gets" and "great" weekend brunches; it's "noisy"
and you might have to share your plank table with others,
but it's "fun" and there are "incredible beers on tap."

SWAN OYSTER DEPOT L M ⇄   26 14 23 $22
1517 Polk (bet. California & Sacramento Sts.),
415-673-1101
■ Slurping down "cherrystones and Anchor Steam draft"
at this Van Ness/Polk 1912 oyster bar is "the most fun you
can have in public"; it's a little pricey, but "quiveringly fresh
seafood", "the warmth of the staff" and the original "if it
ain't broke don't fix it" tile decor might make it the "best
raw bar in the universe"; boosters brag that it has "better
clam chowder than Boston" too.

Sweet Heat 🅻🅂🄼   17 | 14 | 16 | $13
2141 Polk St. (bet. Broadway & Vallejo St.), 415-775-1055
1725 Haight St. (bet. Cole & Shrader Sts.), 415-387-8845
3324 Steiner St. (bet. Chestnut & Lombard Sts.), 415-474-9191
■ Fans of these "cheap and cheerful", "wave of the future", "healthy and tasty" Mexicans praise the "great burritos", "excellent fish tacos" and terrific "tequila selection" and also love the fact that "they deliver"; a minority is not so sweet on the Heat, insisting it "needs more oomph."

Tadich Grill 🅻🄼   21 | 19 | 19 | $29
240 California St. (bet. Front & Battery Sts.), 415-391-1849
◩ Supposedly the "surly waiters are a thing of the past", but someone forgot to inform the gruff and grumpy staff at this "old school", "male dominated" Downtown seafood landmark that's been doling out "perfect grilled" fish and soggy sides for almost 150 years; no reserving means there can be "frustrating waits" for the cozy booths, but most think it's "SF at its best" and "hope it's always around."

Tanuki 🅻🅂🄼   ∇ 21 | 13 | 17 | $23
4419 California St. (6th Ave.), 415-752-5740
◪ There's "fresh sushi" and "good sashimi" at this "authentic" Richmond District Japanese; it's off the beaten path and the "atmosphere is boring", but "excellent prices" add to its appeal.

Tarantino's 🅻🅂🄼   ∇ 15 | 16 | 15 | $31
206 Jefferson St. (Taylor St.), 415-775-5600
◪ Locals consider this Fisherman's Wharf Italian seafooder an "adequate" "tourist destination" with a "wonderful view" but not much more; although some say it "consistently improves", most maintain it's "nothing out of the ordinary."

THEP PHANOM 🅂🄼   26 | 18 | 20 | $22
400 Waller St. (Fillmore St.), 415-431-2526
■ "Be sure to try the specials" at this lower Haight-Ashbury Thai, which takes the honors again this year for "best Thai in SF"; despite the "crummy neighborhood" and "funky living room" ambiance, it's "always crowded" and "what a wine list"; the hosts are "charming" and the affordable tab makes it "a pearl at bargain prices"; just call it "Thep-phenomenal!"

Thirsty Bear Brewing Co. 🅻🅂🄼   17 | 15 | 16 | $23
661 Howard St. (3rd St.), 415-974-0905
◪ This "cavernous" and "always animated" SOMA microbrew and tapas joint has a "cold, industrial interior" and "hectic, unprofessional service", but it's still a hit with twentysomething after-work types who prop themselves on stools and sample "fabulous and creative" vs. "ersatz" Spanish fare; after a few "smooth beers", some say "I feel like I'm in Catalonia, Catalunya . . . whatever!"

Ti Couz 🅻🆂🅼　　　22　17　17　$17
3108 16th St. (bet. Valencia & Guerrero Sts.), 415-252-7373
■ "Love at first bite" Mission District French where "extremely long waits" mean nothing when the end result is "incredible" sweet and savory crêpes washed down with mason jars of red wine or cider; the neighborhood's "dumpy", but the hip, "upscale crowd" eats it all up.

Timo's 🆂🅼　　　20　15　16　$22
842 Valencia St. (bet. 19th & 20th Sts.), 415-647-0558
Ghirardelli Sq., 900 North Point (Larkin St.), 415-440-1200 🅻
■ The Ghirardelli Square offspring of the original "funky" Mission Spanish has "great trappings" and a fab view of the Bay; both offer "dependable and tasty" tapas in a colorful, "fun and jumpin'" atmosphere, but some report "the service needs help"; the sangria-soaked crowd can be overly "festive" at times, so "don't let them seat you next to the snake-filled bar."

Tommaso's 🆂　　　22　17　19　$21
1042 Kearny St. (Broadway), 415-398-9696
■ The reason it "feels like old North Beach" is this "cozy" Italian has been around since 1935, and you don't stay in business that long without serving a "consistently good" brick-oven pie; while it also features a full menu of traditional Italian food, everyone's fixated on the "can't go wrong" pies.

Tommy's Joynt ●🅻🆂🅼⇄　　　14　15　12　$14
1101 Geary Blvd. (Van Ness Ave.), 415-775-4216
☑ You'll "feel like you're in New Jersey" at this "meat, meat and more meat" Traditional American "fixture" on Van Ness with "so what do you want?" service; it's "a little grungy", but there's an "enormous beer selection" and "all you can eat pickles" to boot; and where else can you get brisket and buffalo stew past midnight?

Tommy Toy's Chinoise 🅻🆂🅼　　　25　25　24　$50
655 Montgomery St. (bet. Washington & Clay Sts.), 415-397-4888
■ "Drop a fork and they are there in seconds" at this Downtown "magical" blend of French and Chinese ("don't expect to find kung pao chicken here"); the "lavish interior" draws a power crowd that laps up the "doting" service and recommends that you "get the signature dinner . . . period"; all agree it's "in a class by itself and so are the prices."

Tonga Restaurant & Hurricane Bar 🆂🅼　　　14　25　17　$26
Fairmont Hotel, 950 Mason St. (California St.), 415-772-5278
☑ The "faux rainstorms are a hoot" at this "gimmicky" Nob Hill Asian with "beyond cheap" Polynesian decor in the Fairmont Hotel; cynics think "it's been out of date since 1972" and many are surprised to hear that "people eat here", but "everyone should go once" for a drink with a group.

Ton Kiang ᴸ ˢ ᴹ　　23 | 14 | 18 | $20
3148 Geary Blvd. (Spruce St.), 415-752-4440
5821 Geary Blvd. (bet. 22nd & 23rd Aves.), 415-387-8273
■ "The dim sum rules" as do the "family-style" Hakka dishes at this "unpretentious" Richmond Chinese duo where you can always count on "scrumptious", "impeccably fresh", "carefully cooked dishes"; even those who have "no clue what [they're] eating" know that it's some of the "best Chinese in SF"; be prepared for "rushed" service and, since it's a "destination" that draws crowds, "go early."

Top of the Mark ◉ ˢ　　– | – | – | M
Mark Hopkins Inter-Continental Hotel, 1 Nob Hill (bet. California & Mason Sts.), 415-616-6916
They're now serving tea Monday–Friday at this deluxe bar high atop the Mark Hopkins Inter-Continental Hotel, but it's still mainly a place to have a (pricey) drink and enjoy the breathtaking panoramic view of one of the world's most beautiful cities; bar menu available till 10:30 PM.

Tortola ᴸ　　18 | 15 | 16 | $18
UCSF Medical Ctr., 500 Parnassus Ave., Millberry Union Bldg. (2nd Ave.), 415-731-8670 ⇗ ᴹ
3640 Sacramento St. (bet. Locust & Spruce Sts.), 415-929-8181 ˢ
Stonestown Galleria, 3251 20th Ave. (Winston St.), 415-566-4336 ⇗ ᴹ
Crocker Galleria, 50 Post St., 3rd. fl. (bet. Kearny & Montgomery Sts.), 415-986-8678 ⇗ ᴹ
☑ "Handy" "neighborhood" Mexicans with a "California twist" offering "good tamales" and "upscale burritos" made with "fresh ingredients"; critics claim the chain "doesn't compare to real" south of the border fare, but it's "a great place for the family" so "bring the kids and let 'em scream."

Town's End Restaurant & Bakery ᴸ ˢ　　21 | 17 | 19 | $21
2 Townsend St. (Brannan St.), 415-512-0749
■ "Those little muffins are a must" as is the "awesome bread" at this SOMA bakery/cafe where you can "bring the kids" and enjoy one of SF's best breakfasts in the "blossoming neighborhood" called South Beach; "confused service" is par for the course, but for "good American fare without pretense" it's "irresistible."

Trattoria Contadina ˢ ᴹ　　20 | 18 | 20 | $26
1800 Mason St. (Union St.), 415-982-5728
☑ "Watch the cable cars go by" while enjoying "solid" pastas at this "cute", "homey" North Beach Italian; some claim the menu items "could use more variety" and less cream, but a "friendly staff" helps make it "a nice corner restaurant" where "out-of-towners are charmed."

Trio Cafe 🅻🆂Ⓜ⇆ ▽ 17 | 14 | 17 | $16
1870 Fillmore St. (bet. Bush & Sutter Sts.), 415-563-2248
■ "Superb" bowls of latte are the signature drink at this casual, affordable Pacific Heights Eclectic whose "proximity to Fillmore shops" makes it a great lunch pit stop; while not ambitious, "what they do, they do right."

Tu Lan 🅻Ⓜ⇆ 22 | 5 | 12 | $11
8 Sixth St. (Market St.), 415-626-0927
☑ It's a "cramped, noisy, bad service" kind of place in a "dodgy neighborhood" ("take your bodyguard") Downtown, but the fact that "you can get stuffed for five bucks" on "sensational" Vietnamese food may make all the hassles worth it; "I love this pit."

2223 Restaurant & Bar 🅻🆂Ⓜ 23 | 19 | 19 | $32
2223 Market St. (bet. Noe & Sanchez Sts.), 415-431-0692
■ Foodies from crosstown finally have a Castro destination in John Cunin's (Cypress Club) "loud", "totally hip" bistro on Market Street; reviewers "like the energy" and "enjoy every fabulous bite" of American "food that shines"; the "casual and classy" flower-filled room wins votes too, which just goes to prove that "presentation is key, love."

Universal Cafe 🅻🆂 23 | 18 | 19 | $30
2814 19th St. (bet. Bryant & Harrison Sts.), 415-821-4608
■ "Sit at the counter and watch them create" at this "hip", "high-tech food hangout" in an "out of the way", semi-industrial Mission area; the "clean, inspiring" California fare from chef Julia McClaskey has everyone raving "wonderful"; drat – "another secret out!"

U.S. Restaurant 🅻 15 | 11 | 16 | $17
431 Columbus Ave. (bet. Green & Stockton Sts.), 415-362-6251
☑ North Beach "greasy ladle" Italian with an "authentic staff", a "spartan" interior and a clientele consisting of "policemen and old ladies"; "heaping loads of food . . . cheap" is the attraction – just "wish it had more flavor."

Valentine's Cafe 🆂Ⓜ ▽ 20 | 16 | 19 | $20
1793 Church St. (30th St.), 415-285-2257
■ "Occasional flashes of brilliance" illuminate this "artsy" Mission Vegetarian where the owners "clearly love what they do"; while the dining area may be "too small, too crowded", there's an "excellent range" of menu options with an international theme.

Val 21 🆂Ⓜ 21 | 17 | 19 | $26
995 Valencia St. (21st St.), 415-821-6622
■ "Spiffy" and "consistent" Mission New American offering a "short but ever-changing menu" of "health food and Cal cuisine" (including the "best virtually unknown brunch in town") backed up by "solid service" and "good" Val-ue prices; a few find the "LA nouveau" fare "bland" and "too pricey for beans", but most say "very pleasant all around."

Venticello 🖥️Ⓜ️   22 | 23 | 21 | $32
1257 Taylor St. (Washington St.), 415-922-2545
■ This "dressy Northern Italian" on Nob Hill is a "sexy spot" with "beautiful surroundings" and a "fun but small bar"; "delicious" food and an "infectiously nice staff" make it a great place "for indulging yourself" or "a date."

Vertigo 🇱Ⓜ️   22 | 24 | 21 | $42
Transamerica Pyramid, 600 Montgomery St. (Battery St.), 415-433-7250
■ "Hitchcock would go psycho" for this "dizzying" Downtown Californian where "close attention to detail" results in "innovative" fusion cuisine; service can be "disorganized" and the design is a bit "cold" for some ("can you say cement?"), but the "breathlessly trendy" scene is hot and there are "beautiful people galore" enjoying what many call "superb food and decor."

Vicolo 🇱🖥️Ⓜ️   21 | 11 | 12 | $16
201 Ivy St. (bet. Franklin & Gough Sts.), 415-863-2382
■ "Irresistible cornmeal-crusted pizza", "terrific topping combos" and "fantastic salads" are the focus at these "upscale" pizzerias; the Civic Center location is "a pre-concert favorite" for a quick bite before Beethoven.

Vivande Porta Via 🇱🖥️Ⓜ️   23 | 16 | 19 | $30
2125 Fillmore St. (bet. California & Sacramento Sts.), 415-346-4430
☑ "Looks like a deli, eats like a great Italian" – Carlo Middione's "tightly crowded" Pacific Heights trattoria offers "authentic" Italian fare that's "better for lunch than dinner" and "the best takeout in SF" that's "a must for picnics"; dissenters deem it "way too expensive for a plate of pasta" and "patronizing service."

Vivande Ristorante 🇱🖥️Ⓜ️   21 | 23 | 20 | $38
Opera Plaza, 670 Golden Gate Ave. (bet. Franklin St. & Van Ness Ave.), 415-673-9245
■ Carlo Middione "has a special style" and puts out some "top-notch peasant food" at his classy, flashy, mostly Sicilian Italian in Opera Plaza; the dining room is "beautifully designed" and the "knowledgeable staff" will guide you through the "outstanding regional dishes" and the daring all-Italian wine list; it's pricey, but "scores high on all accounts."

Wa-Ha-Ka Oaxaca Mexican Grill 🇱🖥️Ⓜ️   16 | 13 | 14 | $12
1489 Folsom St. (11th St.), 415-861-1410
1980 Union St. (Buchanan St.), 415-775-4145
☑ While the yuppie "crowd can be unbearable" at this "no lard" Cal-Mex duo, the staff is "sweet" and the duck burritos and swordfish tacos are fresh, fast and "fairly authentic"; but don't tell that to miffed Mex mavens who ask "healthy Mexican – where's the fun in that?"

Washington Square Bar & Grill L S M
18 | 19 | 18 | $31

1707 Powell St. (Union St.), 415-982-8123

■ "Who can argue with tradition?" – "atmosphere is the number one attraction" at this American classic with a "clubby bar" and great "old boy" atmosphere; "your fellow diners might be propped up", but the "good seafood" and other "typical North Beach" fare is "very reliable"; live jazz helps keep the ambiance "bustling."

Waterfront, The L S M
– | – | – | E

Pier 7, Embarcadero (Broadway), 415-391-2696

This Wharfside American is undergoing a major relaunch: chef Bruce Hill (ex Oritalia) has been brought on board to take the helm in the kitchen, so expect big improvements in the menu; decor renovations include outdoor dining and a more sophisticated upstairs dining room, which should make the already wonderful view even better.

WOODWARD'S GARDEN S
26 | 15 | 22 | $35

1700 Mission St. (Duboce St.), 415-621-7122

■ Chef-owners Margie Conard and Dana Tommasino are "working miracles" at reasonable prices in their tiny Mission District Californian tucked under the freeway; "the venue doesn't do these gals justice", but "as soon as you step inside it's lovely" with "unpretentious" ambiance, "try so hard" service and "some of the most original cooking in town"; N.B. airflow problems have reportedly been fixed since last year.

World Wrapps L S M
15 | 10 | 13 | $10

2257 Chestnut St. (bet. Pierce & Scott Sts.), 415-563-9727

2227 Polk St. (bet. Green & Vallejo Sts.), 415-931-9727

☑ Defenders of this "inexpensive", "cool concept" chain praise the "enormous" wrappers stuffed with "innovative", "filling" foods like Jamaican jerk and samurai salmon; detractors snap "not everything belongs in a wrap" – it's "the kitchen sink wrapped in a tortilla" – and say they're "tired of this trend"; as for the decor, all agree "what decor? – just take the food and go."

Wu Kong L S M
18 | 15 | 14 | $25

One Rincon Ctr., 101 Spear St. (bet. Mission & Howard Sts.), 415-957-9300

☑ "Elegant" SOMA Chinese praised for a "wide and superb Hong Kong and Shanghai menu" and "delicious dim sum"; but a growing number of critics claim it's "overrated", "overpriced" and has "snooty service"; unfortunately, an across-the-board drop in ratings supports their point of view.

Yabbies Coastal Kitchen S M   23 | 21 | 21 | $32
2237 Polk St. (bet. Green & Vallejo Sts.), 415-474-4088
■ "Watch out", there's a "new seafood king in town";
Mark Lusardi (ex Vertigo) serves "superb", "fresh" grilled
fish including signature yabbies (Australian for crawfish)
at this "relaxed, unpretentious" Van Ness/Polk newcomer
that most are calling "a favorite"; a "cheerful staff", big
choice of wines by the glass, raw bar and vegetarian
options make it a contender for "best new restaurant."

Yank Sing L S M   24 | 16 | 18 | $22
427 Battery St. (bet. Washington & Clay Sts.), 415-781-1111
49 Stevenson Pl. (bet. 1st & 2nd Sts.), 415-541-4949
■ "Two words: dim sum" – these Downtown Chinese
dumpling darlings offer "simply the best" version of the
dish anywhere, but the most "you can say about the decor is
it's clean"; while the little plates stack up and "seem to
keep going up in price", who cares – "I'm addicted!"

Yaya Cuisine L S   20 | 20 | 19 | $25
1220 Ninth Ave. (Lincoln Way), 415-566-6966
■ "Tranquil" and "dramatically lit" Inner Sunset Middle
Eastern where there are "no ordinary dishes" on the
"inventive" menu; "the tagines are a must" and dishes
like "date pasta with walnuts" are "great for vegetarians";
while "Mesopotamian cuisine is not for all", adventuresome
diners nod Ya, Ya, "try it."

Yet Wah L S M   15 | 14 | 14 | $18
Pier 39, Fisherman's Wharf (Embarcadero), 415-434-4430
5328 Diamond Hts. Blvd. (Duncan St.), 415-282-0788
2140 Clement St. (23rd Ave.), 415-387-8040
☑ "Chung King on white tablecloths" is the take on these
"harmless" Americanized Chinese namesakes; "personable
waiters" serve "tourist-style dishes", so you might want to
"take mom when she visits", but most locals just ask "why?"

Yoshida-Ya L S M   21 | 18 | 19 | $29
2909 Webser St. (Union St.), 415-346-3431
☑ Aficionados of this Union Street Japanese yakitori house
"love the little hibachis" at the tables and "top-notch"
sushi, and advise "be sure to sit upstairs" in the "nice and
quiet" tatami-lined room; all agree prices are "outrageous",
but that's why it's called "totally authentic Japanese dining."

Yoyo Bistro L S M   ▽ 21 | 21 | 20 | $35
Miyako Hotel, 1611 Post St. (Laguna St.), 415-922-7788
☑ A "unique" and pricey Japantown French-Californian
bistro with an Asian tilt and "beautifully presented" but
"small portions"; while some find the "fusion food"
"inventive", others say it "needs excitement", so you'll
have to put your own spin on this yoyo.

Yuet Lee ◐ L S M ⇗ 21 | 6 | 13 | $18
1300 Stockton St. (Broadway), 415-982-6020
3601 26th St. (bet. Valencia & Guerrero Sts.), 415-550-8998
■ "Great, cheap", "bright and bare" Chinese seafood joints with late-night hours ("fantastic salt and pepper prawns" at 2 AM) and "fast service"; while the "terrible decor" makes them all the more "authentic", they sure could use sprucing up.

Yukol Place Thai Cuisine S M ▽ 20 | 14 | 18 | $21
2380 Lombard St. (bet. Pierce & Scott Sts.), 415-922-1599
☑ There's a "nice new location" for this "best Marina Thai" proffering "fabulous pad Thai" and other "high-quality cooking"; while some rate it only "average", there's "sweet service" and locals think it's a "wonderful neighborhood place."

Zaré on Sacramento L M – | – | – | M
568 Sacramento St. (Montgomery St.), 415-291-9145
This moderate Downtown Mediterranean newcomer with a six-course vegetarian tasting menu is the domain of "very friendly" chef-owner Hoss Zaré, whom write-ins credit with putting out some "excellent", "strongly flavored" food; they say "you'll be Zaré you went elsewhere."

Zarzuela L M 22 | 17 | 20 | $28
2000 Hyde St. (Union St.), 415-346-0800
■ There's always a crowd at this Van Ness/Polk Spaniard that's "tops for tapas" (including "the only really good octopus in town") and there's an abundance of "fine sherry the way it's meant to be served"; "friendly" waiters who "should be stand-ups" keep the mood festive, but do take a cab 'cuz "parking is a joke."

Zax 23 | 18 | 22 | $34
2330 Taylor St. (bet. Columbus Ave. & Francisco St.), 415-563-6266
■ The cuisine "hits all the notes" at this "intimate" chef-owned North Beach Californian with French and Mediterranean accents; although it's "off the beaten path", "great soufflés" and other "perfect" dishes lead customers to call it "a gem" that's "worth the effort."

Zazie L S M 21 | 19 | 19 | $22
941 Cole St. (bet. Carl St. & Parnassus Ave.), 415-564-5332
☑ "Cute atmosphere" Cole Valley French run by "nice local folk", where patio brunching on "great ginger pancakes" are "what neighborhood places are all about"; "wonderful bouillabaisse" and other "dishes you can't normally get" also make it "a good value" for the price.

Zingari   ▽ 19 | 20 | 20 | $37
Donatello Hotel, 501 Post St. (Mason St.), 415-885-8850
⬛ Being located on the site of former favorite Donatello
leaves this "pricey" Downtown Italian with a lot to live up
to; while not many surveyors have sampled it, those who
have are split: some say there's "good calamari" and other
"authentic Italian cooking", while others declare it's
"disappointing" and "doesn't live up" to its predecessor.

Zinzino 🆂🅼   21 | 20 | 21 | $27
2355 Chestnut St. (bet. Scott & Divisadero Sts.),
415-346-6623
⬛ "Bold flavors" make this Marina Italian stand out from
the crowd; there's "lots of energy" at work here, from the
"helpful staff" and from the kitchen, which turns out "paper-
thin pizzas" and other "impressive food"; surveyors say it's
"much improved" and a "rising star."

ZUNI CAFE 🅞🅛🆂   23 | 20 | 18 | $34
1658 Market St. (bet. Franklin & Gough Sts.), 415-552-2522
⬛ "The whiners can go elsewhere" say devotees of this
"see and be seen" Civic Center Mediterranean where "the
Caesar salad is an institution"; "they keep it up year after
year", offering a "versatile top-notch menu", sidewalk
oyster bar, the "best Bloody Marys in town" and "people-
watching", which causes many to call it the "quintessential
SF restaurant"; though Zuniphobes find it "self-important",
several report "attitude has recently improved."

East of San Francisco

	F	D	S	C

Ajanta L S M   23 | 18 | 21 | $21
1888 Solano Ave. (The Alameda), Berkeley,
510-526-4373
■ "Wonderful erotic murals" provide a stimulating
backdrop at this Berkeley Indian lauded as one of the
"most creative in the Bay Area" (as "if Alice Waters were
born in New Delhi"); "new delights monthly", "beautiful
presentation" and "friendly owners" are among the
reasons why many say "I eat here a lot."

Alexander Ristorante L S M   ∇ 17 | 19 | 16 | $29
65 Moraga Way (Brookwood St.), Orinda, 510-253-1322
◪ "California cuisine meets Italian" at this Orinda spot
where "indifferent service" mars the "attempt at SF style";
some say they "love it every time", but others call it "run of
the mill" and advise "you can do lots better" in the East Bay.

Bay Wolf L S M   24 | 20 | 23 | $40
9853 Piedmont Ave. (Rio Vista), Oakland, 510-655-6004
■ "Michael Wild knows how to run a restaurant" and that's
why this "high-caliber" Cal-Mediterranean is one of the
"absolutely most consistent" in the Oakland area; admirers
howl about the "low-key" decor, outdoor deck, "innovative
regional specials", "caring" service and "great wine list."

Bette's Oceanview Diner L S M   21 | 17 | 18 | $15
1807A Fourth St. (Hearst Ave.), Berkeley, 510-644-3230
■ This "too cool" Berkeley diner with a "fabulous '50s
Formica feel" offers "healthy portions" of some of the
"best" pancakes, bacon and eggs in the Bay Area, with
one-hour lines to prove it; sure the waits are "purgatory",
but that's the price you pay for the "perfect breakfast" ...
hey, "we couldn't see any ocean."

Bighorn Grill L S M   ∇ 14 | 17 | 12 | $29
2410 San Ramon Valley Blvd. (Crow Canyon Rd.), San Ramon,
510-838-5678
◪ "Finally, a place for meatarians to eat" in the tofu zone;
this "nicely decorated" San Ramon American cooks up "big
portions" of grilled meats and barbecue, but it's way "too
loud" and you might get "treated as an afterthought"; while
"ok for San Ramon", by most standards it's pretty "ordinary" –
"even a Kuleto interior can't save a sinking kitchen."

Blackhawk Grille L S M 21 | 22 | 20 | $34
Blackhawk Plaza, 3540 Blackhawk Plaza Circle (bet. Crow Canyon Rd. & Camino Tassajara), Danville, 510-736-4295
"Best door handles in the Bay Area" . . . and "the pizzettas are to die for" too at this upmarket waterside Danville Cal-Mediterranean; expect "nose in the air attitude" along with "outstanding food" and "one of the best wine lists around"; combine it with a visit to the neighboring Behring Car Museum for a "fun trip."

Blue Nile L S 19 | 14 | 15 | $15
2525 Telegraph Ave. (bet. Parker & Dwight Sts.), Berkeley, 510-540-6777
"No utensils, eat with your hands" are "perfect rules for the college crowd" that patronizes this crowded and inexpensive Berkeley Ethiopian; supporters think it's the "best" of its kind in the Bay Area, but others claim it's "indistinguishable from numerous others"; P.S. the honey wine will reportedly "get you in the mood" for romance.

Bridges Restaurant & Bar L S M 22 | 25 | 21 | $39
44 Church St. (Hartz Ave.), Danville, 510-820-7200
"East meets West" at this Danville Californian–Pacific Rim in an "elegant", "very pretty" flower-filled setting; when the "cross-riffing works it's exciting", but the "stunning" fare "can be hit or miss"; at a minimum, it's a "nice place for city people to escape to."

Bucci's L M 20 | 19 | 18 | $25
6121 Hollis St. (bet. 61st & Powell Sts.), Emeryville, 510-547-4725
"It's like eating in a gallery" at this popular Emeryville Italian-Mediterranean with reasonable prices on "great Caesar salads" and "marvelous pizzas"; the tables might be a bit "underserviced" by the "up-and-coming artist" staff, but most think it's a "fun" place and call it "a winner."

CAFE AT CHEZ PANISSE L M 26 | 22 | 23 | $36
1517 Shattuck Ave. (bet. Cedar & Vine Sts.), Berkeley, 510-548-5049
"The tuna carpaccio had me weeping" at Alice Waters' "timeless" Berkeley Californian with a "sophisticated yet casual ambiance" and "stellar service"; it's "a little cramped" and surveyors suggest going at "weird hours" to avoid the crowds (no reservations), but with more menu choices than Chez Panisse downstairs, the "very seductive" food sets a "benchmark of freshness and simplicity"; in sum, "close to perfection at affordable prices."

Café Chêneville L S ▽ 21 | 20 | 18 | $26
499 Ninth St. (Washington St.), Oakland, 510-893-5439
There's a "small but interesting menu" at this "inventive" Mediterranean; while some say it "needs to come together", most maintain "they try hard" and label it "a bright light" in an "up-and-coming" Downtown Oakland neighborhood.

Cafe de Bordeaux 🇱🇸🇲 | – | – | – | E |
326 Seventh St. (Harrison St.), Oakland, 510-891-2338
The few reviewers who've frequented this expensive
Oakland French-Asian say it's "consistently good" and the
"lunch deals can't be beat", but at least one customer
considers it "a bit of a rip-off" for the price.

Cafe Fanny 🇱🇸🇲 | 22 | 13 | 15 | $14 |
1603 San Pablo Ave. (Cedar St.), Berkeley, 510-524-5447
◪ "Baked goat cheese is a cliché, but no one does it better"
say fans of Alice Waters' breakfast and lunch "parking lot
cafe" where some complain that you "pay more for the
privilege of standing up" at the "crowded" chic zinc counter
to munch on "excellent sandwiches" or sip "latte in a bowl";
while the foodigentsia swears that there's "intellectual
soul food" to be found here, the unsmitten sniff "trend and
pretense in Berkeley – what's new?"

Cafe Rouge 🇱🇸🇲 | 19 | 19 | 18 | $32 |
1782 Fourth St. (Delaware St.), Berkeley, 510-525-1440
◪ This "classy" French bistro and charcuterie run by Zuni
alumni "has potential" but at press time "hasn't quite gotten
it together"; it's on a stretch of Fourth Street in Berkeley's
gourmet ghetto that has "historic" resonance for Bay Area
foodies, but "amateur hour" service from "puzzled waiters"
can mar some otherwise "excellent food"; keep checking
'cuz maybe it just "needs time to grow and smooth out."

California Cafe 🇱🇸🇲 | 20 | 19 | 20 | $27 |
1540 N. California Blvd. (bet. Civic Dr. & Bonanza St.),
Walnut Creek, 510-938-9977
See review in North of San Francisco Directory.

Cha Am Thai 🇱🇸🇲 | 20 | 14 | 17 | $17 |
1543 Shattuck Ave. (Cedar St.), Berkeley, 510-848-9664
See review in San Francisco Directory.

Chevys 🇱🇸🇲 | 14 | 13 | 15 | $17 |
650 Ellinwood Way (Contra Costa Blvd.), Pleasant Hill,
510-685-6651
See review in San Francisco Directory.

CHEZ PANISSE 🇱🇲 | 27 | 24 | 26 | $61 |
1517 Shattuck Ave. (bet. Cedar & Vine Sts.), Berkeley,
510-548-5525
▉ "Legendary" – there's no other word for Alice Waters'
"refined" and expensive "national shrine" of California
cuisine housed in a "cozy" Arts and Crafts cottage in
North Berkeley; "they tell you what to eat" on the fixed
menu, which gets pricier as the weekend approaches, but
with "impeccable", "perfectly composed meals" most
"don't mind"; despite "small portions," "Alice can do no
wrong" and her restaurant is "a mecca" for foodies.

Citron S M   23 | 18 | 21 | $38
5484 College Ave. (bet. Taft & Lawton Sts.), Oakland,
510-653-5484
☑ "Thirtysomething dining at its best" is the reason this
Oakland French-Mediterranean is reportedly "gaining on
Chez Panisse"; "homey decor", "fabulous service" that
pays "attention to every detail" and "smashing good food"
mean the new owners "keep improving" what was already
an East Bay favorite; some think it's "good but not worth a
drive", others just "wish it were in SF."

Doug's BBQ L S M   ▽ 23 | 7 | 15 | $35
3600 San Pablo Ave. (36th St.), Emeryville, 510-655-9048
☑ "When you're feeling carnivorous" come to this
Emeryville barbecue joint and dig into "the best BBQ in
the East Bay"; there are unusual offerings like lamb, goat
and "deep-fried turkey" that make for "good messy food."

Fat Apple's L S M   18 | 12 | 16 | $14
1346 Martin Luther King Jr. Blvd. (Rose St.), Berkeley,
510-526-2260
7525 Fairmont Ave. (Colusa St.), El Cerrito, 510-528-3433
■ "Zero frills" East Bay siblings that have "all those
American goodies" like "excellent grilled hamburgers",
pumpkin pancakes that "light up your day" and "dependable
desserts"; it's strictly WYSIWYG and "they should reevaluate
the waiters", but it's "great for what it is."

Faz L S M   18 | 19 | 17 | $26
600 Hartz Ave. (Diablo Rd.), Danville, 510-838-1320
5121 Hopyard Rd., Pleasanton, 510-460-0444
See review in San Francisco Directory.

Gertie's Chesapeake   18 | 15 | 18 | $25
Bay Cafe L S
1919 Addison St. (Martin Luther King Jr. Blvd.), Berkeley,
510-841-2722
☑ "Aunt Gertie's soul is in her crab cakes" at this "relaxed"
bargain seafood house convenient to the Berkeley Repertory
Theater; "slow service" can be a bit over-relaxed and some
think it's just "boring", but others suggest "reliable" is an
appropriate term of endearment for this "old, quiet" place.

Ginger Island L S M   17 | 17 | 17 | $26
1820 Fourth St. (Hearst St.), Berkeley, 510-644-0444
☑ Ginger-infused vodka martinis, housemade ginger ale and
the "best curry noodles anywhere" still float some boats
at this "happy, colorful" Berkeley Californian with Asian
accents where they're "not afraid of spicing it up"; although
several say the "overrated fusion cooking" is "slipping",
gourmet Gilligans vote it "the place to be marooned on a
steamy summer day."

Grissini 🄻🅂🄼   – – – M
Concord Hilton Hotel, 1970 Diamond Blvd. (Willow Pass Rd.), Concord, 510-680-1700

"Better than most hotel restaurants" might just be a nice way of saying that this "heavy Italian" in the Concord Hilton is pretty average; but the staff "works hard to make you happy" and there are some interesting wines by the glass.

Jade Villa 🄻🅂🄼   18 11 13 $17
800 Broadway (bet. 8th & 9th Sts.), Oakland, 510-839-1688

◼ The "only decent dim sum in the East Bay" ("greasy but satisfying") is offered at this "loud", "barnlike" Chinese in Oakland's Chinatown; too bad it's served by "cranky" waiters who "can't understand that people want things their way when they eat out."

Johnny Love's 🄻🄼   8 10 9 $20
1448 S. Main St. (Newell Ave.), Walnut Creek, 510-934-4199
See review in San Francisco Directory.

Jordan's 🄻🄼   – – – E
Claremont Resort, 41 Tunnel Rd. (bet. Ashby & Domingo Aves.), Oakland, 510-843-3000

This makeover of the former Pavilion Restaurant at the Claremont Resort made its debut post-*Survey*; the American food has some Asian and spa-food tendencies, and jazz on weekends helps make it "a great place for a special occasion"; "breathtaking views" of the Golden Gate Bridge and the San Francisco skyline add to the attraction.

Kirala 🄻🅂🄼   23 14 16 $26
2100 Ward St. (Shattuck Ave.), Berkeley, 510-549-3486

◼ There's "a line before it even opens" at this "no reservations" Berkeley Japanese with an "awesome", "cool robata grill" and "the best sushi in the East Bay"; even though the prices are "reasonable", it can get expensive "because you want everything", especially some of the more unusual items such as monkfish liver ("a special treat") or deep-fried ice cream.

Lalime's 🅂🄼   25 20 23 $36
1329 Gilman St. (Nielson Ave.), Berkeley, 510-527-9838

◼ "Chez Panisse lite" is how devotees describe this endearing Berkeley Mediterranean where there's a "different prix fixe" menu and à la carte choices every few nights; the Provençal colors and changing artwork add to the "culinary adventure" for the "very Brooklyn crowd" that patronizes it; N.B. you can subscribe to the restaurant's newsletter for upcoming menus or download the info from its Web site.

La Mediterranee 🄻🄼   20 14 19 $17
2936 College Ave. (Ashby Ave.), Berkeley, 510-540-7773
See review in San Francisco Directory.

Lark Creek L S M   20 | 20 | 19 | $33
1360 Locust St. (Mt. Diablo Blvd.), Walnut Creek,
510-256-1234

⊠ Bradley Ogden's East Bay lark (with a South Bay sibling)
has "atmosphere inside and out" with "cute birdhouse"
decor and an upscale but "relaxing" ambiance; there's
"solid" American food and "enthusiastic service" too, but
the less impressed sniff "potatoes and meat loaf – a
culinary experience?" and claim they "don't compare" with
Ogden's Larkspur original.

Le Marquis L S   ▽ 24 | 19 | 24 | $40
Plaza Shopping Ctr., 3524B Mt. Diablo Blvd. (bet. Oak Hill
Rd. & 1st St.), Lafayette, 510-284-4422

▨ "A sleeper in a strip mall", this "old-style" French
frequented by "older wealth" "deserves special mention"
for its "excellent food", "great wine list" and "quiet
elegance"; there's a new terrace for outdoor dining and a
new menu, but it may still be "too stuffy for young couples."

Long Life Vegi House L S M   15 | 8 | 13 | $13
2129 University Ave. (bet. Shuttuck Ave. & Oxford St.),
Berkeley, 510-845-6072

⊠ Even with "bountiful portions" at a "cheap" tab, not
everyone is won over by this Berkeley Vegetarian; "it can
be very good if you know what to order" (some say "stay
away from the mock meat"), but it can also be "grease
galore" with "unsubtle flavors."

Mama's Royal Cafe L S M ⇄   ▽ 20 | 14 | 18 | $13
4012 Broadway (bet. 40th & 41st Sts.), Oakland, 510-547-7600

▮ This "wonderfully eccentric" and inexpensive Oakland
American has a "funky atmosphere" as well as "outstanding
omelets" and other "great breakfast specialties"; it may
be "worth the wait", but some critics remind us that, no
matter how royal, "a luncheonette is still a luncheonette."

Nan Yang L S   ▽ 21 | 15 | 19 | $20
6048 College Ave. (Claremont Ave.), Oakland, 510-655-3298

▨ "The garlic noodles make you melt" and "the ginger salad
is excellent" at this "deserving" Oakland Burmese that's
now down to one location; it's a "well watched-over family
restaurant with integrity" and a "creative menu" of "light,
tasty, delicate" dishes that devotees declare are "unlike
any other Asian cuisine."

New Gulf Coast Grill S   ▽ 13 | 11 | 15 | $23
(fka Gulf Coast Bar & Grill)
736 Washington St. (8th St.), Oakland, 510-836-3663

⊠ "Erratic hours" make it seem like this Oakland grill "is
never open" (it closes at 9:30 PM), but it can be a "great
place to go before a Warriors game" with its "good Cajun-
Creole cuisine", "great jambalaya" and "nice people" to
serve you a "taste of New Orleans."

O Chame **L** **M**　　22　21　20　$26
1830 Fourth St. (Hearst St.), Berkeley, 510-841-8783
◪ David Vardy's "unique" "nouvelle Japanese" in Berkeley
scores big with Buddhist foodists for "excellent", "elegantly
made" noodle dishes doled out in a "calm and cool" setting;
it's reportedly "where other chefs go" for lessons in "perfect
execution"; detractors complain about the price and
"minimalist food that's minimally filling."

Oliveto Cafe & Restaurant **L** **S** **M**　　23　19　19　$39
5655 College Ave. (Keith St.), Oakland, 510-547-5356
▪ "The food sparkles" at this Oakland Italian restaurant
and cafe where "steady improvements" by Chez Panisse
alumnus Paul Bertolli are paying off; his "elegantly crafted
meals" are "really a departure" from run-of-the-mill
pastas and service is "knowledgeable", making it "a
place to visit again"; if you can't wait for dinner, there's
"great cappuccino and pastries for breakfast"; "micro
portions" are the big complaint.

Omnivore **S**　　▽　17　15　20　$24
*3015 Shattuck Ave. (bet. Emerson & Ashby Sts.), Berkeley,
510-848-4346*
◪ There's "good lamb" and "heavenly" ravioli with
Gorgonzola at this moderate Berkeley Californian, but
otherwise surveyors say the "always changing menu" is
"hit or miss"; for those with high expectations, it's "not
memorable" though "nice for a date."

Pacific Fresh **L** **S** **M**　　▽　17　16　16　$25
*550 Ellenwood Way (Contra Costa Blvd.), Pleasant Hill,
510-827-3474*
See review in South of San Francisco Directory.

Pasta Pomodoro **L** **S** **M**🍃　　18　12　16　$13
5500 College Ave. (Lawton St.), Oakland, 510-923-0900
See review in San Francisco Directory.

Picante Cocina Mexicana **L** **S** **M** ▽　21　12　14　$12
*1328 Sixth St. (bet. Gilman & Camilia Sts.), Berkeley,
510-525-3121*
▪ "Long before wraps became trendy" this "kid-tolerant",
"superior taqueria" in Berkeley was turning out "clean-
tasting Mexican" (including "the best burritos") at
"bargain prices"; on the down side, it's "loud, crowded
and haphazard" and there's "no table service."

Plearn Thai Cuisine **L** **S** **M**　　19　13　15　$18
*2050 University Ave. (Shattuck Ave.), Berkeley,
510-841-2148*
◪ This budget Berkeley Thai is still an East Bay "favorite"
and a "good value", but veterans say they're "resting on
their laurels" with "shabby" "decor that needs updating";
still, it's a "good intro for those unfamiliar with the cuisine."

Prima Trattoria L S M   ▽ 23 | 22 | 22 | $34 |
1522 N. Main St. (bet. Bonanza & Lincoln Sts.), Walnut Creek, 510-935-7780

■ "Beautiful people" dine on "yummy" Italian at this "lively and romantic" suburban trattoria that "excels in antipasti" and has a "great wine program" (including many offerings by the glass); it's "a little pricey", but that's to be expected at "one of the stars in Walnut Creek."

Pyramid Alehouse L S M   14 | 18 | 16 | $17 |
901 Gilman St. (bet. 7th & 8th Sts.), Berkeley, 510-528-9880

◪ "More of a theme park than a brewpub", this "big, big, big" Berkeley alehouse is "a hip new spot to chill after work" with a "huge beer and ale selection"; "the kitchen needs help", but there's some "nice pub food" and "with enough beer who cares about the food?"

Restaurant Peony L S M   ▽ 23 | 17 | 18 | $19 |
Pacific Renaissance Plaza, 388 Ninth St. (bet. Franklin & Webster Sts.), Oakland, 510-286-8866

■ You can always count on a "good meal" at this "upscale dim sum" place in Oakland's Chinatown that also offers some "exotic dinner dishes"; regulars rave that it's "comparable to Harbor Village" and deserves "more good words" – this peony is blooming.

Ristorante Salute L S M   ▽ 19 | 21 | 18 | $27 |
1900 Esplanade Dr. (Regatta St.), Richmond, 510-215-0803

■ "A sweetheart of a restaurant" located on the Richmond waterfront proffering pastas that are "palate pleasers" and some "good Italian seafood" as well; "gracious service" and outdoor dining persuade most that it's an "excellent neighborhood place."

Rivoli S M   25 | 19 | 23 | $38 |
1539 Solano Ave. (Nielson St.), Berkeley, 510-526-2542

■ "The smell of olives wafts through the room" (and "backyard raccoons add to the atmosphere") at this popular Berkeley Cal-Mediterranean "keeper" where "you can always count on tasting something incredible" from the continually changing menu; "caring service" makes it "a pleasure to be there" and some suggest it might just be "Chez Panisse at half the price."

Rue de Main L   ▽ 21 | 19 | 21 | $35 |
22622 Main St. (bet. B & C Aves.), Hayward, 510-537-0812

■ "Hayward's finest" is a Classic French "oasis in dreadful suburbia"; the decor is "unmatched" and the "fine food" and "quiet, romantic" ambiance make it a "special event" kind of place; "it may be all there is in Hayward, but that's what the automobile is for."

Santa Fe Bar & Grill L S M   19   21   20 $31
*1310 University Ave. (bet. Bonar & Acton Sts.), Berkeley,
510-841-4740*
◪ A jump in decor scores reflects a "fabulously redone"
garden (where "they grow their own salad makings") and
the addition of a cigar-friendly patio to this Berkeley
American housed in a "beautiful, spacious room" that was
formerly a train station; "the food is not at all daring", but
"the favorites are here" (including "heavenly" duck) and
some hold out hope that once it evolves "it's gonna be nifty."

Saul's Restaurant & Deli L S M   15   10   14 $15
1475 Shattuck Ave. (Vine St.), Berkeley, 510-848-DELI
◪ The Bay Area deli wars continue as the faithful ("I cross
the bridge for deli here"), the resigned ("it ain't perfect, but
it's all we've got"), the conciliatory ("great pickles") and
the scornful ("get out of town, already") converge on this
reasonable Berkeley facsimile; "I'm a NYer and I'm spoiled",
but "generously portioned sandwiches" help ease the exile.

Scott's Seafood Grill & Bar L S M   18   17   18 $29
2 Broadway (Embarcadero), Oakland, 510-444-3456
See review in San Francisco Directory.

Siam Cuisine L S M   ▽ 20   15   18 $19
*1181 University Ave. (bet. Curtis St. & San Pablo Ave.),
Berkeley, 510-548-3278*
◪ Look beyond the "tacky decor" and you'll find "excellent
true Thai food" at this "good value" Berkeley spot; regulars
recommend the "great curries and seafood" but warn that
the "hot dishes are really hot."

Skylight Cafe M   ▽ 18   17   18 $26
2320 Central Ave. (bet. Park & Oak Sts.), Alameda, 510-865-4615
■ "Alameda's nicest place" is a "very friendly" and
moderately priced neighborhood Italian with "a small well-
planned menu" and "great desserts"; the handful who've
happened upon it call it "a wonderful small-town restaurant."

Soizic L S   20   18   19 $26
300 Broadway (3rd St.), Oakland, 510-251-8100
◪ It's "a brave attempt" – a "cool" midrange French bistro
in Oakland's Jack London Square with a "light", "airy",
"industrial chic" dining room; the "artsy good food" is
sometimes "fabulous", sometimes "disappointing", but
it's "a little treasure of eccentricity" and several still call it
"one of Oakland's best dining spots."

Spenger's Fish Grotto L S M   11   11   13 $22
1919 Fourth St. (University Ave.), Berkeley, 510-845-7771
◪ "Plop plop, fizz fizz" – "battered and fried" is how most
describe this Berkeley seafood "landmark" where iceberg
lettuce goes perfectly with "overcooked fish" and the
staff is "incomprehensible"; a few find it "dependable", but
more carp "no self-respecting fish would be seen here."

Spiedini L S M   22 | 21 | 20 | $30 |
101 Ygnacio Valley Rd. (Oakland Blvd.), Walnut Creek,
510-939-2100
The "energy is good" at this East Bay trattoria offering "excellent spit-roasted Italian food" and "consistently good pasta dishes" in a "modern", "glitzy without being ritzy" setting; it "can get noisy" and some say it's "tired", but it's still a favorite in this neck of the woods.

Thornhill Cafe L S M   ▽ 22 | 18 | 21 | $32 |
5761 Thornhill Dr. (Grisborne St.), Oakland, 510-339-0646
"Personal hospitality" from "jolly waiters" and "innovative French food with Asian touches" from chef Chai make this eclectic Oakland "hideaway" a hit; "the salmon is fantastic, the sweetbreads a treat" and most of our surveyors agree it's one "marvelous restaurant."

Tourelle L S M   20 | 25 | 21 | $38 |
3565 Mt. Diablo Blvd. (Oak Hill Rd.), Lafayette,
510-284-3565
Reviewers report that this Lafayette Californian in a "beautiful setting" with garden tables has "lots of class"; the "imaginative and often spectacular dishes" are "caringly prepared" and there's generally "good service" (with a tiny tad of "'tude"), making it a "nice place for a leisurely evening"; the disappointed declare that the "uneven" "food doesn't match the decor."

Uzen L M   ▽ 21 | 16 | 17 | $24 |
5415 College Ave. (Lawton Ave.), Oakland, 510-654-7753
"Try for the tatami room" at this "intimate, stylish" Oakland place offering "Japanese food with an imaginative twist" and a "nice selection of sakes"; doesn't everyone claim that their own "nice neighborhood sushi bar" serves the "best sushi in the Bay Area"? . . . so who's to argue?

Venezia L S M   18 | 19 | 18 | $24 |
1799 University Ave. (Grant St.), Berkeley, 510-849-4681
"Clothes hanging from the ceiling" is part of the "amusing back alley decor" at this "always jolly", "trustworthy and tasty" Venetian-style trattoria; it's "a little chaotic" (i.e. "it feels like you're in Italy"), but the "waiters are always attentive" and the big bowls of pasta are "dependable."

Vic Stewart's S M   ▽ 21 | 23 | 21 | $38 |
850 S. Broadway (Newell St.), Walnut Creek,
510-943-5666
"You must ask for a train car and take your best friends" to this "clubby", "expensive" Walnut Creek steakhouse that gets two thumbs up for "best spot in the East Bay for beef"; the railroad motif and dining car decor create a "fabulous atmosphere" and the "great martinis" can put some steam in your engine.

WENTE VINEYARDS L S M | 26 | 26 | 24 | $38 |

5050 Arroyo Rd. (Wetmore Rd.), Livermore, 510-456-2450
■ This highly rated destination Californian in Livermore offers "superb food" and an "outstanding wine list", but it's the "gorgeous" garden setting and "unreal views of the hills" that make it "worth the drive", especially for brunch; it's a "terrific getaway" ... and "I haven't found a better pork chop."

World Wrapps L S M | 15 | 10 | 13 | $10 |

1372 Locust St. (Bonanza St.), Walnut Creek, 510-930-9777
See review in San Francisco Directory.

Yoshi's at Jack London Square L S M | 18 | 19 | 18 | $25 |

510 Embarcadero W. (bet. Clay & Washington Sts.), Oakland, 510-652-9200
☑ New and more elegant Oakland quarters for this jazz and Japanese club ("what a combination") have some wondering "will it play in Jack London Square?"; while there's only "average sushi" and other "typical Japanese dishes", aficionados go for the "terrific music" nightly.

Zachary's Chicago Pizza L S M ⊄ | 24 | 11 | 15 | $14 |

1853 Solano Ave. (Fresno St.), Berkeley, 510-525-5950
5801 College Ave. (Oak Grove St.), Oakland, 510-655-6385
■ "The constant crowd tells all" at these "unsurpassed" East Bay pie joints whose deep-dish versions ("spinach and mushroom, the best") are "pizza heaven – it's that simple"; since the "wait is torture", you might want to "get it to go" even if that means a long haul: "I'd drive 10 miles for this pizza ... oh, wait, I just did."

Zza's Trattoria L S M   ▽ | 19 | 13 | 17 | $20 |

552 Grand Ave. (MacArthur Blvd.), Oakland, 510-839-9124
☑ For many, this "funky", "informal", child-friendly Oakland Italian is "the best place I know that lets you draw on the tables"; sure there are "adolescents at the helm" and the "obnoxious neon sign" near the kitchen is "unsettling", but it's a "good standby" "for a quick dinner."

North of San Francisco

| F | D | S | C |

Adriana's 🇱Ⓜ   ▽ | 18 | 13 | 18 | $25 |
999 Andersen Dr. (Bellam St.), San Rafael, 415-454-8000
☒ "Noisy" midrange San Rafael Italian with a "traditional Italian menu" that's "dependable but not exciting"; still, there are some "good pastas" and the outdoor patio makes up for the "large, uninspired dining room."

Alta Mira 🇱ⓈⓂ | 16 | 23 | 17 | $32 |
Alta Mira Hotel, 125 Bulkley Ave. (Harrison Ave.), Sausalito, 415-332-1350
☒ Too bad "you can't eat the view" at this strategically located Sausalito spot because the "unimaginative" Continental cuisine doesn't impress reviewers; but even with "unexplained lapses in service", locals sometimes "go for drinks" – it's "where we can look at our city."

Atlas Peak Grill Ⓢ | – | – | – | M |
3342 Vichy Ave. (Hwy. 121), Napa, 707-253-1455
A stone country cottage setting distinguishes this Napa American write-in run by the family that owns Alfred's in the city; there's outdoor dining in summer on trademark steaks and wine country regional cuisine.

AUBERGE DU SOLEIL 🇱ⓈⓂ | 25 | 28 | 23 | $55 |
Auberge du Soleil Inn, 180 Rutherford Hill Rd. (Silverado Trail), Rutherford, 707-967-3111
☒ "Get your 'I've been there' ticket punched here": the "glorious" view from the terrace overlooking the Napa Valley makes this "idyllic" American a true destination; the menu of wine country fare features some "outstanding" dishes, though it's a tough comparison with the setting; service can be "snooty" and the tab is always large (unless you opt for drinks at sunset), but most think it's "worth the price for admission" to "heaven."

Avenue Grill ⓈⓂ | 18 | 16 | 18 | $29 |
44 E. Blithedale Ave. (Sunnyside Ave.), Mill Valley, 415-388-6003
☒ There's "a bit of a scene" at this "reasonably priced" Mill Valley American where the "noisy but fun energy" suggests it's a "great hometown place" that "hangs in there even as competition grows"; gripers growl "fading" and "overpriced for the quality."

Babette's
25 | 19 | 23 | $46

464 First St. E. (bet. Spain & Napa Sts.), Sonoma,
707-939-8921

■ Get in on the feast at this "fabulous new find in Sonoma" with "marvelously original decor", "homey but elegant" ambiance and "eclectic" New French fare from "a chef who knows what he's doing"; to cut the cost, try the "delightful prix fixe" or sit in the "casual" bar bistro.

Barnaby's By The Bay ⓁⓈⓂ
– | – | – | M

12938 Sir Francis Drake Blvd., Inverness, 415-669-1114

"A beautiful site wasted on a fifth-rate roadhouse" is how one critic sums up this Inverness barbecue and seafood place in a "pleasant" location along the edge of Tomales Bay; supporters insist "people who don't like it don't understand fresh seafood"; your call, mate.

Bistro Don Giovanni ⓁⓈⓂ
23 | 22 | 22 | $34

4110 Hwy. 29 (bet. Salvador Ave. & Oak Knoll), Napa,
707-224-3300

■ "The Scalas know the right formula" at this Napa Valley Italian lauded as "the only place in the wine country for pasta"; there's a "relaxing", "warm" atmosphere that "feels like home but tastes better" thanks to "handed-down family recipes" and a "friendly, professional staff" that "reminds us of what a restaurant should be"; "it's a favorite for the right reasons."

Bistro Ralph ⓁⓈⓂ
23 | 19 | 22 | $32

109 Plaza St. (Center St.), Healdsburg, 707-433-1380

■ "Eat at the bar and you'll see a Who's Who of the wine world" at this "compelling" New American–Mediterranean where "high rustic dishes" from owner-chef Ralph Tingle are served by a "fast, friendly staff"; "people actually drive from SF just for dinner" and sigh "lucky Healdsburg!"

BOLERO ⓁⓈⓂ
18 | 26 | 18 | $32

125 E. Sir Francis Drake Blvd. (near the Larkspur Ferry),
Larkspur, 415-925-9391

☒ A "romantic" Larkspur Spanish newcomer in a "captivating" "historic" brickyard setting; while your enjoyment of the "many paellas" and tapas "depends on specific choices", no one questions the "Barcelona by the Bay" feel; P.S. the "great acoustics" make the live flamenco on Friday–Saturday nights even better.

Boonville Hotel ⓁⓈⓂ
▽ 23 | 22 | 22 | $31

14050 Hwy. 128 (Lambert Ln.), Boonville, 707-895-2210

■ We hear nothing but praise for this Cal-Mediterranean in "charming, rustic" and appropriately named Boonville; "interesting, creative fare", "unpretentious service" and "local Anderson Valley wines" make it a "great getaway"; if it gets late, you can always "stay at the hotel."

Brava Terrace L S M 21 21 18 $35
3010 St. Helena Hwy. N. (Lodi Ln.), St. Helena,
707-963-9300

☑ "The food has spunk" because chef Fred Halpert "has a deft touch" at this St. Helena New American in a "beautiful", "warm" space with a trademark terrace for "very pleasant outdoor dining" offering "great views of the Valley"; service can be "uneven", but overall most are "glad tourists don't venture this far north."

Brix L S M 23 24 21 $38
7377 St. Helena Hwy. (Washington St.), Napa,
707-944-2749

▪ Respondents are blown away by "an Asian breeze across Napa Valley"; this "upscale" fusion newcomer has voters "impressed" with its "stylish decor" and "delicious, innovative food" from a "genius" chef who puts out some of the "best fish this side of Hawaii" and "work of art" desserts; the "still green" staff may be the compromise to an experience that's otherwise "outstanding."

Bubba's Diner L S M 20 15 19 $20
566 San Anselmo Ave. (Magnolia St.), San Anselmo,
415-459-6862

▪ Chef Stephen Simmons (ex Lark Creek Inn) "redefines the diner" at this "very casual" San Anselmo American with "lots of personality" including "red vinyl booths" and "fried green tomatoes"; you'll need a shoehorn to get in", but once you do expect "delicious down-home dinners" (and breakfasts and lunches too); it's "great fun!"

Buckeye Roadhouse L S M 22 22 21 $31
15 Shoreline Hwy. (Hwy. 101), Mill Valley, 415-331-2600

▪ "The Buckeye hits the bull's-eye" at this Mill Valley American with a "comfy", "rustic", "hunting lodge" atmosphere; it's an "unhurried" "place to go for a no-nonsense, pat-your-tummy meal" including "great s'mores pie", pork chops and "anything with mashed potatoes"; throw in "courteous service" and you see why reservations are highly recommended.

Cacti L S M ▽ 19 20 20 $27
1200 Grant Ave. (2nd St.), Novato, 415-898-2234

☑ While this Southwestern is "great on the Novato scale", by other yardsticks "the quality varies"; everyone agrees that the former church setting is "classy."

Cactus Cafe L S M ▽ 19 15 19 $17
393 Miller Ave. (LaGoma St.), Mill Valley, 415-388-8226

☑ Inexpensive "run of the Mill" Valley Mexican with "burritos the size of hand grenades" and "fast" service; the more prickly say "the basement parking lot decor detracts" and that "Marin needs a decent Mexican restaurant."

Cafe Beaujolais 🅂 Ⓜ   25 | 21 | 22 | $38
961 Ukiah St. (bet. Evergreen & School Sts.), Mendocino,
707-937-5614
■ Margaret Fox's "must in Mendocino" offers "distinctive"
"heartfelt" New American–Californian cuisine in a
"homegrown" atmosphere ("ask for the garden room");
it's "dinner-only now", but don't arrive too late in the evening
or you may miss the fantastic "homemade breads."

California Cafe 🅛 🅂 Ⓜ   20 | 19 | 20 | $27
The Village at Corte Madera, 1736 Redwood Hwy.
(Paradise Dr.), Corte Madera, 415-924-2233
☑ "For a shopping mall restaurant", this Californian chainlet
with branches around the Bay Area serves "healthy but
attractive food" that's "surprisingly good"; the feel is
"formula" and depending on location service can be "a
trial", but there's "something for everyone" on the menu.

Caprice ◐🅂Ⓜ   ▽ 18 | 25 | 20 | $36
2000 Paradise Dr. (Mar West St.), Tiburon, 415-435-3400
☑ Historically, the "million-dollar view" "right over the
water" was the sole attraction at this "intimate, romantic"
Tiburon Californian; however, several scouts tell us the
food's "much improved", though you wouldn't know it
from the rating; either way, it's a safe Sunday brunch
destination or "place to take out-of-towners."

Catahoula 🅛 🅂 Ⓜ   24 | 21 | 21 | $35
Mount View Hotel & Spa, 1475 Lincoln Ave. (Washington Ave.),
Calistoga, 707-942-2275
■ "If chef Jan cooks for you, it's heaven" at this "noisy",
lively" Calistoga American specializing in "gutsy, delicious"
Cajun-Creole cuisine like "wonderful gumbo", pizzas with
"pizazz" and "the most original appetizers in all of Napa";
the service doesn't operate at the same level, but the
"exciting food" more than makes up for it.

CHATEAU SOUVERAIN 🅛 🅂   23 | 26 | 23 | $34
400 Souverain Rd. (Hwy. 101, Independence Ln. exit),
Geyserville, 707-433-3141
■ "A lovely dining room" with a smoky fireplace and a patio
with a "spectacular" view of Alexander Valley vineyards
are the draw at this dine-in-the-vines French bistro in
sunny Sonoma; there's a "limited but well-done menu"
and "great service", and for the quality it's an "excellent
value"; N.B. open Friday–Sunday, lunch and dinner.

Chevys 🅛 🅂 Ⓜ   14 | 13 | 15 | $17
Bon Air Shopping Ctr., 302 Bon Air Dr. (Sir Francis Drake
Blvd.), Greenbrae, 415-461-3203
See review in San Francisco Directory.

DOMAINE CHANDON L S M   26 | 26 | 26 | $52
1 California Dr. (Hwy. 29), Yountville, 707-944-2892
■ The indoor room is "reminiscent of an airport lounge", but a "beautiful park-like setting" makes for "sublime" outdoor dining at this très pricey New French on the premises of Napa's most famous producer of sparkling wine; alas, chef Philippe Jeanty has departed, but with experienced chef de cuisine Robert Curry stepping in to fill Jeanty's very large sabots, chances are it will remain "perfect in every way."

Downtown Bakery and   24 | 11 | 17 | $11
Creamery L S M ⊅
308 Center St. (Matheson St.), Healdsburg, 707-431-2719
■ Some ask "why include" this Sonoma bakery on the *Survey*?; how about 'cuz our reviewers are stuck on their sticky buns, "amazing brownies" and "great cinnamon rolls" – "my car drives there all by itself."

El Paseo S M   22 | 25 | 25 | $40
17 Throckmorton Ave. (bet. E. Blithedale & Miller Aves.), Mill Valley, 415-388-0741
■ Sounds Spanish, but it's actually a "great old" Classic French; the "very romantic" ambiance makes it "the ultimate spot for a tête-à-tête" and the service is "particularly good" too; a few wish for a "lighter touch", but when you need a "special occasion place" this could be it.

Foothill Cafe S   ▽ 23 | 11 | 21 | $30
J & P Shopping Ctr., 2766 Old Sonoma Rd. (Foothill Blvd.), Napa, 707-252-6178
☑ "Crowded" Napa American "overdecorated with chintzy Mexican kitsch" and burdened with an "unprepossessing location in a strip mall"; however, it's "a well-kept local secret" for "excellent food" especially the barbecue dishes.

Frantoio L S M   19 | 21 | 20 | $32
152 Shoreline Hwy. (Hwy. 101), Mill Valley, 415-289-5777
☑ "The olive press works as does most of the menu" at this Mill Valley Mediterranean with a solid decor score despite the fact that it evokes a "Mussolini-era train station" to some; the "extremely agreeable food" including "wonderful risotto" may be "way too rich, but it's top quality."

FRENCH LAUNDRY L S M   28 | 27 | 27 | $73
6640 Washington Ave. (Creek Ave.), Yountville, 707-944-2380
■ "Wow", "wow" and "wow" – Thomas Keller's "brilliant, miraculous food" attains "another level of hedonism" at this ultra-expensive Napa New American with a Classic French accent; the "perfect room" has "an otherworldly glow" and even if the food comes in "tweezer portions", the "amazing little masterpieces arrive continuously"; a few could do with less starch in the "standoffish staff", but most call it "perfection in the Valley."

Frog & The Peach ⅬⅬⅯ　　20 | 18 | 19 | $32
106 Throckmorton Ave. (bet. Bernard & Miller Sts.), Mill Valley, 415-381-3343
☑ We received a mixed salad of comments on Nancy Mootz's (Vertigo) Mill Valley newcomer with "odd decor" ("colander light fixtures") but "soothing colors"; "great addition" to the dining scene with "superperfect entrees" and a "good wine list" vs. "cannot find anything on the menu to eat" and "uneven service"; in any case, "the name alone is a draw."

Fusilli Ristorante ⅬⅯ　　– | – | – | M
620 Jackson St. (W. Texas St.), Fairfield, 707-428-4211
No surprises at this Fairfield twin of San Rafael's Pasta Prego: "stereotypical Italian" offering "good, stable" pasta dishes in a "mall ambiance."

General's Daughter ⅬⅬⅯ　　21 | 24 | 20 | $35
400 W. Spain St. (4th St. W.), Sonoma, 707-938-4004
▣ A "gussied-up", "tearoomish" restored historic Victorian house with a "beautiful garden" is the setting for this Sonoma New American; the food may be "cunning copycat Californian", but it's still "excellent", especially the "beyond reproach" lunch; service can be "negligent" on occasion, but it's "one of Sonoma's brightest spots."

Gira Polli Ⅼ Ⅿ　　21 | 14 | 18 | $21
590 E. Blithedale Ave. (Camino Alto), Mill Valley, 415-383-6040
See review in San Francisco Directory.

Guaymas ⅬⅬⅯ　　19 | 22 | 18 | $26
5 Main St. (Tiburon Blvd.), Tiburon, 415-435-6300
▦ "Take the ferry from SF" to this "hip, high-end" waterfront Mexican in Tiburon with "jaw-dropping views of the Bay"; then sit outside under the heat lamps and enjoy "unbeatable margaritas" and some of the "most varied and authentic Mexican in the area"; there are "crowds" and "rushed service", but what a place to spend the afternoon.

Guernica Ⅼ Ⅿ　　▽ 21 | 19 | 22 | $28
2009 Bridgeway (Spring St.), Sausalito, 415-332-1512
☑ "Stick to the house specials" for best results at this "old reliable" Sausalito French-Basque where "the owner supervises" and makes sure it's "always good"; the menu's "not particularly exciting", but the paella can be "superb" and it's backed by "excellent service."

Horizons ⅬⅬⅯ　　▽ 13 | 22 | 16 | $23
558 Bridgeway (Princess St.), Sausalito, 415-331-3232
☑ Expand your horizons with a "classic view of the city from the deck" of this Sausalito American; it's a "'60s-era historic monument" with "beautiful views" and "good Bloody Marys"; too bad the food's "so-so"; N.B. new ownership may mean changes are on the horizon.

Il Fornaio L S M
20 │ 21 │ 19 │ $29

223 Corte Madera Town Ctr. (Paradise Dr., off Hwy. 101),
Corte Madera, 415-927-4400
See review in San Francisco Directory.

Insalata's L S M
24 │ 22 │ 21 │ $31

120 Sir Francis Drake Blvd. (Barber Ave.), San Anselmo,
415-457-7700
■ This "spacious" new San Anselmo Cal-Mediterranean is
an "instant hit" with our surveyors; there are still "bugs to
work out" ("service needs shaping"), but "Heidi is a star"
and her "gutsy food" is "a taste treat"; can an eatery with
a name like this have anything less than "awesome salads"?

John Ash & Co. L S M
23 │ 24 │ 22 │ $44

Vintners Inn, 4330 Barnes Rd. (bet. River Rd. & Hwy. 101),
Santa Rosa, 707-527-7687
☑ Former owner John Ash, a pioneer of California cuisine,
"started it all" in Sonoma and "his spirit still pervades"
this "steep" American "jewel in the vineyards"; the "nice
folks" that run the place now offer "innovative cuisine"
that can be impressive, but "they need to be on their
toes" since there are "too many good restaurants in the
area"; "if you count fields of grapevines as decor", it's
also "one of the area's most beautiful restaurants."

Kasbah S
▽ 19 │ 21 │ 21 │ $41

200 Merrydale Rd. (Willow St.), San Rafael, 415-472-6666
☑ "It's true Moroccan right down to the belly dancers" at
this San Rafael spot where the "carefully prepared" food
is "exceeded only by the exotic decor"; even if staring at
midriffs isn't your scene, it's "fun one time."

Kenwood L S
24 │ 22 │ 23 │ $37

9900 Hwy. 12 (Warm Springs Rd.), Kenwood, 707-833-6326
■ "Try the sweetbreads" at this "upscale roadside cafe"
in Kenwood that's an "old favorite" for a "versatile, burgers-
to-haute-cuisine menu" and a "cozy", "charming" outdoor
patio with a view of the vineyards; bottom line: "a great
place to eat between stops at the wineries."

La Ginestra S
▽ 19 │ 13 │ 17 │ $21

127 Throckmorton Ave. (Miller Ave.), Mill Valley, 415-388-0224
■ "The Aversa family treats all of Mill Valley like guests at
their home" at this recently remodeled Southern Italian–
pizzeria; the "great home cooking" and some "unusual
entrees" at affordable prices make it a "good neighborhood
standby" "where all the locals go for honest food."

La Petite Auberge L S M
▽ 20 │ 19 │ 20 │ $33

704 Fourth St. (Tamalpais Dr.), San Rafael, 415-456-5808
☑ Not much excitement about this "traditional" San Rafael
French in a setting "reminiscent of Europe"; some call the
fare "reliably good" and recommend the sweetbreads, while
others say "too many California influences."

LARK CREEK INN L S M　　23　25　22　$41
234 Magnolia Ave. (Tamalpais Dr.), Larkspur, 415-924-7766
◩ This "lovely" American where "New England meets Marin" in an "idyllic" setting gets mixed comments from surveyors; some consider it "outstanding in every way" with a "very professional staff" and dishes that "always please", while others sense a "slipping giant" – could be that the "chef-owner [Bradley Ogden] has too many commitments."

Las Camelias L S M　　▽ 20　17　19　$23
912 Lincoln Ave. (bet. 3rd & 4th Sts.), San Rafael, 415-453-5850
◪ "If you don't go, you'll miss out" on some "good quality", "satisfying, refined Mexican" at this San Rafael haunt that's been a local favorite and a "bargain" for almost 20 years; admirers add that the Fregosos are "tremendous hosts."

Left Bank L S M　　21　22　21　$34
507 Magnolia Ave. (Ward St.), Larkspur, 415-927-3331
◩ Reactions to Roland Passot's "bustling", "noisy", "cosmopolitan" Larkspur French bistro are like a raging debate amongst Left Bank intellectuals; supporters argue that it's a "fun", "relaxed" place with some items (lamb sandwich, steak frites, onion tart) that can be "magical"; lamentors insist the menu is "limited" and the service "slow"; vive la différence!

Madrona Manor S M　　▽ 22　23　21　$41
Madrona Manor Country Inn, 1001 Westside Rd. (bet. Mill St. & W. Dry Creek Rd.), Healdsburg, 800-258-4003
◩ "Creative and surprising" is the take on this expensive and "deservedly popular" Healdsburg Californian-International with "spectacular cuisine", "quaint decor" and an "idyllic setting" amid nine acres of gardens; a few find it "not as good as it thinks", but with "gracious service" most think it's "excellent all around."

Marin Joe's ◐ L S M　　19　13　19　$24
1585 Casa Buena Dr. (Tamalpais Dr.), Corte Madera, 415-924-2081
◼ "As safe and reliable as your dad's Buick", this "always crowded", "smoky", "late-night" Marin Italian-American with "circa 1959 decor" offers "honest, uncomplicated food" from a "something for everyone", "Pritikin nemesis" menu; the "over-60" crowd recommends sitting "at the counter" and sampling one of the "excellent hamburgers" or "old-fashioned" pastas.

Meadowood Grill ◐ S M　　20　21　20　$32
Meadowood Resort, 900 Meadowood Ln. (bet. Howell Mtn. Rd. & Silverado Trail), St. Helena, 707-963-3646
◼ View "crazy golfers" from the deck of this Napa Mediterranean as you munch on either "good hearty fare" or spa dishes; more urbane customers call it a "pleasant" spot "suited to suburban types", but even they're impressed with the "awesome", "green, wooded" setting.

Meadowood Restaurant Ⓢ Ⓜ | 25 | 24 | 23 | $53 |
Meadowood Resort, 900 Meadowood Ln. (bet. Howell
Mtn. Rd. & Silverado Trail), St. Helena, 707-963-3646
■ This "laid-back", French-Californian at the Meadowood
Resort has fans who claim it goes "head to head with
Auberge du Soleil" for "Napa Valley at its finest"; the prices
"stagger", but the "romantic" ambiance and "elegant,
innovative presentations" "make one feel like a Rockefeller";
apostates cry "staid" and "needs pepping up."

Mikayla Ⓢ Ⓜ   ▽ | 23 | 24 | 23 | $35 |
Casa Madrona Hotel, 801 Bridgeway, Sausalito,
415-331-5888
■ "The roof rolls back" for a "gorgeous view" (especially
when there's a "full moon") at this Marin American on a
"lofty perch" in Sausalito; surprisingly "delicious" food
and "cheerful service" make it a "dependable" choice
when you have "out-of-town guests", or for Sunday brunch.

Mustards Grill Ⓛ Ⓢ Ⓜ | 23 | 20 | 21 | $34 |
7399 St. Helena Hwy. (Hwy. 29), Napa, 707-944-2424
■ "Everything works" at Cindy Pawlcyn's "quintessential
wine country cafe": the "classic American grill" menu, the
"chic" but casual ambiance, the "accommodating, attentive
staff" and the "overwhelming" list of wines; a small minority
sniffs "more Heinz than Grey Poupon", but most don't
mind being "packed in like anchovies" for "the epitome of
California cuisine"; P.S. "be sure to order the onion rings."

Napa Valley Grille Ⓛ Ⓢ Ⓜ | 22 | 20 | 20 | $36 |
Washington Sq., 6795 Washington St. (Hwy. 29 & Madison
St.), Yountville, 707-944-8686
☑ A "comfortable feeling" Yountville Cal-Mediterranean
with a vineyard view, "creative and well-prepared menu"
and an "extremely personable staff"; it's "often overlooked"
but a good "alternative to Mustards."

Napa Valley Wine Train Ⓛ Ⓢ Ⓜ | 17 | 24 | 20 | $53 |
1275 McKinstry St. (1st St.), Napa, 707-253-2111
☑ There may be "better food in nonmoving restaurants",
but this "rolling tourist trap" is "a fun way to see the Valley"
over a bottle of wine, even if the selection is "oddly lacking";
some locals find it "fun once in a while with out-of-towners",
but remember to "skip" the California cuisine (just "make
mine a Dramamine").

North Sea Village Ⓛ Ⓢ Ⓜ   ▽ | 18 | 16 | 14 | $22 |
300 Turney St. (Bridgeway), Sausalito, 415-331-3300
☑ Expect "Cantonese at fair prices" and a "matchless view"
of the Bay at this Sausalito Chinese; some take it as "proof
that good views and good Chinese food rarely mix", but
others go for the "best dim sum in the North Bay"; P.S. as
the score suggests, "service can be aloof."

109

Panama Hotel & Restaurant L S M
▽ 17 | 21 | 19 | $23

4 Bay View St. (B St.), San Rafael, 415-457-3993

◪ "Insist on the patio" at this "fun and funky" (even "kinky") San Rafael American with a "great atmosphere"; the food's "adequate", but the real draw is the swing and jazz on Tuesday nights – a "favorite" with locals.

Pasta Prego L S M
▽ 22 | 18 | 21 | $24

Grapeyard Shopping Ctr., 3260 Jefferson St. (bet. Lincoln & Trancas Sts.), Napa, 707-224-9011

◼ Napa Italian with "strip mall" ambiance but "good bruschetta and seafood"; it may be "boring", but it's "better than most for the price" and "good before the movies."

Piatti L S M
20 | 20 | 20 | $30

625 Redwood Hwy. (Hwy. 101, Seminary Dr. exit), Mill Valley, 415-380-2525
El Dorado Hotel, 405 First St. (Spain St.), Sonoma, 707-996-2351
6480 Washington St. (Oak Circle), Yountville, 707-944-2070

◪ "A chain is a chain is a chain" ... unless it's this "lively", "upscale" Italian version where "you can always rely on the food being good" thanks to "surprisingly skilled" execution in the kitchen; nitpickers stress that "service varies" and claim they're "too commercialized."

Piazza D'Angelo L S M
19 | 20 | 18 | $28

22 Miller Ave. (Throckmorton Ave.), Mill Valley, 415-388-2000

◪ "Busy", "boisterous", "trendy" Marin Italian hangout that's perfect when you're in the mood for "people-watching" or "craving thin-crust pizza"; the food isn't as interesting as the "bar scene", but it's definitely "better than average."

Pinot Blanc L S M
20 | 20 | 19 | $41

641 Main St. (Grayson St.), St. Helena, 707-963-6191

◪ "Too trendy to criticize"? – not according to respondents who report that Joachim Splichal's (of LA's Patina) Napa French bistro "can be fabulous" but for the most part is "uneven" and "has yet to show me anything special"; the staff's "SoCal attitude" doesn't help, but the roomy booths and outdoor seating score points; overall, "still working on it."

Rice Table S
▽ 20 | 14 | 20 | $24

1617 Fourth St. (G St.), San Rafael, 415-456-1808

◼ For the cost of a rijsttafel, you can take "a charming trip to a faraway land" at this Marin Indonesian with a "basic rice table menu" but "truly wonderful food and service"; too bad the decor's "almost gaudy."

Ristorante Fabrizio L S M
▽ 18 | 17 | 19 | $26

455 Magnolia Ave. (Cane St.), Larkspur, 415-924-3332

◪ "Lunch specials" are the way to approach this Larkspur Italian delivering "huge portions" at a great value; some claim "molto ordinario", but there's a "nice family feel" and an "attentive" staff.

Robata Grill & Sushi L S M   ▽ 21 | 18 | 19 | $24
591 Redwood Hwy. (Hwy. 101, Seminary Dr. exit), Mill Valley,
414-381-8400
☑ "If you like sushi", you "can't go wrong" at this Mill Valley
Japanese where "true professionals" put out "great sushi
and sashimi"; don't leave without trying some grilled
vegetables from the "best robata in the Bay Area."

Royal Thai L S M   22 | 15 | 18 | $21
610 Third St. (Irwin St.), San Rafael, 415-485-1074
■ "Consistently" "delicious", "reasonable" San Rafael
Thai (with a SF sib) with a "voluminous menu" that offers
everything from a winning salmon in red curry sauce to
"the best green papaya salad you can find."

Rutherford Grill L S M   – | – | – | M
1180 Rutherford Rd. (Hwy. 29), Rutherford, 707-963-1792
"Get the rotisserie chicken and blue cheese potato chips"
and "fabulous fall-off-the-bone ribs" at this Napa American
"where the local wine crowd eats"; "rapidly turning tables"
means they sometimes "seem to rush you out", but for
"consistent simple food" (including the "best mashed
potatoes" west of Idaho) it's a sure bet.

Sam's Anchor Cafe L S M   13 | 20 | 15 | $21
27 Main St. (Tiburon Blvd.), Tiburon, 415-435-4527
☑ Even with a "great view", it's "hard to relax" on the deck
of this legendary Tiburon American bar and grill because
one of the "killer gulls" may "poop on you and your food"
("I was birded"); nevertheless, it still draws a "trendy"
crowd of "beautiful people" downing "froufrou drinks",
"greasy spoon" burgers and brunch served by "shorty
shorts in the fog" waitresses.

Sand Dollar L S M   ▽ 15 | 17 | 16 | $21
3458 Shoreline Hwy., Stinson Beach, 415-868-0434
☑ Stinson Beach American with a "fun bar" and "great
Sunday morning ambiance" along with "good" soups,
salads and burgers; detractors claim "nice spot, but not
for the food – brown bag it."

Scoma's L S M   17 | 17 | 16 | $30
588 Bridgeway (Princess St.), Sausalito, 415-332-9551
See review in San Francisco Directory.

Showley's L S   ▽ 22 | 20 | 21 | $33
Miramonte Inn, 1327 Railroad Ave. (bet. Hunt & Adams Sts.),
St. Helena, 707-963-1200
■ "The Showleys are warm people" and their staff "tries
hard" at this "country-style" Napa Californian in a historic
building (1870); regulars recommend "lunch outside during
the week" and note that the chocolate hoo hoo has returned.

Sonoma Mission Inn Grille L S M | 20 | 21 | 21 | $38 |
*Sonoma Mission Inn, 18140 Hwy. 12, Boyes Hot Springs
(Boyes Blvd.), Sonoma, 707-939-2415*
◪ The low-fat, "light as air menu at this Sonoma Cal-Med
is "good" and "convenient" to health-conscious types
staying at the inn, but those coming from farther away say
it's "solid and consistent" but "nothing special"; expect a
relaxing atmosphere, even if you haven't had a massage.

Station House Cafe L S M | 19 | 16 | 17 | $22 |
11180 Hwy. 1 (2nd St.), Point Reyes Station, 415-663-1515
◪ Not only is this Marin American cafe a smart choice
"after a long hike at Point Reyes", it's one of only a few
options; hikers recommend the "good breakfasts" in the
"lovely garden" but stress that service can be "slow";
"don't make a special trip", but if you're in the area and
hungry it'll seem like "an oasis."

TERRA S M | 27 | 25 | 26 | $50 |
*1345 Railroad Ave. (bet. Hunt & Adam Sts.), St. Helena,
707-963-8931*
◼ "The squab", no "the quail", no "the sea bass" – voters
can't decide which is more "sublime" at Hiro Sone's Napa
Valley French-Italian with Asian overtones; the "artistic
presentation" of "thrilling cuisine" isn't the only story,
however; an "amazingly romantic" room in an old stone
building, "smooth service" and a savvy wine list turn Terra
into "the best of all worlds"; "Hiro is my hero" and his
restaurant's "a definite repeater."

TRA VIGNE L S M | 24 | 26 | 22 | $38 |
1050 Charter Oak Ave. (Hwy. 29), St. Helena, 707-963-4444
◼ Expect "sexy" "Tuscan ambiance" at this "elegant yet
relaxed" Italian where you must sit outside on the terrace or
in the courtyard to take in the "stunning" setting; it's a
unanimous winner with "superb" food, "fabulous service"
and an "unbelievable wine list" including "their own
grappa"; "no visit to Napa is complete without a visit."

Trilogy L | ▽ 25 | 19 | 23 | $46 |
1234 Main St. (Hunt St.), St. Helena, 707-963-5507
◼ The "best quail in the universe" can be found at this "tiny,
intimate" Napa Cal-French with an "attractive fixed-price
menu" and an "excellent wine list."

Tutto Mare L S M | 18 | 22 | 18 | $32 |
9 Main St. (Tiburon Blvd.), Tiburon, 415-435-4747
◪ "Spellbinding views" from the upper deck are the main
attraction at this "spacious" Tiburon Italian seafooder;
patrons report only "average" and at times "disappointing"
food and say "they haven't gotten it straight yet" ("oysters
have more intelligence than some of the waiters"); until
they do, it's just "another fish place with a view."

Vintner's Court S – | – | – | E
Silverado Country Club, 1600 Atlas Peak (Hardman Ave.), Napa, 707-257-0200
The Friday "seafood-o-rama" buffet is "excellent" at this Napa Pacific Rim dining room in the Silverado Country Club; otherwise it's "too expensive", but you can still have "a most comfortable evening" here.

Wappo Bar Bistro L S M 23 | 20 | 18 | $30
1226 Washington St. (Lincoln Ave.), Calistoga, 707-942-4712
◪ "Service by amateurs" and a "very slow kitchen" are drawbacks, but most appreciate the "creative menu" of "delicious" Eclectic dishes at this Calistoga newcomer with "delightful courtyard" dining; "the food was good, but get your act together."

WILLOWSIDE CAFE S 26 | 17 | 24 | $37
3535 Guerneville Rd. (Willowside Rd.), Santa Rosa, 707-523-4814
◼ Don't let the "understated", rustic, "old red-painted wood building" throw you; this Sonoma American-Med has fine service, "carefully prepared creative food" and a "splendid wine list"; it's well "worth the reservations chase."

Wine Spectator Greystone L S M 20 | 23 | 20 | $42
2555 Main St. (Deer Park Rd.), St. Helena, 707-967-1010
◪ This "fun and colorful" Mediterranean built on the "open kitchen concept" and set in a "beautiful historic building" (the former Christian Brothers winery) in St. Helena has become "a nice part of the Napa scene"; "frequently adventurous" cuisine from graduates of the CIA (upstairs) is "on the rise", if not always "coherent"; the menu of "interesting tapas" might be the best approach.

Yet Wah L S M 15 | 14 | 14 | $18
2019 Larkspur Landing Cir. (Sir Francis Drake Blvd.), Larkspur, 415-461-3631
See review in San Francisco Directory.

South of San Francisco

		F	D	S	C

Amber India 🄻🅂🄼   ▽ | 24 | 17 | 18 | $23

2290 El Camino Real #9 (bet. Rengstorff & Ortega Aves.), Mountain View, 415-968-7511

■ If you live in the South Bay, chances are you already know this "gold standard for Indian food", but city dwellers are catching on; a moderately priced "hidden treasure", it "takes North Indian cuisine to the top level" with some "unusual and most welcome menu choices"; "dressy" but not too dressy ambiance and a "helpful staff" help make this one "worth a 50-mile drive."

Aqui Cal-Mex Grill 🄻🅂🄼🗭   ▽ | 22 | 16 | 14 | $15

1145 Lincoln Ave. (Willow St.), San Jose, 408-995-0381

■ The "nice staff" at this "self-serve" San Jose grill prepares "fresh, healthy and consistent" Cal-Mex; low prices make it a "great deal" that's "good for the genre."

Basque Cultural Center 🄻🅂   ▽ | 18 | 15 | 17 | $24

599 Railroad Ave. (bet. Spruce & Orange Aves.), South San Francisco, 415-583-8091

■ "I never thought I would like oxtail", but at this Peninsula French Basque in a "bizarre neighborhood" you can get some convincing "back to the old country" cuisine at "great value" prices; some say "everything's starting to taste the same", but with "huge portions" of "honest" food, it's a "good embassy" for the Basque cause.

Beausejour 🄻🅂🄼   ▽ | 21 | 16 | 19 | $33

170 State St. (bet. 3rd & 4th Sts.), Los Altos, 415-948-1382

☑ "Romantic and woodsy" Los Altos Asian-French is a "reliable but not inspired" stop with a "good prix fixe" menu and "slow but nice service" in a "bistro setting"; the general take is that it's "dependable."

Bella Vista 🄼 | 20 | 25 | 21 | $44

13451 Skyline Blvd. (5 mi. south of I-92), Woodside, 650-851-1229

■ The name tells you there's a "gorgeous view" from this Woodside French-Italian high on the Skyline Drive; the food is only "ok", but the "romantic" ambiance and "charming waiters" make it a "special occasion destination"; just "make sure it's clear" outside because at these prices "if it's foggy, you lose."

Benihana L S M　　　15 | 16 | 18 | $26
1496 Bayshore Hwy. (bet. Broadway & Millbrae Ave.),
Burlingame, 415-342-5202
2074 Valco Fashion Park (Hwy. 280, Wolfe Rd. exit),
Cupertino, 408-253-1221
See review in San Francisco Directory.

Blue Chalk Cafe L S M　　　15 | 15 | 15 | $22
630 Ramona St. (bet. Hamilton & Forest Sts.), Palo Alto,
415-326-1020
☑ "Cue up and chow down" at this "noisy" Palo Alto pool
hall and American cafe where there's a "touch of Dixie"
to the atmosphere and to the cuisine ("the prawns and
grits are great"); it turns into a "body shop" on weekend
nights, so unless you're into the "thirtysomething" singles
scene, you may want to chalk it up.

Bok Choy L S M　　　▽ 17 | 15 | 15 | $20
2A Stanford Shopping Ctr. (University Ave.), Palo Alto,
415-325-6588
☑ Supporters say "this fine for what it is" Palo Alto Pan-
Asian offers "a variety of dishes" including "quick noodles",
"great curry" and other "clean and healthy" fare; however,
detractors balk that the service "needs help" and it's a
"bummer that they're in a mall."

Brother's Delicatessen L S M　　　17 | 9 | 15 | $15
1351 Howard Ave. (Primrose Ave.), Burlingame,
415-343-2311
■ If you need a "decent corned beef connection", check
out this "plain but high-quality" Burlingame deli with "great
potato pancakes" and "mile-high pastrami sandwiches"; it's
certainly "not NYC", but since it might be "the only halfway
decent deli north of LA", it's "always busy and noisy."

Buffalo Grill L S M　　　19 | 20 | 18 | $29
Hillsdale Mall, 66 31st Ave. (El Camino Real), San Mateo,
415-358-8777
☑ To some, the Pat Kuleto design at this San Mateo
Californian is "classy if a little overdecorated" and there's an
"extreme racket" in the dining room and at the "exhibition
bar"; but "frantic" service manages to keep pace with the
crowds that zip in for "large portions" of "super pork chops
and mashed potatoes" and other "good to indifferent" food;
it's shopping-convenient, so "if you're in the area, why not?"

Cafe Marcella L S　　　▽ 26 | 18 | 25 | $33
368 Village Ln. (N. Santa Cruz & University Aves.), Los Gatos,
408-354-8006
■ This Italian-leaning "Fringale of the South Bay" is a
crowd-pleaser offering "fabulous" food (including "excellent
seafood pasta") and a "great wine list"; a few think it's
"too noisy", but most say "it feels like family " so "I could
eat here every night."

Cafe Trio L M   ▽ 23 | 16 | 20 | $30
15466 Los Gatos Blvd. (Lark Ave.), Los Gatos, 408-356-8129
■ You'll "need a reservation" to get into this "very busy" Los Gatos Californian, which some say is "one of the best in the area"; it's a "lovely spot for good service and fine food."

California Cafe L S M   20 | 19 | 20 | $27
700 Welch Rd. (Quarry St.), Palo Alto, 415-325-2233
2855 Stevens Creek Blvd. (Hwy. 280), Santa Clara, 408-296-2233
See review in North of San Francisco Directory.

Capellini L S M   18 | 19 | 18 | $29
310 Baldwin Ave. (B St.), San Mateo, 415-348-2296
■ "Three levels offer a choice of quiet to loud dining" at this "trendy, happening" San Mateo Italian with a "warm, open" atmosphere; there's a "lively bar scene", good grilled items and some of "the best pastas", but "when will they learn to honor reservations on time?"

Carpaccio L S M   20 | 18 | 19 | $30
1120 Crane St. (Santa Cruz Ave.), Menlo Park, 415-322-1211
◪ "Big plates of rich pasta" at "reasonable prices" make this "pretty" Peninsula Northern Italian a "favorite local restaurant" despite scattered reports that "the staff can be gruff"; whether "the same menu all the time" makes it "very consistent" or "somewhat pedestrian" is your call, but with a "power people" scene in full swing, "to be seen is the principal reason to go."

Casanova L S M   ▽ 24 | 25 | 22 | $48
Fifth St. (bet. Mission & San Carlos Sts.), Carmel, 408-625-0501
■ "Break out the gold bullion" – this "enchanting" French-Italian with an "old European feel" may be one of the "best in Carmel", but you'll pay dearly for the "pricey wine list" and "intimate, romantic" atmosphere in a "cute old house" with a "charming garden"; wallet-watchers suggest going for lunch or Sunday brunch.

Chef Chu's L S M   18 | 15 | 17 | $23
1067 N. San Antonio Rd. (El Camino Real), Los Altos, 415-948-2696
◪ "In Hong Kong they would call it an American restaurant", but in Los Altos they call it "Americanized Chinese"; the food at this veteran "is not exciting, but it's always solid"; "reasonable prices" and "decent service" make it "good for large groups."

Chez Renee L   ▽ 27 | 22 | 23 | $34
9051 Soquel Dr. (Rio del Mar), Aptos, 408-688-5566
■ "This is what dining is all about": "food, decor and service done with style and care" at this upscale Aptos French-Californian that's "by far the best" in the area; a "great wine list" and extensive selection of single-malt scotches also add to the appeal of this "local favorite."

Chez T.J. ▽ | 25 | 22 | 25 | $51 |
938 Villa St. (bet. Bryant & Franklin Sts.), Mountain View, 415-964-7466
☑ A "cozy" and costly South Bay French-American providing "a unique dining experience" with "elegant" prix fixe menus and a "romantic" atmosphere; while critics sniff "pretentiousness defined", supporters save up the bucks to savor it on "special occasions."

Club XIX Ⓛ Ⓢ Ⓜ ▽ | 24 | 27 | 26 | $54 |
The Lodge at Pebble Beach, 17 Mile Dr. (18th Green at the Pebble Beach Golf Links), Pebble Beach, 408-625-8519
■ Hubert Keller (Fleur de Lys) has signed on as a consultant to the kitchen at this "plush" and very pricey Pebble Beach French, so expect the "good food" to get even better; a view of the famous 18th hole adds to the "great setting and ambiance", and "impeccable" service is par for the course.

Covey, The Ⓢ Ⓜ ▽ | 22 | 27 | 25 | $52 |
Quail Lodge Resort & Golf Club, 8205 Valley Greens Dr. (Carmel Valley Rd.), Carmel, 408-824-1581
☑ "An almost perfect meal" can be had at this "deluxe" Carmel Continental at the Quail Lodge with its newly redecorated "beautiful postmodern interior"; some sqawk at the prices, but there are "delicious meaty dishes almost reminiscent of Paris bistro food", leading the majority to conclude "wow, one great place."

Crescent Park Ⓛ Ⓢ Ⓜ | 19 | 19 | 15 | $34 |
546 University Ave. (Webster Ave.), Palo Alto, 415-326-0111
☑ This Palo Alto Mediterranean-American newcomer may be "conservative", but, unlike some conservatives, "shows signs of life"; "some things don't work" – like the "negligent service" and "chilly atmosphere" – but most think it has "great potential" and is "a nice South Bay addition."

Crow's Nest Ⓛ Ⓢ Ⓜ ▽ | 14 | 20 | 16 | $23 |
2218 E. Cliff Dr. (5th Ave.), Santa Cruz, 408-476-4560
☑ "The views sucker you in" to this "perfect location" Santa Cruz seafooder, though the cooking is pretty "mediocre"; a few nestle in anyway for a "very romantic" evening with a "great" vista of "the yacht harbor."

Dal Baffo Ⓛ Ⓜ | 23 | 19 | 21 | $48 |
878 Santa Cruz Ave. (University Dr.), Menlo Park, 415-325-1588
☑ "When you want stuffy", book this "well-established", "very expensive" Continental-Italian where the waiters "read the menu out loud to you, savoring each word"; while some think it's "food for the nouveau riche", others swear they "love these guys" for "good classic cuisine" and "what a wine list!"

117

Duarte's Tavern L S M   19 13 18 $23
202 Stage Rd. (Pescadero Creek Rd.), Pescadero,
415-879-0464
■ "Satisfy your soul" with the "wonderful artichoke soup",
seafood and pies ("like mama used to make – with lard")
at this "rustic, homey" South Coast American tavern
where the staff is "consistently accommodating"; it's
"funky and fun just like it always was" and "the drive
down is spectacular."

Duck Club L S M   ▽ 19 20 20 $38
Stanford Park Hotel, 100 El Camino Real (University Ave.),
Menlo Park, 415-322-1234
◪ Duck in to this "gracious" Peninsula Californian with
"leisurely service" and usually "well-prepared food",
although "changing chefs" means "you never know
when you'll get goosed"; but overall it's "a quality hotel
restaurant" that shouldn't ruffle your feathers.

Emile's L   ▽ 26 22 25 $50
545 S. Second St. (bet. William & Reed Sts.), San Jose,
408-289-1960
◪ "The Grand Marnier soufflé brought tears to my eyes"
(and, most likely, so did the check) at this "first-class"
San Jose Continental where the "redone interior adds a
lot of charm"; but while some call it "the best" in the area",
others gripe "$13 for two scallops doesn't make it" –
"who do they think they're kidding?"

Empress Court L S   – – – M
433 Airport Blvd. (Anza Blvd.), Burlingame, 415-348-1122
"Try the buffet" at this Peninsula Chinese where there's
"ok Cantonese" and "the fresh fish can be good"; the
"banquet hall" provides space for special events and a
"friendly staff" keeps reviewers . . . well, Empressed.

ERNA'S ELDERBERRY   28 27 28 $61
HOUSE L S M
48688 Victoria Ln. (Hwy. 41), Oakhurst, 209-683-6800
■ "Class in an unexpected area" can be found at this
Oakhurst Cal-French; the highly rated food gets curiously
little comment, but most maintain it's "worth the drive"
and ask "who wouldn't fork over the money" for the
"lovely setting", "pampering service" and "over the top
experience"?; "Shangri-La exists – right outside Yosemite!"

Estampas Peruanas L S   – – – M
715 El Camino Real (Broadway), Redwood City,
415-368-9340
Traditional and unusual Peruvian dishes (particularly
seafood) shine at this recent Redwood City entry; a
knowledgeable staff explains the regional specialties
and helps make this a singular South American spot.

Eulipia 🄻🅂   ▽ 20 | 18 | 21 | $31
374 S. First St. (bet. San Carlos & San Salvador Sts.), San Jose, 408-280-6161
◾ "If you must go to Downtown San Jose", this recently revamped, "always crowded" New American may be the ticket with its "large portions" of "well-prepared" food in a "modern setting"; while a few "liked the old format better", the majority maintains it's "always interesting."

Evvia 🄻🅂🄼   22 | 22 | 19 | $34
420 Emerson St. (bet. Lytton & University Sts.), Palo Alto, 415-326-0983
◾ At this "glorious" Greek Palo Alto "in-place" with "great olives" and a "warm fireplace" be prepared for "hard-to-get reservations", waits that would try the patience of Socrates and spotty service "that can spoil or save an evening"; still, most say "if it's not noisy, it's absolutely enchanting" and a candidate for "the best newcomer to the Peninsula."

Faz 🄻🅂🄼   18 | 19 | 17 | $26
1108 N. Mathilda Ave. (Mossett Park Dr.), Sunnyvale, 408-752-8000
See review in San Francisco Directory.

Flea St. Cafe 🄻🅂   22 | 20 | 20 | $31
3607 Alameda de las Pulgas (Avy St.), Menlo Park, 415-854-1226
◾ "A place with personality", this Peninsula New American puts the "accent on organic" and "vegetarian alternatives" and "nourishes the spirit as well as the body" with its "cute and quaint" "country French meets Vermont farmhouse" setting; the food is "yummy", so hop on over for "great pairings of fresh flavors."

Fook Yuen 🄻🅂🄼   24 | 16 | 17 | $24
195 El Camino Real (Millbrae Ave.), Millbrae, 415-692-8600
◪ Many rate this "sophisticated" Chinese with "delicious dim sum" and seafood "the best on the Peninsula"; despite "off-putting service", "it gets packed", so "arrive early."

FRESH CREAM 🅂🄼   25 | 24 | 24 | $54
Heritage Harbor, 99 Pacific St. (Scott St.), Monterey, 408-375-9798
◾ Supporters of this long-standing New French claim it's the "best in Monterey", with "an elegant atmosphere", "outstanding views", "excellent service" and "great presentations"; while faultfinders snipe "it lives up to its name" with "rich" and "heavy food", most conclude "it's a once in a lifetime meal – it has to be at those prices!"

Fung Lum 🄻🅂🄼   ▽ 22 | 21 | 17 | $26
1815 S. Bascom Ave. (bet. Hamilton & Campbell Aves.), Campbell, 408-377-6955
◪ "Quantity and quality" go hand in hand at this Campbell Chinese, but whether you'll be consuming "delicious" Cantonese cooking in a "gaudy" or "elegant" atmosphere is definitely a matter of debate.

Gaylord India Restaurant L S M   17 | 16 | 16 | $27
1706 El Camino Real (near Encinal), Menlo Park, 415-326-8761
See review in San Francisco Directory.

Gervais L   – | – | – | E
Park Naglee Plaza, 1798 Park Ave. (Naglee St.), San Jose, 408-275-8631
While fans of this venerable San Jose French find it "very friendly" with "warm service" and "homey ambiance", critics carp "it's a bit stuffy" and "the food is not at the expected level", particularly for the price.

Gibson L S M   ∇ 21 | 21 | 18 | $32
203 E. Third. Ave. (Ellsworth Ave.), San Mateo, 415-344-6566
☑ "Huge potential" marks this somewhat "self-conscious" San Mateo New American newcomer with "very unusual", "carefully crafted cuisine"; as with most new places, the "service needs work", but most call it a "bright if erratic spot" that might prove to be one of "San Mateo's finest."

Gordon Biersch Brewing L S M   16 | 17 | 15 | $22
640 Emerson St. (bet. Hamilton & Forest Sts.), Palo Alto, 415-323-7723
33 E. San Fernando St. (bet. 1st & 2nd Sts.), San Jose, 408-294-6785
☑ These "yuppie bliss" brewpubs offer "good beer and average food", so "stick to the basics" like "burgers and garlic fries"; they're "loud, crowded" and a "singles scene" for the "college crowd."

Grandview L S M   – | – | – | M
1107 Howard Ave. (bet. Lorton & Highland Aves.), Burlingame, 415-348-3888
An "interior makeover" and "much better food" draw praise from the few who know this Burlingame Chinese, which partisans call "one of the best and most authentic" around.

Hong Kong Flower Lounge L S M   22 | 17 | 16 | $25
51 Millbrae Ave. (El Camino Real), Millbrae, 415-692-6666
☑ Most tout the "fantastic dim sum and Peking duck" at this "quite reliable", "crowded and noisy" Peninsula Cantonese (with an Outer Richmond branch); the decor is the "expected dreary setup" and a few say the service can be "horrible", but there are still some "unique and delicious dishes" and at times it's "almost like Hong Kong."

Iberia L S M   21 | 18 | 18 | $35
Ladera Country Shoppes, 190 Ladera Alpine Rd. (bet. Alpine & La Cuesta), Menlo Park, 415-854-1746
☑ Loyalists like the "mouthwatering" paella and "many unusual dishes" at this pricey Menlo Park Spanish "hideaway" where "venture capitalists come for privacy" and you can "eat outside on a nice evening"; foes find the food "pretty heavy by today's standards", the service "slow" and the experience "spotty."

Il Fornaio L S M   20 | 21 | 19 | $29 |

327 Lorton Ave. (California St.), Burlingame, 415-375-8000
Garden Court Hotel, 520 Cowper St. (University Ave), Palo Alto, 415-853-3888
302 Market St. (San Carlos St.), San Jose, 408-271-3366
See review in San Francisco Directory.

Invitation House L S M   – | – | – | M |

270 Rockaway Beach (Hwy. 1), Pacifica, 415-738-8588
This Pacifica place offers "good Korean and Japanese fare in an unlikely locale"; specialties, which include Asian barbecue and a sushi bar with live lobster and crab, are served in a "warm" atmosphere.

Isobune Sushi L S M   16 | 15 | 15 | $22 |

1451 Burlingame Ave. (El Camino Real), Burlingame, 415-344-8433
See review in San Francisco Directory.

JoAnn's Cafe L S M ⊅   23 | 13 | 20 | $14 |

1131 El Camino Real (bet. Westborough & Hickey Blvds.), South San Francisco, 415-872-2810
■ This "impossible to improve" upon Peninsula coffee shop serves "wonderful, big satisfying" breakfasts and "homelike lunches" with "thankfully, no city attitude"; prices are "cheap", the atmosphere is "relaxed" and "you don't walk out, you waddle."

Juban L S M   – | – | – | M |

1204 Broadway (Laguna Ave.), Burlingame, 415-347-2300
"Clean and not too smoky cook-your-own" Japanese in Burlingame (and a sleek new branch in SF's Japan Center); for some, the hands-on experience is "fun and pleasant", but the less industrious assert at these prices "I'd rather have someone else cook my food."

Kincaid's Bistro L S M   20 | 23 | 21 | $33 |

217 Crossroads Blvd. (Hwy. 1), Carmel, 408-624-9626
■ This Carmel French "real find" has already been discovered by some of our voters who had their "best meal of the year" there; the "charming" bistro fare is "a nice break from California cuisine" and the "French farmhouse decor" makes for a "fun atmosphere"; while it can be "noisy", there are "great views of the bay" and it's "good for business lunches."

Kuleto's Trattoria L S M   18 | 19 | 18 | $31 |

1095 Rollins Rd. (Broadway), Burlingame, 415-342-4922
☑ "It may not be exciting", but "when we don't know where to go, we go to Kuleto's"; this "old standby" Peninsula Italian is also "a great choice near the airport"; the "service is spotty" and it's "too loud", but "it's less hassled than its San Francisco" sister.

La Cumbre Taqueria 🄻🅂🄼 | 20 | 8 | 13 | $9 |
28 North B St. (1st Ave.), San Mateo, 415-344-8989
See review in San Francisco Directory.

La Forêt 🅂   ▽ | 26 | 24 | 23 | $45 |
21747 Bertram Rd. (Almaden Rd.), San Jose,
408-997-3458
▮ You "can't eat the decor" at this "elegant, remote" and "very romantic" San Jose New French "hideaway", but you can feast on a "great wild game menu" and "excellent duck"; it's expensive, but voters say the forest is enchanted and "all-around wonderful."

La Luna Bistro 🄻🄼   ▽ | 20 | 17 | 18 | $30 |
1137 Chestnut St. (bet. Oak Grove St. & Santa Cruz Ave.),
Menlo Park, 415-324-3810
▨ "Creative" is the word on this intimate new Menlo Park bistro where the food is French with a Latin accent; service is still "erratic", but it's "off to a great start" and respondents hope it shoots the moon.

La Mère Michelle 🄻🅂   ▽ | 21 | 23 | 23 | $43 |
14467 Big Basin Way (3rd St.), Saratoga, 408-867-5272
▨ "A good place to take your favorite elderly aunt", this San Jose Classic French "takes me back to the '60s"; some think it "needs new blood", but it's still a "solid if predictable" performer with "accommodating service" and a "classy" atmosphere.

L'Amie Donia 🄻 | 24 | 18 | 20 | $37 |
530 Bryant St. (bet. University & Hamilton Aves.), Palo Alto,
415-323-7614
▮ A "crowded" but "charming" Palo Alto French bistro where it "doesn't get any better than this for fresh fare" that's "inspired and delicious"; it's a "loud scene" and the "tables are too close for comfort", but the "total attention to detail" and "the food make up for a lot."

La Pastaia 🄻🅂🄼   ▽ | 22 | 22 | 21 | $32 |
Hotel De Anza, 233 W. Santa Clara St. (Almaden Blvd.),
San Jose, 408-286-8686
▨ This San Jose "good Italiano" features "large portions" of "fabulous" pastas as well as an extensive Italian wine list; it can be "noisy", but it's a "good place for a group."

Lark Creek 🄻🅂🄼 | 20 | 20 | 19 | $33 |
Benjamin Franklin Hotel, 50 E. Third Ave. (El Camino Real),
San Mateo, 415-344-9444
See review in East of San Francisco Directory.

Left at Albuquerque 🅛🅢🅜   17 | 18 | 15 | $20
*1100 Burlingame Ave. (California Ave.), Burlingame,
415-401-5700*
*Pruneyard Shopping Ctr., 1875 S. Bascom Ave. (bet.
Hamilton & Campbell Aves.), Campbell, 408-558-1680*
445 Emerson St. (University Ave.), Palo Alto, 415-326-1011
◪ "What frat boys graduate to after keg parties", these
"pickup scene" Southwesterns are "noisy" and "fun",
although you'll get more kicks from the "staggering
selection of tequilas" and "sublime margaritas" than the
"so-so" Tex-Mex food; cynics say "wish I'd turned right",
but hey, dude, "try the Green Monster" and chill.

Le Mouton Noir 🅢🅜   ▽ 27 | 26 | 26 | $52
*14560 Big Basin Way (bet. 4th & 5th Sts.), Saratoga,
408-867-7017*
◼ They've "definitely kept the quality up" at this "timeless"
and "romantic" Saratoga French with "superb" and
"straightforward food" that's "consistently outstanding";
"prices have increased", but order "anything on the menu
and you won't be disappointed."

Le Papillon 🅛🅢🅜   ▽ 26 | 24 | 24 | $44
410 Saratoga Ave. (Kiely Blvd.), San Jose, 408-296-3730
◼ "An established restaurant that keeps current", this
"classy" San Jose New French offers an "updated menu"
of "delicious" food in a "charming" and "quiet setting."

Lion and Compass 🅛🅜   ▽ 18 | 16 | 20 | $33
*1023 N. Fair Oaks Ave. (Weddell St.), Sunnyvale,
408-745-1260*
◪ The "Silicon Valley crowd doesn't seem to mind" the
"expensive lunches" (including a "great carpaccio salad")
at this Sunnyvale New American; critics who growl about
"no decor" and "not a lot of variety" on the menu conclude
it's "ok for a power lunch, but dinner is blah."

Los Gatos Brewing Co. 🅛🅢🅜   18 | 17 | 16 | $25
*130-G N. Santa Cruz Ave. (Grays Ln.), Los Gatos,
408-395-9929*
◪ "Trendy", "crowded" Los Gatos American brewpub
with a "wonderful open space" and a surprising "menu
that's suitable for dinner"; there's a "long wait for tables"
but, as expected, the "bar scene is hot" and "the nut brown
ale is first-rate."

MacArthur Park 🅛🅢🅜   18 | 18 | 18 | $27
*27 University Ave. (bet. Alma & El Camino Real), Palo Alto,
415-321-9990*
See review in San Francisco Directory.

Max's Opera Cafe 🄻🅂🄼   17 | 15 | 16 | $20
1250 Old Bayshore (Broadway), Burlingame,
415-342-6297
711 Stanford Shopping Ctr., Palo Alto, 415-323-6297
See review in San Francisco Directory.

Mio Vicino 🄻🅂🄼   ▽ 21 | 14 | 20 | $22
384 E. Campbell Ave. (Central Ave.), Campbell,
408-378-0335
1290 Benton St. (Monroe St.), Santa Clara, 408-241-9414
■ There's "zero atmosphere" at these "laid-back"
"downscale Kuleto's", but for "spicy Italian food on a
budget" insiders insist they're "always enjoyable" – "try
the specials" and "be sure to get the garlic bread"; watch
out for the "first come, first served policy", which translates
to "long waits on weekends."

Montrio 🄻🅂🄼   23 | 22 | 23 | $38
414 Calle Principal (bet. Franklin & Jefferson Sts.),
Monterey, 408-648-8880
■ "Wonderful times" can be had at this "noisy" New
American in Monterey serving "high-energy Cal cuisine"
that's "bordering on super"; the food is "innovative", "the
decor is very pleasant" and the "service is knowledgeable",
making it "tops in the area."

Moss Beach Distillery 🄻🅂🄼   14 | 22 | 15 | $27
Beach Way & Ocean Blvd. (off Hwy. 1), Moss Beach,
415-728-0220
■ With any luck, recent renovations to this "great for
views, not food" Moss Beach American will not drive
away its fabled ghost (the Blue Lady) that's been known
to appear on occasion; the thing to do here is "get a
Bloody Mary", grab a "burger and blanket" and hit the
deck for the "divine sunset" and "seals in the water."

Osteria 🄻🄼   22 | 15 | 18 | $28
Cardinal Hotel, 247 Hamilton St. (Ramona Ave.), Palo Alto,
415-328-5700
■ There's "cheek to jowl" dining at this "packed" Palo
Alto Northern Italian that some say is the "best in the
Stanford area"; loyalists like the "excellent light cuisine"
with "good pastas and grills" as well as the "stylish yet
low-key setting" and "reasonable prices", but they could
do without the "at times long waits even with reservations."

Pacific Fresh 🄻🅂🄼   ▽ 17 | 16 | 16 | $25
1130 N. Mathilda Ave. (Lockheed Way), Sunnyvale,
408-745-1710
☑ The catch at this Sunnyvale seafooder (with a branch in
Pleasant Hill) is the "so-so fish"; while they're "ok" if "close
to home" and there are "good deal early-bird specials",
those who "expected more" found the duo "disappointing."

PACIFIC'S EDGE L S M   26 │ 27 │ 23 │ $72
Highlands Inn, Hwy. 1 (Highland Dr.), Carmel, 408-622-5445
■ "What a view!" – not to mention "beautifully prepared and presented cuisine" from "accomplished" chef Cal Stamenov at this "class act" Californian at Carmel's Highlands Inn; exemplifying "Pacific Rim creativity", the food makes for an "always unforgettable" meal, especially if you "watch the sun go down" over the coastline; the tab may put you over the edge, but the special-value sunset dinners are affordable and "out of this world."

Palermo L S M   ▽ 19 │ 18 │ 18 │ $26
394 S. Second St. (San Carlos Ave.), San Jose,
408-297-0607
■ "Get ready for garlic" at this "crowded but convenient" San Jose Italian where "exceptional Sicilian" cuisine is served in "healthy portions" that add up to "great value"; there's a "lively crowd" and "noisy" scene, but with "consistently good food" and "classic tiramisu" most "will go back again and again."

Paolo's L M   ▽ 23 │ 24 │ 24 │ $41
333 W. San Carlos St. (bet. Almaden Blvd. & Woz Way),
San Jose, 408-294-2558
▣ Fans of this San Jose veteran near the Performing Arts Center swear it's "still excellent after all these years" and "very Italian, from food to service"; but foes feel it's "hit or miss for classic" cooking and "too expensive."

Parkside Grille L S   – │ – │ – │ M
Village Sq., 884 Portola Rd. (Sand Hill Rd.), Portola Valley,
415-529-9007
Former patrons of Portola Park will find the same owner and the same menu at this New American offering the likes of steak and seafood and "good grilled food" that surveyors find "much improved"; while the owner put money into the renovation, he cut back on the menu prices.

Pasta Moon L M   21 │ 17 │ 17 │ $28
315 Main St. (Hwy. 92), Half Moon Bay, 415-726-5125 S
Oyster Point Marina Inn, 425 Marina Blvd. (Oyster Point
Blvd.), South San Francisco, 415-876-7090
■ "The white chocolate–dipped biscotti are dreamy" and there are some "wonderful, innovative pastas and salads" at these South San Francisco and Half Moon Bay Italian siblings (the latter is "lovely for lunch after a beach walk"); while service can be "snooty and slow", they make a "fun excursion destination for city folks."

Piatti L S M   20 │ 20 │ 20 │ $30
NW corner of 6th & Junipero, Carmel, 408-625-1766
2 Stanford Shopping Ctr., 180 El Camino Real (University
Ave.), Palo Alto, 415-324-9733
See review in North of San Francisco Directory.

Plumed Horse Ⓜ　　▽ 21 | 21 | 20 | $45
14555 Big Basin Way (4th St.), Saratoga, 408-867-4711
☑ "Highfalutin" Saratoga New French featuring "refined food" and a "great wine list"; some feel its plumes have been plucked and the place is getting a bit "dated", but most say don't put it out to pasture yet – it's still an "elegant standby that's worthy of a special occasion"; N.B. there's a separate bistro menu served in the lounge until 11 PM.

Pluto's ⓁⓈⓂ　　19 | 14 | 14 | $12
482 University Ave. (Cowper St.), Palo Alto, 415-853-1556
See review in San Francisco Directory.

Rio Grill ⓁⓈⓂ　　22 | 20 | 20 | $32
Crossroads Shopping Ctr., 101 Crossroads Blvd. (Rio Rd.), Carmel, 408-625-5436
■ "My mother won't shut up about this place" – maybe that's 'cuz this "creative, energetic" Carmel Southwestern is "a sheer delight" with "to-die-for grilled artichokes" and other "heavenly" menu items; the "good-looking staff" gets high marks for service and there's a "kid-friendly atmosphere" too; it's "noisy, but that's because everyone's having such a good time."

Rosti ⓁⓈⓂ　　15 | 13 | 15 | $20
1108 Burlingame Ave. (California Ave.), Burlingame, 415-401-6900
See review in San Francisco Directory.

ROY'S AT PEBBLE BEACH ⓁⓈⓂ　26 | 26 | 24 | $43
The Inn at Spanish Bay, 2700 17 Mile Dr. (Sunset Ave.), Pebble Beach, 408-647-7423
■ "Don't go to Monterey without a trip to Roy's"; this highly rated yet relatively "reasonable" Euro-Asian on the famed 17-Mile Drive offers "sexy appetizers" (like the "absolute indulgence" tuna starter) and other "gorgeous food" with service that "shines" in a dining room sporting a "breathtaking view" of some of the world's priciest sand; "what a place!" . . . and "it's closer than Hawaii."

San Benito House Ⓢ　　▽ 19 | 16 | 19 | $30
356 Main St. (Mill St.), Half Moon Bay, 415-726-3425
■ "I love the coast atmosphere" at this "Half Moon Bay at its best" Californian where the "consistently healthy homemade food" is "well-executed"; "after-dinner coffee by the fire on the patio is an extra treat."

Sardine Factory ⓈⓂ　　▽ 19 | 20 | 19 | $44
701 Wave St. (Prescott St.), Monterey, 408-373-3775
☑ Supporters of this "expensive but worth it" Monterey Continental say the "simple" "older setting" has a certain Steinbeckian Cannery Row appeal and there's a "great wine list", though equally adamant foes feel the "food doesn't match the charm" and call it an "overrated tourist trap."

Scott's Seafood Grill & Bar L S M   18 | 17 | 18 | $29 |
2300 E. Bayshore Rd. (Embarcadero Rd.), Palo Alto,
415-856-1046
185 Park Ave. (bet. Market St. & Almaden Blvd.), San Jose,
408-971-1700
See review in San Francisco Directory.

SENT SOVI S   26 | 23 | 24 | $51 |
14583 Big Basin Way (5th St.), Saratoga, 408-867-3110
■ There's "chicken from heaven" and "lots of talent in
the kitchen" at this New French bistro down in "sleepy
Saratoga"; the "best restaurant on the Peninsula" has a
"stark" and "cramped setting" and the limited, pricey
wine list sours a few, but "fabulous meals" of "creative
French food" make some say "believe the hype."

Sierra Mar L S M   ▽ 25 | 28 | 26 | $52 |
Post Ranch Inn, Hwy. 1 (26 mi. south of Carmel), Big Sur,
408-667-2800
■ "The place to go if you're in love", this "expensive" Big
Sur Californian high above the Pacific boasts both "food
and views that are out of this world"; "make sure the chef
is in the kitchen" and then settle in for a truly "memorable
experience"; expect "fine food", a "wonderful wine list"
and "great surroundings" – "what more could you want?"

Swagat Indian Cuisine L S M   ▽ 22 | 12 | 15 | $20 |
2700 W. El Camino Real (San Antonio Rd.), Mountain View,
415-948-7727
☑ This Mountain View Indian offers "excellent" "tasty
food" at "cheap" prices; the "decor is a little cheesy",
but diners line up" for the "great lunch buffet."

Tarpy's Roadhouse L S M   22 | 23 | 21 | $34 |
2999 Monterey-Salinas Hwy. (Canyon Del Rey), Monterey,
408-647-1444
■ "The wild artwork is great" at this Contemporary
American roadhouse near the Monterey airport; "the
landing pattern is low", so watch out for noise overhead,
especially on the "charming" stone patio; however,
"steadily good" "hearty" food "in an area with few
outstanding restaurants" helps this one really take off.

Tavern Grill S M   ▽ 19 | 16 | 18 | $27 |
1448 Burlingame Ave. (El Camino Real), Burlingame,
415-344-5692
☑ "Have some fun" at this "blue-collar" bar and grill in
Burlingame where often the American "fare gets overlooked
for the crowd"; the scene can be "obnoxious" at times, but,
"believe it or not", there's "unusually good food for a club."

231 ELLSWORTH 🄻 Ⓜ 25 | 21 | 24 | $44
231 S. Ellsworth Ave. (bet. 2nd & 3rd Aves.), San Mateo, 415-347-7231

☑ "Warm and hospitable" San Mateo French that's been "numero uno since it opened" with "outrageously presented and equally tasty" dishes including "spectacularly delicious desserts"; "great prix fixe deals" keep the tab in check and many maintain it's "tops on the Peninsula"; despite solid decor scores, some say it's time to "update the room."

Vicolo 🄻 Ⓢ Ⓜ 21 | 11 | 12 | $16
473 University Ave. (bet. Cowper & Kipling Sts.), Palo Alto, 415-324-4877
See review in San Francisco Directory.

Viognier 🄻 Ⓢ Ⓜ – | – | – | E
222 E. Fourth Ave. (B St.), San Mateo, 415-685-3727
Gary Danko left last year's top-rated Ritz-Carlton Dining Room and is now at home on the range of this San Mateo Mediterranean (named after the trendy white Rhône wine varietal); his style has become more rustic and relaxed, which suits the casual but sophisticated ambiance of the spacious room; expect great things to happen here.

World Wrapps 🄻 Ⓢ Ⓜ 15 | 10 | 13 | $10
1318 Burlingame Ave. (Park Place Ave.), Burlingame, 415-342-9777
201 University Ave. (Emerson Ave.), Palo Alto, 415-327-9777
See review in San Francisco Directory.

Zibibbo 🄻 Ⓢ Ⓜ – | – | – | E
430 Kipling St. (bet. University & Lytton Aves.), Palo Alto, 650-328-6722
Everyone's moving South: chef Jody Denton (LuLu) and partners have just opened this sprawling Palo Alto Mediterranean venture; the open design fills a Victorian house, spills onto outdoor terraces and continues in a former Barbie Doll factory; if it's anything like its SF cousin, it will be a major South Bay hot spot.

Indexes to Restaurants

Special Features and Appeals

TYPES OF CUISINE*

Afghan
Helmand
Massawa

American (New)
Atlas Peak/N
Avenue Grill/N
Avenue 9
Beach Chalet
Big Four
Bighorn Grill/E
Bistro Ralph/N
BIX
Boulevard
Brava Terrace/N
Buchanan Grill
Cafe Beaujolais/N
Cafe For All Seasons
Cafe Kati
Cafe 222
Campton Place
Careme Room
Carnelian Room
Chez T.J./S
Clement St. B&G
Courtyard B&G
Covey/S
dame
Delancey St.
Doidge's
Duck Club/S
Eulipia/S
Firefly
Flea St. Cafe/S
Flying Saucer
Fog City Diner
Foothill Cafe/N
Frascati
French Laundry/N
Garden Court
General's Daughter/N
Gibson/S
Globe
Gordon Biersch
Gordon Biersch/S
Harry Denton's
Harry Denton's Starlight
Hawthorne Lane
Indigo
Infusion
Jordan's/E
Julie's Supper Club
Julius' Castle

Kelly's on Trinity
Kenwood/N
Liberty Cafe
Lion & Compass/S
Marina Central
Maxfield's
Mecca
Meetinghouse
Montrio/S
Moss Beach Distillery/S
Mustards Grill/N
Occidental Grill
One Market
Ovation at Opera
Pacific's Edge/S
Panama Hotel/N
Parkside Grille/S
Pauli's Cafe
Pickled Ginger
Pluto's
Pluto's/S
Rick's
Rotunda
Sally's
Santa Fe B&G/E
Slow Club
Stars
Stars Cafe
Station House/N
Storyville
Tarpy's Roadhse./S
Tavern Grill/S
Town's End
2223 Rest.
Val 21
Willowside Cafe/N
Woodward's

American (Regional)
Auberge du Soleil/N
Avenue Grill/N
Biscuits & Blues
Blue Chalk Cafe/S
Buckeye Roadhse./N
Cacti/N
Catahoula/N
Crescent Park/S
Duarte's Tavern/S
Eddie Rickenbacker's
Elite Cafe
Elroy's
Farallon
Fly Trap

---

* All restaurants are in the City of San Francisco unless otherwise noted (E=East of San Francisco; N=North of San Francisco; S=South of San Francisco).

John Ash & Co./N
Lark Creek/E
Mikayla/N
Rio Grill/S
Terra/N
Wente Vineyards/E

American (Traditional)

Balboa Cafe
Barnaby's/N
Bette's Oceanview/E
Bill's Place
BIX
Blue Light
Bubba's Diner/N
Buckeye Roadhse./N
Buffalo Grill/S
Castagnola's
Cheers Cafe
Chow
Cliff House
Doidge's
Dottie's True Blue
Elite Cafe
Ella's
Fat Apple's/E
Fog City Diner
Gertie's Chesapeake/E
Gira Polli
Gira Polli/N
Gracie's
Hamburger Mary's
Hard Rock Cafe
Hayes St. Grill
Horizons/N
House of Prime Rib
Izzy's
JoAnn's Cafe/S
Kate's Kitchen
Kelly's on Trinity
Lark Creek/E
Lark Creek/S
Lark Creek Inn/N
Lehr Brothers
London Wine Bar
Los Gatos/S
MacArthur Park
MacArthur Park/S
Mama's Girl
Mama's Royal Cafe/E
Max's Diner
Max's Opera Cafe
Max's Opera Cafe/S
Mel's Drive-In
Miss Millie's
Mo's Burgers
Pacific Fresh/E
Pacific Fresh/S
Paragon B&G

Perry's
Pier 23 Cafe
PJ's Oyster Bed
Planet Hollywood
Pyramid Alehse./E
Ritz-Carlton Terrace
Roti
Rutherford Grill/N
Sam's
Sam's Anchor Cafe/N
Sand Dollar/N
Scoma's
Scoma's/N
Sears Fine Food
Tommy's Joynt
Washington Sq.
Waterfront
Zuni Cafe

Asian

Beausejour/S
Betelnut
Bok Choy/S
Cafe de Bordeaux/E
Crustacean
Eos
Ginger Island/E
House
Long Life Noodle
Mandalay
Oritalia
Pickled Ginger
Postrio
Silks
Straits Cafe
Tonga
Vertigo
Yoyo Bistro

Bakeries

Downtown Bakery/N
Fat Apple's/E
Sally's
Town's End

Bar-B-Q

Buckeye Roadhse./N
Doug's BBQ/E
Foothill Cafe/N
Hahn's Hibachi
MacArthur Park
MacArthur Park/S
San Francisco BBQ

Brazilian

Bahia Cabana

Burmese

Irrawaddy
Mandalay
Nan Yang/E

Cajun/Creole

Catahoula/N
Elite Cafe
Jessie's
New Gulf Coast/E
PJ's Oyster Bed

Californian

Aqui/S
A. Sabella's
Bauhaus Art/Rest.
Bay Wolf/E
Bette's Oceanview/E
Bighorn Grill/E
Blackhawk Grille/E
Blue Point
Boonville Hotel/N
Brava Terrace/N
Bridges/E
Buffalo Grill/S
Cactus Cafe/N
Cafe Akimbo
Cafe Beaujolais/N
Cafe/Chez Panisse/E
Cafe Flore
Cafe Majestic
Cafe Marcella/S
Cafe Trio/S
Caffe Centro
California Cafe/E
California Cafe/N
California Cafe/S
Cal. Pizza Kitchen
Caprice/N
Careme Room
Carnelian Room
Cheers Cafe
Chez Panisse/E
Chez Renee/S
Clement St. B&G
Cliff House
Curbside Cafe
Cypress Club
dalla Torre
Doidge's
Domaine Chandon/N
Duck Club/S
Erna's Elderberry/S
Essex Supper Club
Farallon
Firefly
Fly Trap
French Room
Frog & The Peach/N
Garden Court
Garibaldi's
General's Daughter/N
Gibson/S
Ginger Island/E

Grand Cafe
Harry Denton's
Hawthorne Lane
Hayes St. Grill
House
Indigo
Insalata's/N
Jardiniere
John Ash & Co./N
Johnny Love's
Johnny Love's/E
Julie's Supper Club
Julius' Castle
Lalime's/E
La Scene
Le Marquis/E
London Wine Bar
Los Gatos/S
Madrona Manor/N
Marina Central
Ma Tante Sumi
Meadowood Rest./N
Mio Vicino/S
Moose's
Moss Beach Distillery/S
Mustards Grill/N
Napa Valley Grille/N
Napa Valley Wine/N
Nightshade
Occidental Grill
Omnivore/E
Pacific
Pacific's Edge/S
Perry's
Pickled Ginger
PJ's Oyster Bed
Postrio
Rendezvous du Monde
Rivoli/E
Rocco's
Rumpus
San Benito Hse./S
Scott's
Scott's/E
Scott's/S
Showley's/N
Sierra Mar/S
Silks
Sonoma Mission/N
Stars
Terra/N
Top of the Mark
Tortola
Tourelle/E
Trilogy/S
2223 Rest.
Universal Cafe
Valentine's Cafe
Val 21

132

Vertigo
Wa-Ha-Ka
Willowside Cafe/N
Woodward's
Yabbies
Yoyo Bistro
Zax

Cambodian
Angkor Wat

Caribbean
Babaloo Tapas
Caribbean Zone
Cha Cha Cha
Jessie's
Primo Patio

Chinese
Betelnut
Brandy Ho's
Chef Chu's/S
Eliza's
Empress Court/S
Empress of China
Eric's
Fook Yuen/S
Fountain Court
Fung Lum/S
Grandview/S
Great Eastern
Harbor Village
Hong Kong Flower
Hong Kong Flower/S
Hong Kong Villa
House of Nanking
Hunan
Imperial Palace
Jade Villa/E
Kirin
Lichee Garden
Long Life Vegi/E
Mandalay
Mandarin
Mayflower
North Sea Village/N
Ocean
Rest. Peony/E
Tommy Toy's Chinoise
Tonga
Ton Kiang
Wu Kong
Yank Sing
Yet Wah
Yet Wah/N
Yuet Lee

Coffee Shops/Diners
Bette's Oceanview/E
Bubba's Diner/N

Dottie's True Blue
Fog City Diner
JoAnn's Cafe/S
Mama's Royal Cafe/E
Max's Diner
Mel's Drive-In
Sally's
Sears Fine Food

Continental
Alta Mira/N
Big Four
Caprice/N
Coconut Grove
Covey/S
Cypress Club
Dal Baffo/S
Emile's/S
French Room
Hayes & Vine
Julie's Supper Club
Kenwood/N
Old Swiss Hse.
Park Grill
Roy's/Pebble Beach/S
Sardine Factory/S
Schroeder's

Cuban
Primo Patio

Delis
Brother's Deli/S
Caffe Centro
Max's Diner
Max's Opera Cafe
Max's Opera Cafe/S
Saul's/E
Tommy's Joynt

Dim Sum
Betelnut
Fook Yuen/S
Fountain Court
Harbor Village
Hong Kong Flower
Hong Kong Flower/S
Imperial Palace
Jade Villa/E
Lichee Garden
Mayflower
North Sea Village/N
Rest. Peony/E
Tonga
Ton Kiang
Wu Kong
Yank Sing
Yet Wah
Yet Wah/N

Eclectic/International
Cafe de Bordeaux/E
Caffè Greco
Cal. Pizza Kitchen
Carta
Chez Renee/S
Cypress Club
Delancey St.
Dottie's True Blue
Eos
Firefly
French Room
Hayes & Vine
JoAnn's Cafe/S
Kelly's on Trinity
Lalime's/E
Madrona Manor/N
Millennium
Moa Room
Occidental Grill
Oritalia
Palomino
Pier 23 Cafe
Primo Patio
Rooster
Savor
Sierra Mar/S
Stars Cafe
Thornhill Cafe/E
Trio Cafe
2223 Rest.
Valentine's Cafe
Val 21
Viognier/S
Wappo Bar/N
World Wrapps
World Wrapps/E
World Wrapps/S
Yaya Cuisine

Ethiopian
Blue Nile/E
Massawa
Rasselas

French
Aux Delices
Basque Cultural Ctr./S
Bella Vista/S
Cafe Jacqueline
Café Mozart
Casanova/S
Citron/E
Covey/S
El Paseo/N
Essex Supper Club
French Laundry/N
Jardiniere
Kincaid's Bistro/S

La Bergerie
La Mère Michelle/S
La Petite Auberge/N
Le Cyrano
Le Marquis/E
L'Olivier
Madrona Manor/N
Masa's
Rue de Main/E
Terra/N
Thornhill Cafe/E
Ti Couz
231 Ellsworth/S
Zaré

French Bistro
Avenue 9
Baker St. Bistro
Beausejour/S
Bistro Aix
Bistro Clovis
Bizou
Brasserie Chambord
Cafe Bastille
Café Chêneville/S
Cafe Beaujolais/N
Cafe Claude
Cafe de Paris
Cafe Fanny/E
Cafe Rouge/E
Chapeau!
Chateau Souverain/N
City of Paris
Fringale
Guernica/N
Kenwood/N
Kincaid's Bistro/S
La Luna Bistro/S
L'Amie Donia/S
La Petite Auberge/N
Le Central
Le Charm
Left Bank/N
LuLu
Pastis
Pinot Blanc/N
Plouf
Rendezvous du Monde
Rumpus
Scala's Bistro
Soizic/E
South Park
Tommy Toy's Chinoise
Yoyo Bistro
Zax
Zazie

French (New)
Alain Rondelli
Anjou

134

Babette's/N
Bruno's
Cafe de Bordeaux/E
Cassis Bistro
Chapeau!
Charles Nob Hill
Chez Michel
Chez Renee/S
Chez T.J./S
Citron/E
Club XIX/S
Domaine Chandon/N
Emerald Garden
Erna's Elderberry/S
Essex Supper Club
Fleur De Lys
French Room
Fresh Cream/S
Gervais/S
Grand Cafe
Kiss
La Belle Saison
La Folie
La Forêt/S
Le Mouton Noir/S
Le Papillon/S
LuLu
Masa's
Ma Tante Sumi
Meadowood Rest./N
Pacific
Plumed Horse/S
Ritz-Carlton Din. Rm.
Rubicon
Sent Sovi/S
Stars Cafe
Trilogy/N
231 Ellsworth/S
Vertigo
Woodward's

German
Schroeder's
Suppenküche
Tommy's Joynt

Greek
Asimakopoulos
Evvia/S
La Mediterranee
La Mediterranee/E

Hamburgers
Balboa Cafe
Bill's Place
Fat Apple's/E
Gordon Biersch
Gordon Biersch/S
Hamburger Mary's
Hard Rock Cafe

Max's Opera Cafe
Mel's Drive-In
Mo's Burgers
Perry's
Planet Hollywood
Sand Dollar/N

Hawaiian
Rick's

Health Food
Millennium
Pluto's
Pluto's/S

Hungarian
Hungarian Sausage

Indian
Ajanta/E
Amber India/S
Appam
Gaylord India
Gaylord India/S
Indian Oven
Maharani India
North India
Swagat/S

Indonesian
Jakarta
Rice Table/N

Irish
O'Reilly's
Sinead's

Italian
(N=Northern; S=Southern;
N&S=Includes both)
Acquerello (N)
Adriana's/N (N&S)
Albona (N)
Alexander/E (N)
Alioto's (S)
Allegro (N&S)
Antica Trattoria (N&S)
Aperto (N&S)
Armani Cafe (N&S)
Aromi (N)
Basta Pasta (N)
Bella Trattoria (N&S)
Bella Vista/S (N&S)
Bistro Don Giovanni/N (N&S)
Bocce Café (N&S)
Bonta (N&S)
Bruno's (N&S)
Buca Giovanni (N&S)
Bucci's/E (N&S)
Cafe Fanny/E (N)
Cafe Marcella/S (N)

Café Riggio (N&S)
Cafe Tiramisu (N)
Caffe Centro (N)
Caffe Delle Stelle (N)
Caffè Macaroni (N&S)
Caffe Sport (S)
Capellini/S (N)
Capp's Corner (N&S)
Carpaccio/S (N)
Casanova/S (N&S)
Castagnola's (N&S)
Columbus Rist. (N&S)
Correnti's (N&S)
Dal Baffo/S (N&S)
dalla Torre (N&S)
E'Angelo (N)
Eleven Ristorante (N)
Enrico's (N&S)
Ernesto's (N&S)
Fior d'Italia (N)
Fizz Supper Club (N)
Frantoio/N (N&S)
Frascati (N&S)
Fusilli Rist./N (N)
Gira Polli (N)
Gira Polli/N (N&S)
Grissini/E (N)
I Fratelli (N&S)
Il Fornaio (N&S)
Il Fornaio/N (N&S)
Il Fornaio/S (N&S)
Incontro (N&S)
Iron Horse (N)
Jackson Fillmore (S)
Julius' Castle (N)
Kuleto's (N)
Kuleto's Tratt./S (N)
La Felce (N)
Laghi (N)
La Ginestra/N (S)
La Pastaia/S (N&S)
La Traviata (N)
Little Henry's (N&S)
Little Italy (S)
Little Joe's (N)
L'Osteria del Forno (N&S)
Madrona Manor/N (N)
Mangiafuoco (N)
Marin Joe's/N (N)
Mario's Bohemian (N)
Mescolanza (N&S)
Michelangelo Cafe (N&S)
Milano Pizzeria (N&S)
Mio Vicino/S (N&S)
Mozzarella Di Bufala (N&S)
New Joe's (N)
Nightshade (N&S)
Nob Hill Cafe (N)
North Beach (N)

Olive's (N&S)
Oliveto/E (N&S)
Original Joe's (N&S)
Osteria (N)
Osteria/S (N)
Palermo/S (N&S)
Palio d'Asti (N)
Pane e Vino (N)
Paolo's/S (N&S)
Parma (N&S)
Pasta Moon/S (N&S)
Pasta Pomodoro (N&S)
Pasta Pomodoro/E (N&S)
Pasta Prego/N (N)
Piatti/N (N&S)
Piatti/S (N&S)
Piazza D'Angelo/N (N&S)
Prego (N&S)
Prima Trattoria/E (N)
Puccini & Pinetti (N)
Radicchio (N)
Rist. Bacco (N&S)
Rist. Ecco (N&S)
Rist. Fabrizio/N (N)
Rist. Ideale (N)
Rist. Milano (N)
Rist. Salute/E (N&S)
Rose Pistola (N)
Rose's Cafe (N)
Rosti (N)
Rosti/S (N)
San Benito Hse./S (N)
Scala's Bistro (N&S)
Skylight Cafe/E (N&S)
Spiedini/E (N&S)
Splendido (N&S)
Spuntino (N)
Stelline (S)
Stinking Rose (N&S)
Tarantino's (S)
Terra/N (N)
Tommaso's (N&S)
Tratt. Contadina (N&S)
Tra Vigne/N (N&S)
Tutto Mare/N (N&S)
Universal Cafe (S)
U.S. Rest. (N&S)
Venezia/E (N&S)
Venticello (N)
Vicolo (N&S)
Vicolo/S (N&S)
Vivande Porta Via (N&S)
Vivande Rist. (N&S)
Waterfront (N&S)
Zaré (N)
Zingari (N&S)
Zinzino (N&S)
Zuni Cafe (N&S)
Zza's Trattoria/E (N&S)

Japanese

Benihana
Benihana/S
Blowfish Sushi
Cafe Akimbo
Cafe 222
Ebisu
Godzilla Sushi
Hamano Sushi
Invitation House/S
Iroha
Isobune
Isobune/S
Juban
Juban/S
Kabuto Sushi
Kansai
Kirala/E
Kyo-Ya
Maki
Ma Tante Sumi
Matsuya
Mifune
Murasaki
Nippon Sushi
O Chame/E
Osome
Robata Grill/N
Sanppo
Sanraku
Tanuki
Uzen/E
Yoshida-Ya
Yoshi's/E

Jewish

Firefly
Max's Opera Cafe
Max's Opera Cafe/S
Moxie
Saul's/E

Korean

Hahn's Hibachi
Invitation House/S
Korea House
Seoul Garden

Mediterranean

Avenue 9
Bay Wolf/E
Bistro Aix
Bistro Ralph/N
Bizou
Blackhawk Grille/E
Blue Point
Boonville Hotel/N
Brava Terrace/N
Bruno's
Bucci's/E

Café Chêneville/E
Citron/E
Crescent Park/S
Enrico's
Faz
Faz/E
Faz/S
Fizz Supper Club
42 Degrees
Fournou's Ovens
Frantoio/N
Frog & The Peach/N
Garibaldi's
Grissini/E
Insalata's/N
Iron Horse
Lalime's/E
La Mediterranee
La Mediterranee/E
Little City
Meadowood Grill/N
Meadowood Rest./N
Mecca
Moose's
Moxie
Napa Valley Grille/N
Palomino
Panama Hotel/N
PlumpJack
Postrio
Rendezvous du Monde
Rist. Salute/E
Rivoli/E
San Benito Hse./S
Savor
Slow Club
Socca
Tavern Grill/S
Tourelle/E
Viognier/S
Willowside Cafe/N
Wine Spectator/N
Zaré
Zax
Zazie
Zibibbo/S
Zuni Cafe

Mexican/Tex-Mex

Aqui/S
Cactus Cafe/N
Cadillac Bar
Cafe Marimba
Campo Santo
Casa Aguila
Chevys
Chevys/E
Chevys/N
El Balazo

137

Guaymas/N
La Cumbre
La Cumbre/S
La Rondalla
Las Camelias/N
La Taqueria
Leticia's
Mom is Cooking
Pancho Villa
Picante/E
Roosevelt Tamale
Sweet Heat
Tortola
Wa-Ha-Ka

Middle Eastern

La Mediterranee
La Mediterranee/E
Yaya Cuisine

Moroccan

Kasbah/N
Marrakech

Noodle Shops

Iroha
Kansai
Long Life Noodle
Mifune
O Chame/E

Pacific Rim

Bridges/E
Brix/N
Eos
House
Ma Tante Sumi
Pacific
Pacific Cafe
Pacific's Edge/S
Roy's/Pebble Beach/S
Vintner's Court/N

Pizza

Bistro Aix
Cafe Marcella/S
Cal. Pizza Kitchen
La Ginestra/N
Mescolanza
Milano Pizzeria
Mozzarella Di Bufala
Nightshade
Olive's
Pauline's
Piazza D'Angelo/N
Prego
Spuntino
Tommaso's
Vicolo
Vicolo/S
Zachary's/E

Russian

Katia's

Seafood

Alioto's
Aqua
A. Sabella's
Barnaby's/N
Blue Point
Cafe Marcella/S
Caribbean Zone
Castagnola's
Cliff House
Crow's Nest/S
Crustacean
Elite Cafe
Enrico's
Farallon
Fizz Supper Club
Fusilli Rist./N
Gertie's Chesapeake/E
Gibson/S
Great Eastern
Harbor Village
Hayes St. Grill
Horizons/N
House of Prime Rib
Jasmine House
Mandarin
Maxfield's
Maye's Oyster Hse.
McCormick & Kuleto's
Michelangelo Cafe
Moss Beach Distillery/S
Napa Valley Grille/N
New Gulf Coast/E
Old Swiss Hse.
One Market
Original Old Clam Hse.
Pacific Fresh/E
Pacific Fresh/S
Pasta Prego/N
Pier 23 Cafe
PJ's Oyster Bed
Plouf
Primo Patio
Rick's
Ritz-Carlton Terrace
Rocco's
Sam's
Sam's Anchor Cafe/N
Sardine Factory/S
Scoma's
Scoma's/N
Scott's
Scott's/E
Scott's/S
Sierra Mar/S
Sol y Luna

Spenger's/E
Swan Oyster Depot
Tadich Grill
Tarantino's
Ton Kiang
Tutto Mare/N
Vintner's Court/N
Waterfront
Yabbies
Yuet Lee
Zuni Cafe

Singaporean
Straits Cafe

South American
Estampas Peruanas/S

Southern/Soul
Biscuits & Blues
Blue Chalk Cafe/S
Bubba's Diner/N
Elite Cafe
New Gulf Coast/E

Southwestern
Cacti/N
Elroy's
Left at Albuquerque
Left at Albuquerque/S
Rio Grill/S
Savor
Tortola

Spanish
Alegrias
Basque Cultural Ctr./S
Bolero/N
Enrico's
Esperpento
Guernica/N
Iberia/S
Picaro
Sol y Luna
Thirsty Bear
Timo's
Zarzuela

Steakhouses
Alfred's
Atlas Peak/N
Benihana
Crow's Nest/S
Harris'
House of Prime Rib
Izzy's
Lehr Brothers
Morton's of Chicago
Vic Stewart's/E

Swiss
Matterhorn Swiss
Old Swiss Hse.

Thai
Cha Am Thai
Cha Am Thai/E
Dusit Thai
Khan Toke Thai
Manora's
Marnee Thai
Narai
Neecha Thai
Plearn Thai/E
Royal Thai
Royal Thai/N
Samui Thai
San Francisco BBQ
Siam Cuisine/E
Sukhothai
Thep Phanom
Yukol Place

Tibetan
Lhasa Moon

Vegetarian
(Most Chinese, Indian and
Thai restaurants; the
following are good bets)
Bistro Ralph/N
Clement St. B&G
Flea St. Cafe/S
Fleur De Lys
Greens
Long Life Vegi/E
Maharani India
Millennium
Miss Millie's
New Gulf Coast/E
Raw Living Foods
Valentine's Cafe
Val 21
Zaré

Vietnamese
Aux Delices
Cordon Bleu
Emerald Garden
Golden Turtle
Jasmine House
Kim's of Saigon
La Vie
Le Soleil
Mai's
Slanted Door
Tu Lan

NEIGHBORHOOD LOCATIONS

SAN FRANCISCO

Bernal Heights
Hungarian Sausage
Liberty Cafe

Castro/Noe
Cafe Flore
Chow
dame
Eric's
Firefly
Hahn's Hibachi
Hamano Sushi
La Mediterranee
Leticia's
Little Italy
Ma Tante Sumi
Matsuya
Mecca
Miss Millie's
Nippon Sushi
Pasta Pomodoro
Rist. Bacco
Savor
2223 Rest.
Yet Wah

Chinatown
Empress of China
Great Eastern
House of Nanking
Hunan
Imperial Palace
Lichee Garden
Yuet Lee

Civic Center
Bahia Cabana
Bistro Clovis
Caffe Delle Stelle
Careme Room
Carta
Eliza's
Hayes & Vine
Hayes St. Grill
Incontro
Indigo
Jardiniere
Max's Opera Cafe
Millennium
Ovation at Opera
Spuntino
Stars
Stars Cafe
Stelline

Suppenküche
Vicolo
Vivande Rist.
Zuni Cafe

Downtown
Alfred's
Anjou
Aqua
Armani Cafe
Biscuits & Blues
Brasserie Chambord
Cafe Akimbo
Cafe Bastille
Cafe Claude
Café Mozart
Cafe Tiramisu
Cafe 222
Cal. Pizza Kitchen
Campton Place
Carnelian Room
Chevys
City of Paris
Dottie's True Blue
Essex Supper Club
Farallon
Faz
Fizz Supper Club
Fleur De Lys
Fog City Diner
French Room
Garden Court
Gaylord India
Globe
Gracie's
Grand Cafe
Harbor Village
Harry Denton's Starlight
Hunan
Il Fornaio
Iron Horse
Kansai
Kelly's on Trinity
Kuleto's
Kyo-Ya
La Scene
Le Central
Lehr Brothers
L'Olivier
London Wine Bar
MacArthur Park
Marrakech
Masa's
Maxfield's

Morton's of Chicago
New Joe's
Occidental Grill
Original Joe's
Pacific
Palio d'Asti
Park Grill
Pastis
Perry's
Pier 23 Cafe
Planet Hollywood
Plouf
Postrio
Puccini & Pinetti
Rendezvous du Monde
Rotunda
Rubicon
Rumpus
Sam's
Sanraku
Scala's Bistro
Schroeder's
Scott's
Sears Fine Food
Silks
Sol y Luna
Splendido
Tadich Grill
Tommy Toy's Chinoise
Tortola
Tu Lan
Vertigo
Yank Sing
Zaré
Zingari

Haight-Ashbury

Cha Cha Cha
El Balazo
Eos
Indian Oven
Kate's Kitchen
Massawa
Storyville
Sweet Heat
Thep Phanom
Zazie

Japantown

Benihana
Iroha
Isobune
Juban
Korea House
Maki
Mifune
Nightshade
Sanppo
Seoul Garden
Yoyo Bistro

Marina

Babaloo Tapas
Bistro Aix
Buchanan Grill
Cafe Marimba
Columbus Rist.
E'Angelo
Greens
Hahn's Hibachi
Izzy's
Marina Central
Olive's
Paragon B&G
Parma
Pasta Pomodoro
Pluto's
Rosti
Scott's
Sweet Heat
World Wrapps
Yukol Place
Zinzino

Mission

Blowfish Sushi
Bruno's
Dusit Thai
Esperpento
Flying Saucer
La Cumbre
La Rondalla
La Taqueria
La Traviata
Mangiafuoco
Moa Room
Mom is Cooking
Moxie
Original Old Clam Hse.
Pancho Villa
Pauline's
Picaro
Roosevelt Tamale
Rooster
Slanted Door
Ti Couz
Timo's
Universal Cafe
Valentine's Cafe
Val 21
Woodward's
Yuet Lee

Nob Hill

Big Four
Charles Nob Hill
Fournou's Ovens
Nob Hill Cafe
Ritz-Carlton Din. Rm.
Ritz-Carlton Terrace

Tonga
Top of the Mark
Venticello

North Beach

Allegro
Basta Pasta
BIX
Bocce Café
Brandy Ho's
Buca Giovanni
Cafe Jacqueline
Caffè Greco
Caffè Macaroni
Caffe Sport
Campo Santo
Capp's Corner
Correnti's
Cypress Club
dalla Torre
Enrico's
Fior d'Italia
Gira Polli
Helmand
House
Julius' Castle
La Felce
Little City
Little Joe's
L'Osteria del Forno
Mama's Girl
Mario's Bohemian
Michelangelo Cafe
Moose's
Mo's Burgers
North Beach
O'Reilly's
Pasta Pomodoro
Rist. Ideale
Rose Pistola
Stinking Rose
Tommaso's
Tratt. Contadina
U.S. Rest.
Washington Sq.
Zax

Pacific Heights

Cafe Kati
Curbside Cafe
Elite Cafe
Ella's
Garibaldi's
Godzilla Sushi
Jackson Fillmore
Kim's of Saigon
La Mediterranee
Meetinghouse
Mozzarella Di Bufala
Oritalia
Osteria

Pauli's Cafe
Rasselas
Tortola
Trio Cafe
Vivande Porta Via

Potrero Hill

Aperto
Asimakopoulos
Eliza's
Sally's
San Francisco BBQ
Slow Club

Richmond

Alain Rondelli
Angkor Wat
Bauhaus Art/Rest.
Beach Chalet
Bella Trattoria
Bill's Place
Blue Point
Café Riggio
Chapeau!
Cheers Cafe
Clement St. B&G
Cliff House
Courtyard B&G
Ernesto's
Fountain Court
Hong Kong Flower
Hong Kong Villa
Jakarta
Jasmine House
Kabuto Sushi
Katia's
Khan Toke Thai
Kirin
La Belle Saison
La Bergerie
Laghi
La Vie
Le Cyrano
Le Soleil
Mai's
Mandalay
Mayflower
Mel's Drive-In
Mescolanza
Murasaki
Narai
Ocean
Pacific Cafe
Royal Thai
Sinead's
Socca
Straits Cafe
Tanuki
Ton Kiang
Yet Wah

SOMA

Appam
Bizou
Boulevard
Cadillac Bar
Caffe Centro
Caribbean Zone
Cha Am Thai
Chevys
Delancey St.
Eddie Rickenbacker's
Eleven Ristorante
Elroy's
Fly Trap
42 Degrees
Fringale
Gordon Biersch
Hamburger Mary's
Harry Denton's
Hawthorne Lane
Hunan
Infusion
Jessie's
Julie's Supper Club
Kiss
Le Charm
Long Life Noodle
LuLu
Manora's
Max's Diner
One Market
Palomino
Pickled Ginger
Primo Patio
Rist. Ecco
Roti
South Park
Thirsty Bear
Town's End
Wa-Ha-Ka
Wu Kong

Sunset

Avenue 9
Cafe For All Seasons
Casa Aguila
Chevys
Ebisu
House
Marnee Thai
Milano Pizzeria
Mozzarella Di Bufala
Pasta Pomodoro
PJ's Oyster Bed
Pluto's
Raw Living Foods
Rick's
Sukhothai
Tortola
Yaya Cuisine

Union Street

Alegrias
Baker St. Bistro
Balboa Cafe
Betelnut
Blue Light
Bonta
Cafe de Paris
Cassis Bistro
Doidge's
Irrawaddy
Left at Albuquerque
Lhasa Moon
Mel's Drive-In
North India
Osome
Pane e Vino
Perry's
PlumpJack
Prego
Radicchio
Rose's Cafe
Samui Thai
Wa-Ha-Ka
Yoshida-Ya

Van Ness/Polk

Acquerello
Antica Trattoria
Aromi
Aux Delices
Cafe Majestic
Coconut Grove
Cordon Bleu
Crustacean
Emerald Garden
Frascati
Golden Turtle
Hahn's Hibachi
Hard Rock Cafe
Harris'
House of Prime Rib
I Fratelli
Johnny Love's
La Folie
Little Henry's
Maharani India
Mario's Bohemian
Matterhorn Swiss
Maye's Oyster Hse.
Neecha Thai
Rist. Milano
Rocco's
Swan Oyster Depot
Sweet Heat
Tommy's Joynt
World Wrapps
Yabbies
Zarzuela

Wharf
Albona
Alioto's
A. Sabella's
Castagnola's
Chez Michel
Gaylord India
Mandarin

McCormick & Kuleto's
Old Swiss Hse.
Scoma's
Tarantino's
Timo's
Waterfront
Yet Wah

BEYOND SAN FRANCISCO
East

Alameda
Skylight Cafe

Berkeley
Ajanta
Bette's Oceanview
Blue Nile
Cafe/Chez Panisse
Cafe Fanny
Cafe Rouge
Cha Am Thai
Chez Panisse
Fat Apple's
Gertie's Chesapeake
Ginger Island
Kirala
Lalime's
La Mediterranee
Long Life Vegi
O Chame
Omnivore
Picante
Plearn Thai
Pyramid Alehse.
Rivoli
Santa Fe B&G
Saul's
Siam Cuisine
Spenger's
Venezia
Zachary's

Concord
Grissini

Danville
Blackhawk Grille
Bridges
Faz

El Cerrito
Fat Apple's

Emeryville
Bucci's
Doug's BBQ

Hayward
Rue de Main

Lafayette
Le Marquis
Tourelle

Livermore
Wente Vineyards

Oakland
Bay Wolf
Café Chêneville
Cafe de Bordeaux
Citron
Jade Villa
Jordan's
Mama's Royal Cafe
Nan Yang
New Gulf Coast
Oliveto
Pasta Pomodoro
Rest. Peony
Scott's
Soizic
Thornhill Cafe
Uzen
Yoshi's
Zachary's
Zza's Trattoria

Orinda
Alexander

Pleasant Hill
Chevys
Pacific Fresh

Pleasanton
Faz

Richmond
Rist. Salute

San Ramon
Bighorn Grill

Walnut Creek
California Cafe
Johnny Love's
Lark Creek

Prima Trattoria
Spiedini
Vic Stewart's
World Wrapps

North

Marin
Adriana's
Alta Mira
Avenue Grill
Barnaby's
Bolero
Bubba's Diner
Buckeye Roadhse.
Cacti
Cactus Cafe
California Cafe
Caprice
Chevys
El Paseo
Frantoio
Frog & The Peach
Fusilli Rist.
Gira Polli
Guaymas
Guernica
Horizons
Il Fornaio
Insalata's
Kasbah
La Ginestra
La Petite Auberge
Lark Creek Inn
Las Camelias
Left Bank
Marin Joe's
Mikayla
North Sea Village
Panama Hotel
Piatti
Piazza D'Angelo
Rice Table
Rist. Fabrizio
Robata Grill
Royal Thai
Sam's Anchor Cafe
Sand Dollar
Scoma's
Station House
Tutto Mare
Yet Wah

Mendocino
Boonville Hotel
Cafe Beaujolais

Napa
Atlas Peak
Auberge du Soleil
Bistro Don Giovanni
Brava Terrace
Brix
Catahoula
Domaine Chandon
Foothill Cafe
French Laundry
Meadowood Grill
Meadowood Rest.
Mustards Grill
Napa Valley Grille
Napa Valley Wine
Pasta Prego
Piatti
Pinot Blanc
Showley's
Terra
Tra Vigne
Trilogy
Vintner's Court
Wappo Bar
Wine Spectator

Rutherford
Rutherford Grill

Sonoma
Babette's
Bistro Ralph
Chateau Souverain
Downtown Bakery
General's Daughter
John Ash & Co.
Kenwood
Madrona Manor
Piatti
Sonoma Mission
Willowside Cafe

South

Half Moon Bay
Pasta Moon
San Benito Hse.

Monterey/Carmel
Casanova
Club XIX

Covey
Fresh Cream
Kincaid's Bistro
Montrio
Pacific's Edge
Piatti
Rio Grill
Roy's/Pebble Beach
Sardine Factory
Sierra Mar
Tarpy's Roadhse.

Peninsula
Basque Cultural Ctr.
Bella Vista
Benihana
Blue Chalk Cafe
Bok Choy
Brother's Deli
Buffalo Grill
California Cafe
Capellini
Carpaccio
Crescent Park
Dal Baffo
Duck Club
Empress Court
Estampas Peruanas
Evvia
Flea St. Cafe
Fook Yuen
Gaylord India
Gibson
Gordon Biersch
Grandview
Hong Kong Flower
Iberia
Il Fornaio
Isobune
JoAnn's Cafe
Juban
Kuleto's Tratt.
La Cumbre
La Luna Bistro
L'Amie Donia
Lark Creek
Left at Albuquerque
MacArthur Park
Max's Opera Cafe
Osteria
Parkside Grille
Pasta Moon
Piatti

Pluto's
Rosti
Scott's
Tavern Grill
231 Ellsworth
Vicolo
Viognier
World Wrapps
Zibibbo

San Jose
Amber India
Aqui
Beausejour
Benihana
Cafe Marcella
Cafe Trio
California Cafe
Chef Chu's
Chez T.J.
Emile's
Eulipia
Faz
Fung Lum
Gervais
Il Fornaio
La Forêt
La Mère Michelle
La Pastaia
Left at Albuquerque
Le Mouton Noir
Le Papillon
Lion & Compass
Los Gatos
Mio Vicino
Pacific Fresh
Palermo
Paolo's
Plumed Horse
Scott's
Sent Sovi
Swagat

Santa Cruz
Chez Renee
Crow's Nest

South Coast
Duarte's Tavern
Invitation House
Moss Beach Distillery

Yosemite-Oakhurst
Erna's Elderberry

SPECIAL FEATURES AND APPEALS

Breakfast

(All hotels and the following standouts)

Baker St. Bistro
Bette's Oceanview/E
Bubba's Diner/N
Cafe Fanny/E
Caffe Centro
Caffè Greco
Casa Aguila
Casanova/S
Doidge's
Dottie's True Blue
Downtown Bakery/N
Duarte's Tavern/S
Ella's
Greens
Il Fornaio
Il Fornaio/N
Jade Villa/E
JoAnn's Cafe/S
Kate's Kitchen
Kelly's on Trinity
Lichee Garden
Mama's Girl
Mama's Royal Cafe/E
Mandarin
Miss Millie's
Mo's Burgers
Paolo's/S
Pluto's
Pluto's/S
Rendezvous du Monde
South Park
Station House/N
Town's End
Universal Cafe
Zazie
Zuni Cafe

Brunch

(Best of many)

Aperto
Avenue 9
Baker St. Bistro
Bette's Oceanview/E
Blackhawk Grille/E
Bubba's Diner/N
Buckeye Roadhse./N
Café Chêneville/E
Cafe For All Seasons
Cafe 222
California Cafe/N
Campton Place
Carta
Casanova/S

Chapeau!
Doidge's
Dottie's True Blue
Elite Cafe
Ella's
Erna's Elderberry/S
Flea St. Cafe/S
Fournou's Ovens
French Room
Frog & The Peach/N
Garibaldi's
General's Daughter/N
Grand Cafe
Greens
Il Fornaio
Il Fornaio/N
Il Fornaio/S
JoAnn's Cafe/S
John Ash & Co./N
Kate's Kitchen
Katia's
La Forêt/S
La Mère Michelle/S
Lark Creek/E
Lark Creek/S
Lark Creek Inn/N
Le Mouton Noir/S
Liberty Cafe
LuLu
Mama's Girl
Mama's Royal Cafe/E
Meadowood Rest./N
Mikayla/N
Miss Millie's
Mom is Cooking
Montrio/S
Moose's
Moxie
Napa Valley Grille/N
Pacific
Pacific's Edge/S
Park Grill
Pasta Moon/S
Piazza D'Angelo/N
Picante/E
PJ's Oyster Bed
Postrio
Rendezvous du Monde
Rio Grill/S
Ritz-Carlton Terrace
Sonoma Mission/N
Station House/N
Suppenküche
Tarpy's Roadhse./S
Thornhill Cafe/E
Ti Couz

Tourelle/E
Town's End
2223 Rest.
Universal Cafe
Valentine's Cafe
Val 21
Vintner's Court/N
Vivande Rist.
Wente Vineyards/E
Zazie

Buffet Served
(Check prices, days
and times)
Alexander/E
Alta Mira/N
Amber India/S
Baker St. Bistro
Cafe 222
Careme Room
Castagnola's
Cliff House
Duck Club/S
Empress of China
Gaylord India
Jordan's/E
Left at Albuquerque
Lhasa Moon
Maharani India
Meadowood Rest./N
Mikayla/N
Mom is Cooking
New Gulf Coast/E
Pacific Fresh/E
Pacific's Edge/S
Panama Hotel/N
Rio Grill/S
Ritz-Carlton Terrace
Roy's/Pebble Beach/S
Skylight Cafe/E
Stelline
Swagat/S
Top of the Mark
U.S. Rest.
Vintner's Court/N
Yet Wah

Business Dining
Aqua
Big Four
Boulevard
Brasserie Chambord
Campton Place
Carnelian Room
Cypress Club
Emile's/S
42 Degrees
Fournou's Ovens
French Room

General's Daughter/N
Harris'
Hawthorne Lane
Hayes St. Grill
House of Prime Rib
Il Fornaio
Iron Horse
John Ash & Co./N
La Folie
Le Central
Little City
L'Olivier
London Wine Bar
MacArthur Park
Mandarin
Masa's
Matterhorn Swiss
McCormick & Kuleto's
Moose's
North Beach
One Market
Pacific
Pacific Fresh/E
Park Grill
PlumpJack
Postrio
Ritz-Carlton Din. Rm.
Rubicon
Sam's
Sol y Luna
Splendido
Stars
Tadich Grill
Tommy Toy's Chinoise
231 Ellsworth/S
Vertigo
Vintner's Court/N
Vivande Rist.
Washington Sq.
Waterfront
Yukol Place
Zuni Cafe

Caters
(Best of many)
Amber India/S
Aperto
Aqua
Avenue 9
Bauhaus Art/Rest.
Bistro Ralph/N
Blackhawk Grille/E
Blue Nile/E
Bok Choy/S
Boonville Hotel/N
Boulevard
Brava Terrace/N
Brix/N
Bubba's Diner/N

Caffè Macaroni
California Cafe/S
Careme Room
Casanova/S
Cha Am Thai
Cha Am Thai/E
Cha Cha Cha
dame
Eleven Ristorante
Emerald Garden
Emile's/S
Eulipia/S
Evvia/S
Flea St. Cafe/S
Fleur De Lys
Fountain Court
Frantoio/N
French Laundry/N
Fusilli Rist./N
Garibaldi's
Gira Polli
Gira Polli/N
Globe
Helmand
Hong Kong Flower
Indian Oven
Insalata's/N
JoAnn's Cafe/S
John Ash & Co./N
Kasbah/N
Katia's
Kelly's on Trinity
Kuleto's Tratt./S
La Folie
Lalime's/E
La Mediterranee
La Mediterranee/E
La Pastaia/S
Las Camelias/N
Left Bank/N
Le Marquis/E
Le Mouton Noir/S
Le Papillon/S
Long Life Noodle
LuLu
MacArthur Park/S
Maharani India
Mandarin
Mecca
Mescolanza
Millennium
Mio Vicino/S
Miss Millie's
Mom is Cooking
Montrio/S
Napa Valley Grille/N
New Gulf Coast/E
Nightshade
North India

Pacific's Edge/S
Pane e Vino
Paolo's/S
Park Grill
Pasta Moon/S
Pasta Prego/N
Pauline's
Pickled Ginger
Pinot Blanc/N
Plouf
Rendezvous du Monde
Rio Grill/S
Rose's Cafe
Rumpus
Samui Thai
Sent Sovi/S
Siam Cuisine/E
Sonoma Mission/N
Storyville
Suppenküche
Tarpy's Roadhse./S
Thornhill Cafe/E
Ton Kiang
Valentine's Cafe
Val 21
Vicolo
Vicolo/S
Vic Stewart's/E
Vivande Porta Via
Yank Sing
Yoyo Bistro
Zaré
Zibibbo/S
Zza's Trattoria/E

Cigar Friendly
A. Sabella's
Auberge du Soleil/N
Balboa Cafe
Basta Pasta
Bauhaus Art/Rest.
Big Four
Bighorn Grill/E
Biscuits & Blues
Bistro Don Giovanni/N
Blue Light
Bruno's
Buchanan Grill
Buckeye Roadhse./N
Buffalo Grill/S
Cafe de Paris
Cafe Majestic
Caribbean Zone
Casanova/S
Covey/S
Crustacean
Cypress Club
Dal Baffo/S
Erna's Elderberry/S

Essex Supper Club
Fly Trap
General's Daughter/N
Julius' Castle
La Mère Michelle/S
Lehr Brothers
Le Papillon/S
Maxfield's
Morton's of Chicago
North Beach
Occidental Grill
Palermo/S
Palomino
Paolo's/S
Paragon B&G
Park Grill
Pier 23 Cafe
Prima Trattoria/E
Rio Grill/S
Schroeder's
Sol y Luna
Tavern Grill/S
Timo's
Tra Vigne/N
Vic Stewart's/E
Wente Vineyards/E
Wine Spectator/N

Dancing/Entertainment

(Check days, times and performers for entertainment; D=dancing)

Alegrias (flamenco guitar)
Alexander/E (D/varies)
Alta Mira/N (piano)
Angkor Wat (Cambodian dance)
A. Sabella's (piano)
Bahia Cabana (D/Brazilian)
Bauhaus Art/Rest. (D/varies)
Beach Chalet (varies)
Big Four (piano)
Biscuits & Blues (D/blues)
BIX (jazz)
Blackhawk Grille/E (piano)
Bocce Café (jazz)
Bolero/N (flamenco)
Brasserie Chambord (varies)
Bridges/E (guitar)
Bruno's (jazz)
Cadillac Bar (guitar/singing servers)
Cafe Bastille (D/blues/jazz)
Cafe Claude (blues/jazz)
Cafe de Paris (D/world)
Cafe Majestic (piano)
Cafe 222 (piano)
California Cafe/E (piano)
California Cafe/N (piano)
California Cafe/S (piano)

Caprice/N (piano)
Caribbean Zone (D/Latin music)
Cliff House (piano)
Coconut Grove (D/varies)
Crescent Park/S (jazz)
Crow's Nest/S (D/varies)
Cypress Club (jazz)
El Balazo (guitar)
Eleven Ristorante (varies)
Enrico's (jazz)
Essex Supper Club (D/DJ/jazz)
Estampas Peruanas/S (Peruvian music)
Fizz Supper Club (jazz)
Fly Trap (jazz)
42 Degrees (jazz)
French Room (piano)
Garden Court (D/jazz/piano)
Gordon Biersch/S (jazz/swing)
Gracie's (jazz)
Guaymas/N (mariachi)
Harris' (jazz)
Harry Denton's (D)
Harry Denton's Starlight (D/varies)
Hawthorne Lane (piano)
Hungarian Sausage (varies)
Infusion (guitar)
Invitation House/S (jazz)
Iron Horse (jazz)
Jardiniere (piano)
Johnny Love's (D)
Johnny Love's/E (D/varies)
Jordan's/E (D/jazz)
Julie's Supper Club (blues/jazz)
Kasbah/N (belly dancer)
Katia's (accordion/guitar)
Khan Toke Thai (Thai dancing)
Kuleto's (piano)
La Mère Michelle/S (D/varies)
Lark Creek Inn/N (jazz/piano)
La Rondalla (mariachi)
La Scene (jazz pianist)
Left Bank/N (jazz)
MacArthur Park/S (piano)
Mandarin (island music)
Marin Joe's/N (jazz/piano)
Mario's Bohemian (jazz trio)
Marrakech (belly dancer)
Maxfield's (jazz)
Max's Opera Cafe (singing servers)
Mecca (varies)
Milano Pizzeria (blues/jazz)
Moose's (jazz)
One Market (jazz/piano)
Ovation at Opera (piano)
Pacific (piano)
Pacific's Edge/S (singer)

Palomino (jazz)
Panama Hotel/N (jazz/r&b/soul)
Paolo's/S (piano)
Paragon B&G (varies)
Park Grill (piano)
Pier 23 Cafe (D/varies)
PJ's Oyster Bed (D/varies)
Plumed Horse/S (D/bands)
Prima Trattoria/E (jazz/piano)
Rasselas (jazz)
Rick's (piano)
Ritz-Carlton Din. Rm. (harp)
Ritz-Carlton Terrace (varies)
Rose Pistola (jazz)
Roy's/Pebble Beach/S
   (Brazilian/jazz trio)
Santa Fe B&G/E (piano)
Saul's/E (varies)
Schroeder's (D/bands)
Showley's/N (jazz)
Sol y Luna (D/flamenco/salsa)
Sonoma Mission/N (piano)
Stars (piano)
Station House/N (jazz)
Storyville (jazz)
Timo's (D/flamenco/harp)
Tonga (D/bands)
Top of the Mark (D/jazz/swing)
Tutto Mare/N (jazz)
Vertigo (piano)
Vic Stewart's/E (varies)
Vintner's Court/N (D/jazz)
Vivande Rist. (jazz
   vocalist/piano)
Wappo Bar/N (varies)
Washington Sq. (jazz)
Yoshi's/E (jazz)
Yoyo Bistro (jazz)
Zingari (piano)
Zuni Cafe (piano)

Delivers/Takeout

(Nearly all Asians, coffee
shops, delis, diners and
pasta/pizzerias deliver or do
takeout; here are some
interesting possibilities;
D=delivery, T=takeout; call to
check range and charges,
if any)
Ajanta/E (T)
Alegrias (T)
Alioto's (T)
Allegro (T)
Amber India/S (D,T)
Antica Trattoria (T)
Aperto (T)
Aqui/S (T)

Armani Cafe (T)
Aromi (T)
A. Sabella's (D,T)
Asimakopoulos (T)
Aux Delices (D)
Avenue Grill/N (T)
Avenue 9 (T)
Balboa Cafe (T)
Barnaby's/N (T)
Big Four (T)
Bighorn Grill/E (T)
Biscuits & Blues (T)
Bistro Aix (T)
Bistro Ralph/N (T)
Blackhawk Grille/E (T)
Blue Nile/E (T)
Blue Point (T)
Bocce Café (T)
Bolero/N (T)
Bonta (T)
Brasserie Chambord (D,T)
Brava Terrace/N (T)
Bubba's Diner/N (T)
Buca Giovanni (T)
Bucci's/E (T)
Buchanan Grill (T)
Buckeye Roadhse./N (T)
Buffalo Grill/S (T)
Cafe Akimbo (T)
Cafe Bastille (T)
Cafe Claude (T)
Cafe de Bordeaux/E (D)
Cafe de Paris (D,T)
Cafe Marcella/S (T)
Cafe Marimba (T)
Cafe Rouge/E (T)
Cafe Trio/S (T)
Caffe Centro (T)
Caffe Delle Stelle (D)
Caffè Greco (T)
Caffe Sport (T)
Capellini/S (T)
Caprice/N (T)
Caribbean Zone (T)
Carpaccio/S (T)
Casanova/S (T)
Cha Cha Cha (T)
Chow (T)
City of Paris (T)
Clement St. B&G (T)
Coconut Grove (T)
Columbus Rist. (T)
Correnti's (T)
Courtyard B&G (T)
Crescent Park/S (T)
Crustacean (T)
Curbside Cafe (T)
Dal Baffo/S (T)
dalla Torre (T)

Pyramid Alehse./E (T)
Raw Living Foods (D,T)
Rendezvous du Monde (T)
Rick's (T)
Rio Grill/S (T)
Rist. Bacco (T)
Rist. Ecco (T)
Rist. Fabrizio/N (T)
Rist. Ideale (T)
Rist. Milano (T)
Rist. Salute/E (T)
Rivoli/E (D,T)
Robata Grill/N (T)
Rocco's (D,T)
Rooster (D,T)
Rose's Cafe (T)
Roti (T)
Royal Thai (T)
Roy's/Pebble Beach/S (T)
Rue de Main/E (T)
Rumpus (T)
Rutherford Grill/N (T)
Sand Dollar/N (T)
Sanppo (T)
Sanraku (T)
Santa Fe B&G/E (D)
Sardine Factory/S (D,T)
Savor (T)
Sears Fine Food (T)
Showley's/N (D,T)
Skylight Cafe/E (T)
Slanted Door (T)
Socca (T)
Sol y Luna (T)
Spiedini/E (T)
Splendido (T)
Stars Cafe (T)
Stelline (T)
Storyville (T)
Tadich Grill (T)
Tarpy's Roadhse./S (D,T)
Tavern Grill/S (T)
Thornhill Cafe/E (T)
Timo's (T)
Tra Vigne/N (T)
Tutto Mare/N (D)
2223 Rest. (T)
Valentine's Cafe (T)
Val 21 (T)
Vic Stewart's/E (T)
Vivande Porta Via (D,T)
Waterfront (T)
Yoshida-Ya (T)
Zachary's/E (T)
Zazie (T)
Zibibbo/S (T)
Zinzino (T)
Zuni Cafe (T)

Dining Alone

(Other than hotels, coffee
shops, sushi bars and places
with counter service)
Alegrias
Beach Chalet
Bill's Place
Biscuits & Blues
Clement St. B&G
Cordon Bleu
Elite Cafe
Hamburger Mary's
House of Nanking
Infusion
La Rondalla
Long Life Noodle
Matterhorn Swiss
Mo's Burgers
Pasta Pomodoro
Pasta Pomodoro/E
PJ's Oyster Bed
Raw Living Foods
South Park
Spuntino
Swan Oyster Depot
Tommy's Joynt
Waterfront
Yukol Place

Fireplaces

Auberge du Soleil/N
Betelnut
Big Four
Blue Chalk Cafe/S
Boonville Hotel/N
Brava Terrace/N
Brix/N
Buckeye Roadhse./N
Café Mozart
Casanova/S
Chateau Souverain/N
Chevys
Chez Renee/S
Chez T.J./S
Cliff House
Correnti's
Covey/S
Crescent Park/S
Crow's Nest/S
Dal Baffo/S
Duck Club/S
El Paseo/N
Erna's Elderberry/S
Evvia/S
Fook Yuen/S
French Laundry/N
Fresh Cream/S
Grand Cafe
Guaymas/N

Harris'
Horizons/N
House of Prime Rib
Izzy's
John Ash & Co./N
Kenwood/N
Kincaid's Bistro/S
Lark Creek Inn/N
Left Bank/N
Le Mouton Noir/S
Los Gatos/S
LuLu
MacArthur Park
MacArthur Park/S
Madrona Manor/N
Meadowood Rest./N
Mikayla/N
Oliveto/E
Pacific
Pacific's Edge/S
Palermo/S
Paragon B&G
Perry's
Piatti/N
Piatti/S
Plumed Horse/S
Prima Trattoria/E
Rio Grill/S
Roti
Rutherford Grill/N
Sand Dollar/N
Sardine Factory/S
Scott's/S
Sierra Mar/S
Storyville
Tarpy's Roadhse./S
Tavern Grill/S
Timo's
Tourelle/E
Tutto Mare/N
Venticello
Vic Stewart's/E
Wine Spectator/N
Zibibbo/S

Health/Spa Menus

(Most places cook to order to
meet any dietary request; call
in advance to check; almost
all Chinese, Indian and other
ethnics have health-
conscious meals, as do
the following)
Auberge du Soleil/N
French Room
Meadowood Rest./N
O Chame/E
Paolo's/S
Sonoma Mission/N

Historic Interest

(Year opened; *building)
1849 Tadich Grill
1860 Garden Court*
1861 Original Old Clam Hse.
1862 General's Daughter/N*
1863 Cliff House
1867 Maye's Oyster Hse.
1867 Sam's
1870 Showley's/N*
1876 Woodward's*
1882 Wine Spectator/N*
1884 Terra/N*
1886 Fior d'Italia
1895 Schroeder's
1900 U.S. Rest.
1905 San Benito Hse./S
1909 Rotunda*
1912 Swan Oyster Depot
1916 Castagnola's
1920 A. Sabella's
1920 Sam's Anchor Cafe/N
1922 Julius' Castle*
1925 Beach Chalet*
1926 Panama Hotel/N
1927 Bella Vista/S
1928 Alioto's*
1934 French Room
1937 Original Joe's

Hotel Dining

Abigail Hotel
  Millennium
Alta Mira Hotel
  Alta Mira/N
Auberge du Soleil Inn
  Auberge du Soleil/N
Benjamin Franklin Hotel
  Lark Creek/S
Boonville Hotel
  Boonville Hotel/N
Campton Place Hotel
  Campton Place
Cardinal Hotel
  Osteria/S
Casa Madrona Hotel
  Mikayla/N
Clift Hotel, The
  French Room
Concord Hilton Hotel
  Grissini/E
Donatello Hotel
  Zingari
Fairmont Hotel
  Tonga
Garden Court Hotel
  Il Fornaio/S
Handlery Hotel
  New Joe's

Harbor Court Hotel
  Harry Denton's
Highlands Inn
  Pacific's Edge/S
Hotel De Anza
  La Pastaia/S
Hotel Galleria Park
  Brasserie Chambord
Hotel Griffon
  Roti
Hotel Monaco
  Grand Cafe
Hotel Nikko San Francisco
  Cafe 222
Huntington Hotel
  Big Four
Inn at Spanish Bay
  Roy's/Pebble Beach/S
Lodge at Pebble Beach
  Club XIX/S
Madrona Manor Country Inn
  Madrona Manor/N
Majestic Hotel, The
  Cafe Majestic
Mandarin Oriental Hotel
  Silks
Mark Hopkins Inter-Continental
  Top of the Mark
Maxwell Hotel
  Gracie's
Meadowood Resort
  Meadowood Grill/N
  Meadowood Rest./N
Miramonte Inn
  Showley's/N
Miyako Hotel
  Yoyo Bistro
Monticello Inn
  Puccini & Pinetti
Mount View Hotel & Spa
  Catahoula/N
Pan Pacific Hotel
  Pacific
Park Hyatt San Francisco
  Park Grill
Post Ranch Inn
  Sierra Mar/S
Prescott Hotel
  Postrio
Quail Lodge
  Covey/S
Renaissance Standard Court
  Fournou's Ovens
Ritz-Carlton San Francisco
  Ritz-Carlton Din. Rm.
  Ritz-Carlton Terrace

Sheraton Palace
  Garden Court
  Kyo-Ya
  Maxfield's
Silverado Country Club
  Vintner's Court/N
Sir Francis Drake Hotel
  Harry Denton's Starlight
  Scala's Bistro
Sonoma Mission Inn
  Sonoma Mission/N
Stanford Park Hotel
  Duck Club/S
Villa Florence Hotel
  Kuleto's
Vintage Court Hotel
  Masa's
Vintners Inn
  John Ash & Co./N
Warwick Regis Hotel
  La Scene

"In" Places

Alain Rondelli
Appam
Aqua
Beach Chalet
Betelnut
Bette's Oceanview/E
Biscuits & Blues
BIX
Bizou
Boulevard
Brava Terrace/N
Bridges/E
Bruno's
Buckeye Roadhse./N
Cafe/Chez Panisse/E
Caribbean Zone
Catahoula/N
Chez Panisse/E
Cypress Club
Eleven Ristorante
Elite Cafe
Emile's/S
Enrico's
Eos
Firefly
Fleur De Lys
Flying Saucer
Fringale
General's Daughter/N
Greens
Harry Denton's
Hawthorne Lane
Hayes & Vine
Johnny Love's/E
Julie's Supper Club
Lark Creek Inn/N

Left Bank/N
Little City
Max's Diner
Mecca
Michelangelo Cafe
Moose's
Mustards Grill/N
Oliveto/E
One Market
Pastis
Perry's
Plouf
PlumpJack
Postrio
Rose Pistola
Rubicon
Slanted Door
South Park
Stars
Stars Cafe
Suppenküche
Tommaso's
Tra Vigne/N
2223 Rest.
Val 21
Vertigo
Vivande Rist.
Washington Sq.
Waterfront
Zuni Cafe

Jacket Required

Acquerello
Bauhaus Art/Rest.
BIX
Cafe Majestic
Campton Place
Carnelian Room
Citron/E
Club XIX/S
Covey/S
Dal Baffo/S
Erna's Elderberry/S
Fleur De Lys
French Room
Garden Court
Harry Denton's Starlight
Masa's
Meadowood Rest./N
One Market
Scott's
Scott's/E
Scott's/S
Zingari

Late Late – After 12:30

(All hours are AM)
Basta Pasta (1)
Caffè Greco (1)

Globe (1)
Great Eastern (1)
Infusion (1)
La Rondalla (3)
Mel's Drive-In (1)
Milano Pizzeria (1)
Planet Hollywood (1)
Tommy's Joynt (1:30)
Yuet Lee (3)

Meet for a Drink

(Most top hotels and the
following standouts)
Balboa Cafe
BIX
Blue Light
Bruno's
Buchanan Grill
Cacti/N
Caribbean Zone
Catahoula/N
Cliff House
Courtyard B&G
Cypress Club
Eleven Ristorante
Elroy's
Enrico's
Eos
Fly Trap
General's Daughter/N
Gordon Biersch
Gordon Biersch/S
Hamburger Mary's
Hard Rock Cafe
Il Fornaio
Il Fornaio/N
Infusion
Izzy's
Johnny Love's/E
Julie's Supper Club
La Rondalla
Left Bank/N
L'Olivier
London Wine Bar
Mecca
Moose's
Mustards Grill/N
North Beach
One Market
O'Reilly's
Palomino
Perry's
Plouf
Prego
Santa Fe B&G/E
Stars
Stars Cafe
Thirsty Bear
Tommy's Joynt

Tra Vigne/N
Vivande Rist.
Washington Sq.

Noteworthy Newcomers (16)

Amber India/S
Antica Trattoria
Babette's/N
Beach Chalet
Chapeau!
Farallon
Globe
Indigo
Jardiniere
Ovation at Opera
Pyramid Alehse./E
Rocco's
Thirsty Bear
Viognier/S
Wappo Bar/N
Yabbies

Noteworthy Closings (19)

Act IV
Backstage
Bardelli's
Bistro M
China Moon Cafe
Ciao Ristorante
Eastside Oyster Bar & Grill/N
Heights
Hyde Street Bistro
Ivy's
JT's Bistro
Lanzone's Place
La Pergola
Le Trou Restaurant Francais
Miss Pearl's Jam House
Rosmarino
Ruby's
Stars Oakville Cafe/N
Vanessi's

Offbeat

Betelnut
Biscuits & Blues
Cafe Fanny/E
Caffe Sport
Campo Santo
Caribbean Zone
Carta
Cha Cha Cha
Coconut Grove
Cypress Club
Delancey St.
Dottie's True Blue
Flying Saucer
Hamburger Mary's
Helmand

Julius' Castle
Katia's
La Rondalla
Lhasa Moon
Long Life Noodle
Mario's Bohemian
Marrakech
Max's Diner
Millennium
Mom is Cooking
O'Reilly's
Panama Hotel/N
Pauline's
Picaro
Plouf
Rasselas
Raw Living Foods
Roosevelt Tamale
Rooster
Sol y Luna
Stinking Rose
Storyville
Straits Cafe
Suppenküche
Sweet Heat
Ti Couz
Tommy's Joynt
Tonga
World Wrapps
World Wrapps/E
World Wrapps/S
Yaya Cuisine
Yoshi's/E

Outdoor Dining

(G=garden; P=patio;
S=sidewalk; T=terrace;
W=waterside)
Adriana's/N (P)
Alta Mira/N (G)
Anjou (S)
Aqui/S (P)
Armani Cafe (S)
Aromi (P)
Atlas Peak/N (G)
Auberge du Soleil/N (T)
Baker St. Bistro (S)
Bay Wolf/E (T)
Beach Chalet (W)
Betelnut (P)
Bighorn Grill/E (P)
Bill's Place (G,P)
Bistro Aix (G,S)
Bistro Don Giovanni/N (P)
Bistro Ralph/N (P)
Blackhawk Grille/E (P,T,W)
Blue Chalk Cafe/S (P)
Bocce Café (G,P)
Bok Choy/S (P,S)

157

Boonville Hotel/N (G,P)
Brava Terrace/N (G,T)
Bridges/E (P)
Bucci's/E (P)
Buckeye Roadhse./N (P)
Buffalo Grill/S (P)
Cacti/N (P)
Cafe Bastille (T)
Cafe Claude (S,T)
Cafe de Paris (P,S,T)
Cafe Fanny/E (S)
Cafe Flore (P,S)
Cafe Rouge/E (T)
Cafe Tiramisu (S)
Cafe Trio/S (P)
Caffe Centro (G,P)
Caffe Delle Stelle (P)
Caffè Greco (P)
Caffè Macaroni (S)
California Cafe/N (P)
California Cafe/S (P)
Caribbean Zone (P)
Carta (S)
Casanova/S (G,P,T)
Castagnola's (S)
Chateau Souverain/N (P)
Cheers Cafe (P)
Chevys (P)
Chevys/E (P)
Chevys/N (P)
Chez Renee/S (P)
Chez T.J./S (P)
Citron/E (P)
Cliff House (W)
Club XIX/S (P,W)
Covey/S (W)
Crescent Park/S (T)
Crow's Nest/S (T,W)
Crustacean (T)
Curbside Cafe (S)
Domaine Chandon/N (P)
Duck Club/S (G,P)
El Paseo/N (G,P,T)
Elroy's (T)
Enrico's (P)
Erna's Elderberry/S (G,T)
Esperpento (S)
Faz (P,T)
Faz/E (G,P,T)
Faz/S (P)
Fizz Supper Club (G,P,S)
Flea St. Cafe/S (T)
42 Degrees (P)
Frantoio/N (P)
French Laundry/N (G,P)
Fresh Cream/S (W)
Gaylord India (W)
General's Daughter/N (G,P)
Gertie's Chesapeake/E (P)

Gibson/S (P)
Ginger Island/E (P)
Gordon Biersch (P,W)
Gordon Biersch/S (P)
Greens (W)
Grissini/E (P)
Guaymas/N (P,T,W)
Hahn's Hibachi (S)
Harry Denton's (S,T,W)
Horizons/N (P,W)
Insalata's/N (P)
Invitation House/S (P)
Iron Horse (S)
John Ash & Co./N (T)
Johnny Love's/E (P)
Julius' Castle (T)
Kenwood/N (G)
Kuleto's Tratt./S (P)
La Cumbre/S (G,P,S,W)
La Forêt/S (W)
La Luna Bistro/S (P,T)
La Mediterranee (P,S)
La Mediterranee/E (S,T)
La Mère Michelle/S (T)
L'Amie Donia/S (P)
La Pastaia/S (P,S)
Lark Creek/E (P,S)
Lark Creek/S (S)
Lark Creek Inn/N (P,W)
Le Charm (P)
Left at Albuquerque (S)
Left at Albuquerque/S (G)
Left Bank/N (T)
Le Marquis/E (G,P,T)
Le Mouton Noir/S (P)
Lion & Compass/S (G)
Little City (S)
Long Life Noodle (S)
MacArthur Park (P)
MacArthur Park/S (P)
Madrona Manor/N (T)
Mangiafuoco (S)
Marin Joe's/N (P)
Mario's Bohemian (S)
McCormick & Kuleto's (W)
Meadowood Rest./N (T)
Mel's Drive-In (P)
Mikayla/N (W)
Miss Millie's (P)
Mom is Cooking (G,P)
Moss Beach Distillery/S (P,W)
Moxie (S)
Nan Yang/E (P)
Napa Valley Grille/N (P)
New Gulf Coast/E (P,S)
Nightshade (P)
O Chame/E (P)
Olive's (P)
Oliveto/E (S)

Palermo/S (G,P,T)
Palomino (P,W)
Panama Hotel/N (G,P)
Pane e Vino (S)
Paolo's/S (P,T,W)
Park Grill (T)
Parkside Grille/S (G,P)
Pasta Pomodoro/E (P)
Pasta Prego/N (P)
Pastis (P)
Perry's (S)
Piatti/N (P,W)
Piatti/S (P)
Picante/E (G,P)
Pickled Ginger (P)
Pier 23 Cafe (G,P,S,T,W)
Pinot Blanc/N (P)
Pluto's (S)
Prego (S)
Prima Trattoria/E (P,S)
Primo Patio (G,P)
Pyramid Alehse./E (P)
Rendezvous du Monde (S)
Rio Grill/S (P)
Rist. Fabrizio/N (P)
Rist. Salute/E (P)
Ritz-Carlton Terrace (P,T)
Rooster (S)
Rose Pistola (S)
Rose's Cafe (S)
Rosti/S (P)
Roti (S,W)
Roy's/Pebble Beach/S (P)
Rumpus (P)
Rutherford Grill/N (P)
Sally's (S)
Sam's Anchor Cafe/N (P,W)
Sand Dollar/N (P)
Santa Fe B&G/E (P)
Savor (P)
Scoma's (W)
Scoma's/N (W)
Scott's (P)
Scott's/E (P,T,W)
Scott's/S (G,P)
Sent Sovi/S (P)
Showley's/N (P)
Sierra Mar/S (T,W)
Slow Club (S)
Sol y Luna (P)
Sonoma Mission/N (P)
Spiedini/E (P)
Splendido (P)
Station House/N (G,P)
Straits Cafe (P)
Sweet Heat (S,T)
Tarpy's Roadhse./S (P)
Tavern Grill/S (P)
Thirsty Bear (P)

Thornhill Cafe/E (P)
Timo's (P,T)
Tonga (W)
Tourelle/E (G,P)
Town's End (P,W)
Tra Vigne/N (G,P,T)
Trilogy/N (P)
Tutto Mare/N (T)
Universal Cafe (S)
Valentine's Cafe (S)
Vertigo (G)
Vicolo/S (P,S)
Vic Stewart's/E (P)
Vivande Rist. (P)
Wappo Bar/N (G,P)
Wine Spectator/N (T)
World Wrapps (S)
World Wrapps/E (S)
World Wrapps/S (S)
Yank Sing (P)
Yet Wah/N (P)
Zazie (P)
Zibibbo/S (G,P,S,T)
Zinzino (G,S)
Zza's Trattoria/E (W)

Outstanding Views
Alioto's
Alta Mira/N
A. Sabella's
Auberge du Soleil/N
Barnaby's/N
Beach Chalet
Bella Vista/S
Blackhawk Grille/E
Caprice/N
Carnelian Room
Castagnola's
Cliff House
Club XIX/S
Covey/S
Crow's Nest/S
dalla Torre
Domaine Chandon/N
Empress of China
Fresh Cream/S
Gaylord India
Gordon Biersch
Gordon Biersch/S
Greens
Guaymas/N
Harbor Village
Harry Denton's
Horizons/N
Julius' Castle
La Forêt/S
Mandarin
McCormick & Kuleto's
Meadowood Rest./N

Mikayla/N
Moss Beach Distillery/S
North Sea Village/N
Old Swiss Hse.
Pacific's Edge/S
Palomino
Paolo's/S
Roti
Sam's Anchor Cafe/N
Scoma's
Scoma's/N
Sierra Mar/S
Splendido
Tarpy's Roadhse./S
Tutto Mare/N
Vintner's Court/N
Waterfront

Parking/Valet

(L=parking lot;
V=valet parking;
*=validated parking)

Acquerello (L)
Adriana's/N (L)
Albona (V)
Alexander/E (L)
Alfred's (V)
Alta Mira/N (L,V)*
Amber India/S (L)
Antica Trattoria*
Aqua (V)
Aqui/S (L)
Aromi (V)
A. Sabella's*
Atlas Peak/N (L)
Auberge du Soleil/N (V)
Avenue Grill/N (L)
Babaloo Tapas (L)
Bahia Cabana (L)
Balboa Cafe (V)
Basque Cultural Ctr./S (L)
Basta Pasta (V)
Bauhaus Art/Rest. (V)
Beach Chalet (L)
Beausejour/S (L)
Bella Vista/S (L)
Benihana/S (L)
Betelnut*
Big Four (V)
Bighorn Grill/E (L,V)
Biscuits & Blues (V)
BIX (V)
Blackhawk Grille/E (L)
Blue Chalk Cafe/S (L)
Blue Point*
Bocce Café (V)
Bok Choy/S (L)
Bolero/N (L)
Boonville Hotel/N (L)

Boulevard (V)
Brasserie Chambord (L)
Brava Terrace/N (L)
Bridges/E (V)
Bruno's (L)
Bucci's/E (L)
Buckeye Roadhse./N (L,V)
Buffalo Grill/S (L)
Cacti/N (L)
Café Chêneville/E (L)
Cafe Claude (L)
Cafe de Paris (L,V)
Cafe Fanny/E (L)
Cafe Kati (V)*
Cafe Majestic (V)
Cafe Marcella/S (L)
Cafe Rouge/E (L)
Cafe Trio/S (L)
Cafe 222 (V)*
California Cafe/E (V)
California Cafe/N (L)
California Cafe/S (L)
Campton Place (V)
Capellini/S (V)
Capp's Corner*
Caprice/N (V)*
Caribbean Zone (L)
Carnelian Room (L)
Carpaccio/S (L)
Carta (L)
Cassis Bistro (V)
Castagnola's*
Catahoula/N (L)
Cha Am Thai*
Chateau Souverain/N (L)
Chevys (L)*
Chevys/E (L)
Chez Michel (L)
Chez Renee/S (L)
City of Paris (L,V)*
Cliff House (L)
Club XIX/S (V)
Coconut Grove (V)*
Columbus Rist. (L)
Correnti's*
Courtyard B&G*
Covey/S (L)
Crescent Park/S (L)
Crow's Nest/S (L)
Crustacean*
Cypress Club (V)
Dal Baffo/S (L)
dalla Torre (V)
Delancey St. (V)
Doug's BBQ/E (L)
Duarte's Tavern/S (L)
Duck Club/S (L)*
Eleven Ristorante (V)*
Elroy's (V)

Emerald Garden*
Emile's/S (V)
Enrico's (V)
Eos (L)
Erna's Elderberry/S (L)
Esperpento (L)
Essex Supper Club (V)
Eulipia/S (L)
Evvia/S (L)
Farallon (V)
Fat Apple's/E (L)
Faz (L)
Faz/E (L)
Faz/S (L)
Fior d'Italia (V)
Flea St. Cafe/S (L)
Fleur De Lys (V)
Fly Trap (V)
Fook Yuen/S (L)
42 Degrees (L)
Fournou's Ovens (V)
Frantoio/N (L,V)
French Room (V)
Fresh Cream/S (L)*
Fusilli Rist./N (L)
Garden Court (V)*
Garibaldi's (V)
Gaylord India (L)*
General's Daughter/N (L)
Gervais/S (L)
Ginger Island/E (L)
Gordon Biersch*
Gordon Biersch/S*
Gracie's (V)
Grand Cafe (L,V)*
Greens (L)
Grissini/E (L)
Guaymas/N*
Guernica/N (L)
Harbor Village (V)*
Harris' (V)
Harry Denton's (V)
Harry Denton's Starlight (V)
Hawthorne Lane (V)
Hayes St. Grill (V)*
Helmand (V)
Hong Kong Flower/S (L)*
Hong Kong Villa*
Horizons/N (V)*
House of Nanking (L)
House of Prime Rib (V)*
Il Fornaio (V)
Indigo (V)
Insalata's/N (L)
Invitation House/S (L)
Iroha (L)
Irrawaddy (V)*
Izzy's*
Jardiniere (V)

John Ash & Co./N (L)
Johnny Love's (L)
Johnny Love's/E (L)
Jordan's/E (V)*
Julie's Supper Club (L)
Julius' Castle (V)
Kansai (L)
Kasbah/N (L)
Katia's (L)
Kenwood/N (L)
Kincaid's Bistro/S (L)
Kuleto's Tratt./S (L,V)*
Kyo-Ya (V)
La Cumbre (L)
La Cumbre/S (L)
La Felce (V)
La Folie (V)
La Forêt/S (L)
La Luna Bistro/S (L)
La Mediterranee/E (L)
La Mère Michelle/S (L)
La Pastaia/S (L)
Lark Creek/E (L)*
Lark Creek/S (L)*
Lark Creek Inn/N (L,V)
La Scene (V)
Le Central (V)
Le Cyrano (L)
Left at Albuquerque/S (V)*
Left Bank/N (V)
Lehr Brothers (V)
Le Marquis/E (L)
Le Mouton Noir/S (L)
Le Papillon/S (L)
Leticia's (L)
Lichee Garden (V)
Lion & Compass/S (V)
Little City*
L'Olivier (V)
Los Gatos/S (L)
LuLu (V)
MacArthur Park (V)
MacArthur Park/S (L,V)
Madrona Manor/N (L)
Maharani India*
Maki (L)
Mandarin*
Marina Central (V)
Marin Joe's/N (L,V)
Masa's (V)
Matterhorn Swiss (V)
Maxfield's (V)*
Max's Opera Cafe (L)
Max's Opera Cafe/S (L)
McCormick & Kuleto's (L)*
Meadowood Rest./N (L)
Mecca (V)
Meetinghouse (V)
Mel's Drive-In (L)

Mikayla/N (L,V)*
Mio Vicino/S (L)
Mom is Cooking (L)
Montrio/S (L)
Moose's (V)
Morton's of Chicago (V)
Moss Beach Distillery/S (L)
Napa Valley Grille/N (L)
Napa Valley Wine/N (L)
Narai (V)*
New Gulf Coast/E (L)
Nob Hill Cafe (V)
North Beach (V)
North India (L)
Old Swiss Hse.*
Oliveto/E (L)
One Market (V)
Original Joe's (V)
Osteria (V)
Ovation at Opera (V)
Pacific (V)*
Pacific Fresh/E (L)
Pacific's Edge/S (V)*
Palermo/S*
Palomino (L)*
Paolo's/S (L)*
Park Grill (V)*
Parkside Grille/S (L)
Pasta Prego/N (L)
Perry's*
Piatti/N (L)
Piatti/S (L)
Piazza D'Angelo/N (V)
Picante/E (L)
Pier 23 Cafe (L)
Pinot Blanc/N (L)
PJ's Oyster Bed (L)
Plumed Horse/S (V)
Postrio (V)
Prima Trattoria/E (V)*
Primo Patio (L)
Pyramid Alehse./E (L)
Rest. Peony/E (L)
Rio Grill/S (L)
Rist. Fabrizio/N (L)
Rist. Milano (L)
Rist. Salute/E (L)
Ritz-Carlton Din. Rm. (V)
Ritz-Carlton Terrace (V)
Robata Grill/N (L)
Rocco's (V)
Rose Pistola (V)
Roti (V)
Roy's/Pebble Beach/S (L,V)
Rubicon (V)
Rue de Main/E (L)
Rutherford Grill/N (L)
Sanraku*
Santa Fe B&G/E (L)

Sardine Factory/S (L)
Scala's Bistro (V)
Scoma's (V)
Scoma's/N*
Scott's*
Scott's/E (L,V)
Scott's/S (L)*
Sent Sovi/S (L)
Seoul Garden*
Sierra Mar/S (L,V)
Skylight Cafe/E (L)*
Socca (V)
Sol y Luna*
Sonoma Mission/N (V)
Spenger's/E (L)*
Spiedini/E (V)
Splendido (L)*
Stars (V)
Stars Cafe (V)
Tarantino's*
Tavern Grill/S (L)
Timo's*
Tonga (V)
Ton Kiang (L)
Top of the Mark*
Tortola (V)
Tourelle/E (L,V)
Tratt. Contadina*
Tra Vigne/N (L)
2223 Rest. (L)
Val 21 (L)*
Venezia/E (L)
Venticello (V)
Vertigo (V)
Vic Stewart's/E (L)
Vintner's Court/N (V)
Viognier/S (V)
Vivande Rist. (V)*
Washington Sq. (V)
Waterfront (V)
Wente Vineyards/E (V)
Willowside Cafe/N (L)
Wine Spectator/N (V)
Yabbies*
Yet Wah/N (L)
Yoshida-Ya*
Yoshi's/E (L)*
Yoyo Bistro*
Zibibbo/S (V)
Zingari (L)
Zinzino*
Zuni Cafe (V)

Parties & Private Rooms

(Any nightclub or restaurant
charges less at off-times;
* indicates private rooms
available; best of many)
Alegrias*
Alioto's

162

Alta Mira/N*
Amber India/S*
Aqua*
Armani Cafe
A. Sabella's*
Asimakopoulos*
Auberge du Soleil/N*
Aux Delices*
Avenue Grill/N*
Avenue 9*
Bahia Cabana
Balboa Cafe
Barnaby's/N
Basque Cultural Ctr./S*
Basta Pasta*
Bauhaus Art/Rest.*
Beausejour/S*
Bella Vista/S*
Betelnut*
Big Four*
Bighorn Grill/E*
Bill's Place
Biscuits & Blues
Bistro Aix
Bizou
Blackhawk Grille/E*
Blue Chalk Cafe/S*
Blue Nile/E
Bocce Café
Bok Choy/S
Bolero/N*
Boulevard*
Brandy Ho's*
Brasserie Chambord*
Brava Terrace/N*
Bridges/E
Brix/N*
Brother's Deli/S*
Bucci's/E
Buchanan Grill*
Buckeye Roadhse./N*
Buffalo Grill/S*
Cacti/N
Cadillac Bar*
Cafe Akimbo
Cafe Bastille*
Café Chêneville/E
Cafe Claude
Cafe de Paris*
Cafe Kati*
Cafe Majestic*
Cafe Marimba
Café Mozart*
Cafe Tiramisu*
Cafe 222*
Caffe Delle Stelle*
Caffè Macaroni
California Cafe/E*
California Cafe/N

California Cafe/S*
Capellini/S*
Caprice/N*
Caribbean Zone
Carnelian Room*
Carpaccio/S
Carta*
Casanova/S*
Castagnola's*
Catahoula/N*
Cha Am Thai
Cha Am Thai/E
Chapeau!
Charles Nob Hill*
Chef Chu's/S*
Chevys
Chevys/E*
Chez Michel*
Chez Renee/S*
Chez T.J./S*
City of Paris*
Clement St. B&G
Cliff House*
Club XIX/S*
Coconut Grove*
Columbus Rist.*
Correnti's*
Covey/S*
Crescent Park/S*
Crow's Nest/S*
Crustacean
Cypress Club*
Dal Baffo/S*
dalla Torre*
Delancey St.*
Duarte's Tavern/S*
Duck Club/S*
E'Angelo
Ebisu*
Eleven Ristorante*
El Paseo/N*
Elroy's
Emerald Garden
Emile's/S*
Eos
Erna's Elderberry/S*
Esperpento*
Essex Supper Club*
Eulipia/S
Farallon*
Faz
Faz/E
Faz/S
Fior d'Italia*
Fizz Supper Club*
Flea St. Cafe/S*
Fleur De Lys*
Fly Trap*
Fog City Diner*

Fook Yuen/S*
42 Degrees
Fountain Court*
Fournou's Ovens*
Frantoio/N*
French Laundry/N*
Fresh Cream/S*
Fusilli Rist./N*
Garibaldi's*
Gaylord India*
General's Daughter/N*
Gervais/S*
Gibson/S
Globe*
Golden Turtle
Gordon Biersch
Gordon Biersch/S*
Gracie's
Grand Cafe*
Grandview/S*
Grissini/E*
Guaymas/N*
Guernica/N*
Hahn's Hibachi
Harbor Village*
Harris'*
Harry Denton's*
Harry Denton's Starlight
Hawthorne Lane*
Hayes St. Grill
Helmand
Hong Kong Flower*
Hong Kong Flower/S*
Hong Kong Villa*
Horizons/N
House of Prime Rib*
Hungarian Sausage
Il Fornaio
Il Fornaio/N
Imperial Palace*
Indigo*
Infusion
Insalata's/N
Invitation House/S*
Iron Horse*
Irrawaddy
Izzy's
Jade Villa/E*
Jakarta*
Jardiniere*
Jasmine House*
John Ash & Co./N
Johnny Love's/E*
Jordan's/E*
Julie's Supper Club*
Julius' Castle*
Kasbah/N*
Katia's
Korea House*

Kuleto's*
Kuleto's Tratt./S*
Kyo-Ya*
La Felce
La Folie
La Forêt/S*
La Luna Bistro/S
La Mère Michelle/S*
La Pastaia/S*
La Petite Auberge/N*
Lark Creek/E
Lark Creek/S
Lark Creek Inn/N*
La Rondalla
Las Camelias/N
La Scene
La Traviata
Left Bank/N*
Lehr Brothers*
Le Mouton Noir/S*
Le Papillon/S*
Leticia's*
Lion & Compass/S*
Little City*
Little Italy
L'Olivier*
London Wine Bar*
Los Gatos/S
LuLu*
MacArthur Park*
MacArthur Park/S*
Madrona Manor/N*
Maharani India
Mandalay
Mandarin
Marina Central*
Marin Joe's/N
Masa's*
Maxfield's*
Mayflower*
McCormick & Kuleto's*
Meadowood Rest./N*
Mecca*
Mel's Drive-In
Mikayla/N*
Millennium
Mio Vicino/S
Miss Millie's*
Mom is Cooking*
Montrio/S*
Moose's*
Morton's of Chicago*
Moss Beach Distillery/S*
Moxie*
Nan Yang/E*
Napa Valley Grille/N*
Napa Valley Wine/N
New Gulf Coast/E*
New Joe's*

164

North Beach*
North India*
North Sea Village/N*
Occidental Grill
Old Swiss Hse.*
Oliveto/E*
Omnivore/E
One Market*
Original Joe's
Original Old Clam Hse.*
Osome*
Pacific
Pacific Fresh/E*
Pacific Fresh/S*
Pacific's Edge/S*
Palermo/S*
Palio d'Asti*
Panama Hotel/N*
Pancho Villa
Paolo's/S*
Paragon B&G
Parkside Grille/S*
Pasta Moon/S*
Pauline's*
Pauli's Cafe
Perry's*
Piatti/N*
Piatti/S*
Pickled Ginger
Pinot Blanc/N*
PJ's Oyster Bed*
Planet Hollywood
Plearn Thai/E*
Plumed Horse/S*
PlumpJack*
Postrio*
Prego*
Prima Trattoria/E*
Primo Patio
Pyramid Alehse./E*
Rendezvous du Monde*
Rest. Peony/E*
Rick's*
Rio Grill/S
Rist. Bacco
Rist. Ecco
Rist. Fabrizio/N*
Rist. Milano*
Rist. Salute/E*
Ritz-Carlton Din. Rm.*
Ritz-Carlton Terrace
Robata Grill/N
Rocco's
Rooster
Rosti/S
Roti*
Rotunda
Royal Thai
Roy's/Pebble Beach/S

Rubicon*
Rue de Main/E
Rumpus*
Sam's*
Samui Thai
San Benito Hse./S
Sanraku
Santa Fe B&G/E
Sardine Factory/S*
Scala's Bistro*
Schroeder's*
Scoma's/N
Scott's*
Scott's/E*
Scott's/S*
Sent Sovi/S*
Seoul Garden*
Showley's/N*
Siam Cuisine/E
Socca*
Sonoma Mission/N*
Spenger's/E*
Spiedini/E*
Splendido*
Spuntino
Stars*
Stars Cafe*
Station House/N*
Stinking Rose*
Storyville*
Sukhothai
Suppenküche*
Sweet Heat*
Tadich Grill
Tanuki*
Tarantino's*
Tarpy's Roadhse./S*
Tavern Grill/S*
Terra/N*
Thep Phanom
Thirsty Bear*
Thornhill Cafe/E*
Timo's*
Tommy Toy's Chinoise*
Tonga
Ton Kiang*
Top of the Mark
Tourelle/E*
Tratt. Contadina*
Tra Vigne/N*
2223 Rest.*
U.S. Rest.
Uzen/E*
Venticello
Vertigo*
Vicolo
Vicolo/S
Vic Stewart's/E*
Viognier/S*

Vivande Rist.*
Wa-Ha-Ka
Wappo Bar/N*
Washington Sq.
Waterfront
Wente Vineyards/E*
Wine Spectator/N*
World Wrapps
World Wrapps/E
World Wrapps/S
Wu Kong*
Yank Sing
Yet Wah*
Yet Wah/N
Yoshida-Ya*
Yoshi's/E
Yoyo Bistro*
Zaré
Zarzuela
Zibibbo/S*
Zingari*
Zinzino*
Zza's Trattoria/E*

People-Watching

Alain Rondelli
Avenue Grill/N
Beach Chalet
Betelnut
Bette's Oceanview/E
Bruno's
Buckeye Roadhse./N
Cafe/Chez Panisse/E
Cafe Flore
Chez Panisse/E
Cypress Club
Eleven Ristorante
Enrico's
Essex Supper Club
Fly Trap
General's Daughter/N
Gordon Biersch
Gordon Biersch/S
Hard Rock Cafe
Harry Denton's
Johnny Love's
Johnny Love's/E
La Rondalla
Le Central
Little City
Long Life Noodle
Mecca
Moose's
One Market
Park Grill
Perry's
Postrio
Rose Pistola
Rubicon

Storyville
Top of the Mark
Vertigo
Zuni Cafe

Power Scenes

Alain Rondelli
Aqua
BIX
Blackhawk Grille/E
Boulevard
Cafe/Chez Panisse/E
Chez Panisse/E
Cypress Club
42 Degrees
Hawthorne Lane
La Folie
Le Central
Masa's
Maxfield's
Moose's
North Beach
Occidental Grill
One Market
Park Grill
Postrio
Rubicon
Stars
Stars Cafe
Vertigo
Vintner's Court/N
Vivande Rist.
Washington Sq.
Waterfront
Zuni Cafe

Pre-Theater/Early Bird Menus

(Call to check prices, days and times)
Cafe 222
California Cafe/E
Chapeau!
City of Paris
Gira Polli
Gira Polli/N
Indigo
Little Italy
New Gulf Coast/E
North India
Pacific Fresh/E
Paolo's/S
Rick's
Ritz-Carlton Terrace
Scott's/S
Tarantino's
Tourelle/E

Prix Fixe Menus

(Call to check prices, days and times)

Ajanta/E
Alta Mira/N
Anjou
Baker St. Bistro
Biscuits & Blues
Bistro Aix
Bok Choy/S
Cafe Beaujolais/N
Campton Place
Capp's Corner
Careme Room
Carnelian Room
Chapeau!
Chez Panisse/E
Chez T.J./S
Emile's/S
Empress of China
Erna's Elderberry/S
Esperpento
Eulipia/S
Flea St. Cafe/S
French Room
Greens
Hong Kong Flower
Imperial Palace
Kasbah/N
Kincaid's Bistro/S
La Folie
La Mère Michelle/S
L'Amie Donia/S
La Scene
Le Mouton Noir/S
Lhasa Moon
L'Olivier
Madrona Manor/N
Mandarin
Masa's
Ma Tante Sumi
Meadowood Rest./N
Mom is Cooking
Moss Beach Distillery/S
Napa Valley Wine/N
New Gulf Coast/E
North India
Pacific
Pacific Fresh/E
Paolo's/S
Rice Table/N
Ritz-Carlton Din. Rm.
Sanraku
Sierra Mar/S
Socca
Sol y Luna
Sonoma Mission/N
South Park

Stelline
Tonga
Top of the Mark
Trilogy/N
231 Ellsworth/S
Wente Vineyards/E
Wu Kong

Pubs/Bars/ Microbreweries

Beach Chalet
Bill's Place
Buchanan Grill
Courtyard B&G
Crow's Nest/S
Gordon Biersch
Grand Cafe
Kuleto's Tratt./S
Los Gatos/S
Old Swiss Hse.
O'Reilly's
Perry's
Pyramid Alehse./E
Thirsty Bear
Tommy's Joynt
Washington Sq.

Quiet Conversation

Alegrias
Alfred's
Antica Trattoria
Cafe/Chez Panisse/E
Café Mozart
Campton Place
Charles Nob Hill
Chez Panisse/E
Domaine Chandon/N
El Paseo/N
Fournou's Ovens
Incontro
John Ash & Co./N
Lalime's/E
Liberty Cafe
L'Olivier
Madrona Manor/N
Masa's
PlumpJack
Ritz-Carlton Din. Rm.
San Benito Hse./S
Sent Sovi/S
231 Ellsworth/S
Vintner's Court/N

Raw Bars

Blowfish Sushi
Blue Point
Cafe de Paris
Cafe Rouge/E
Cliff House
Elite Cafe

Farallon
Faz
Faz/E
Faz/S
Fog City Diner
Gertie's Chesapeake/E
Globe
Il Fornaio/N
LuLu
McCormick & Kuleto's
One Market
Pacific Fresh/E
Ritz-Carlton Terrace
Rocco's
Roti
Spenger's/E
Stars Cafe
Yabbies
Zibibbo/S

Reservations Essential

Albona
Antica Trattoria
Auberge du Soleil/N
Babette's/N
Bauhaus Art/Rest.
Benihana/S
Bistro Aix
Bistro Don Giovanni/N
Bruno's
Buckeye Roadhse./N
Cafe de Bordeaux/E
Cafe Marcella/S
Café Mozart
Cafe Rouge/E
Cafe Tiramisu
Cafe Trio/S
Careme Room
Carnelian Room
Cassis Bistro
Catahoula/N
Chapeau!
Chateau Souverain/N
Chez Michel
Chez Panisse/E
Citron/E
Club XIX/S
Coconut Grove
Columbus Rist.
Crustacean
dalla Torre
Eleven Ristorante
Emerald Garden
Erna's Elderberry/S
Firefly
Fleur De Lys
Fook Yuen/S
Fournou's Ovens
French Room

Fringale
Gervais/S
Guaymas/N
Harris'
Jasmine House
Jessie's
Julius' Castle
La Folie
La Mère Michelle/S
Lark Creek/S
La Traviata
Le Charm
Little Italy
Los Gatos/S
LuLu
Mangiafuoco
Masa's
Matterhorn Swiss
Mom is Cooking
New Gulf Coast/E
Occidental Grill
Oliveto/E
Pacific's Edge/S
Palermo/S
Pastis
PlumpJack
Postrio
Prima Trattoria/E
Rist. Salute/E
Roy's/Pebble Beach/S
Rumpus
Sierra Mar/S
Sonoma Mission/N
Stars
Tonga
Tra Vigne/N
Trilogy/N
Venticello
Zax

Romantic Spots

Acquerello
Alegrias
Alexander/E
Aqua
Buca Giovanni
Cafe/Chez Panisse/E
Cafe Jacqueline
Café Mozart
Casanova/S
Cassis Bistro
Charles Nob Hill
Chez Michel
Chez Panisse/E
Chez Renee/S
Covey/S
Domaine Chandon/N
El Paseo/N
Emile's/S

Erna's Elderberry/S
Fleur De Lys
French Room
Fresh Cream/S
Gaylord India
Gaylord India/S
General's Daughter/N
Globe
Jardiniere
John Ash & Co./N
Julius' Castle
La Folie
La Forêt/S
La Petite Auberge/N
Lark Creek Inn/N
Le Mouton Noir/S
L'Olivier
Madrona Manor/N
Masa's
Matterhorn Swiss
Meadowood Rest./N
Mikayla/N
Ovation at Opera
Pacific's Edge/S
Rooster
San Benito Hse./S
Sent Sovi/S
Sierra Mar/S
Storyville
Terra/N
231 Ellsworth/S
Venticello
Vintner's Court/N
Waterfront
Woodward's

Saturday – Best Bets

(B=brunch; L=lunch;
best of many)
Ajanta/E (L)
Amber India/S (L)
Anjou (L)
Aqui/S (L)
Auberge du Soleil/N (L)
Betelnut (L)
Bette's Oceanview/E (B,L)
Bistro Don Giovanni/N (L)
Blackhawk Grille/E (B)
Boonville Hotel/N (L)
Brava Terrace/N (L)
Brix/N (L)
Bubba's Diner/N (B,L)
Buchanan Grill (B)
Buckeye Roadhse./N (L)
Buffalo Grill/S (L)
Cactus Cafe/N (L)
Cafe Akimbo (L)
Cafe/Chez Panisse/E (L)
Cafe de Paris (B,L)

Cafe Fanny/E (L)
Cafe For All Seasons (B)
Cafe Marcella/S (L)
Cafe Marimba (B,L)
Cafe Rouge/E (L)
Caffe Centro (B,L)
Campton Place (L)
Careme Room (L)
Casa Aguila (L)
Casanova/S (L)
Catahoula/N (L)
Cha Am Thai (L)
Cha Am Thai/E (L)
Cha Cha Cha (L)
Chateau Souverain/N (L)
Chez Panisse/E (L)
City of Paris (L)
Clement St. B&G (B,L)
Cliff House (L)
Club XIX/S (L)
Cordon Bleu (L)
Crow's Nest/S (L)
Crustacean (L)
Curbside Cafe (B,L)
Delancey St. (B,L)
Doidge's (L)
Domaine Chandon/N (L)
Dottie's True Blue (B)
Doug's BBQ/E (L)
Duarte's Tavern/S (L)
Duck Club/S (L)
Dusit Thai (L)
Ebisu (L)
Eddie Rickenbacker's (L)
Elite Cafe (B)
Eliza's (L)
Ella's (B)
Empress Court/S (L)
Enrico's (L)
Eric's (L)
Estampas Peruanas/S (B,L)
Farallon (L)
Fat Apple's/E (L)
Fior d'Italia (L)
Fog City Diner (L)
Fook Yuen/S (L)
Fournou's Ovens (B)
Frantoio/N (L)
French Laundry/N (L)
Frog & The Peach/N (B)
Fung Lum/S (L)
Garden Court (L)
Gaylord India (L)
Gaylord India/S (L)
General's Daughter/N (L)
Ginger Island/E (L)
Gracie's (B,L)
Grand Cafe (B,L)
Grandview/S (L)

Great Eastern (L)
Greens (L)
Guaymas/N (L)
Hahn's Hibachi (L)
Hamburger Mary's (B,L)
Harbor Village (L)
Hard Rock Cafe (L)
Harry Denton's (L)
Hong Kong Flower (L)
Hong Kong Flower/S (L)
Horizons/N (B,L)
House (L)
House of Nanking (L)
Iberia/S (L)
Insalata's/N (L)
Invitation House/S (L)
Iroha (L)
Iron Horse (L)
Isobune (L)
Isobune/S (L)
JoAnn's Cafe/S (B)
John Ash & Co./N (B)
Kate's Kitchen (B,L)
Katia's (L)
Kenwood/N (L)
Khan Toke Thai (L)
Kirin (L)
Kiss (L)
Kuleto's (L)
La Mediterranee (B,L)
La Mediterranee/E (L)
La Mère Michelle/S (L)
La Pastaia/S (L)
Lark Creek/E (L)
Lark Creek/S (B)
La Rondalla (L)
Las Camelias/N (L)
La Taqueria (L)
La Vie (L)
Le Central (L)
Left at Albuquerque (B,L)
Left at Albuquerque/S (L)
Left Bank/N (L)
Lehr Brothers (L)
Le Mouton Noir/S (B)
Le Soleil (L)
Leticia's (L)
Liberty Cafe (B)
Lichee Garden (L)
Little City (L)
Little Joe's (L)
Long Life Vegi/E (L)
Los Gatos/S (L)
L'Osteria del Forno (L)
Maharani India (L)
Mai's (L)
Maki (L)
Mama's Girl (B,L)
Mama's Royal Cafe/E (B)

Mandalay (L)
Mandarin (L)
Mario's Bohemian (L)
Marnee Thai (L)
Massawa (L)
Max's Diner (L)
Max's Opera Cafe (B,L)
Max's Opera Cafe/S (B,L)
Mayflower (L)
McCormick & Kuleto's (L)
Meadowood Rest./N (B)
Mel's Drive-In (B,L)
Michelangelo Cafe (L)
Mifune (L)
Mio Vicino/S (L)
Miss Millie's (B)
Mom is Cooking (B,L)
Montrio/S (L)
Moose's (L)
Mo's Burgers (L)
Moss Beach Distillery/S (L)
Moxie (B)
Mustards Grill/N (L)
Nan Yang/E (L)
Napa Valley Grille/N (L)
Narai (L)
Nob Hill Cafe (L)
North Beach (L)
North Sea Village/N (L)
O Chame/E (L)
Old Swiss Hse. (L)
Olive's (L)
Oliveto/E (L)
O'Reilly's (B)
Osteria/S (L)
Ovation at Opera (L)
Pacific (B)
Pacific's Edge/S (L)
Pane e Vino (L)
Park Grill (B)
Pasta Moon/S (L)
Pauli's Cafe (B,L)
Perry's (B,L)
Piatti/N (L)
Piatti/S (L)
Piazza D'Angelo/N (B,L)
Picante/E (B,L)
Picaro (L)
Pinot Blanc/N (L)
PJ's Oyster Bed (B)
Plearn Thai/E (L)
Pluto's (L)
Pluto's/S (L)
Postrio (B)
Prego (L)
Prima Trattoria/E (L)
Primo Patio (B,L)
Pyramid Alehse./E (L)
Raw Living Foods (B,L)

Rendezvous du Monde (B,L)
Rest. Peony/E (L)
Rio Grill/S (L)
Rist. Fabrizio/N (L)
Rist. Salute/E (B,L)
Ritz-Carlton Terrace (L)
Roosevelt Tamale (L)
Rose Pistola (L)
Rose's Cafe (B,L)
Roy's/Pebble Beach/S (L)
Sally's (L)
Sam's Anchor Cafe/N (B,L)
Samui Thai (L)
Sand Dollar/N (L)
San Francisco BBQ (L)
Sanppo (L)
Saul's/E (B,L)
Scala's Bistro (L)
Seoul Garden (L)
Showley's/N (L)
Siam Cuisine/E (L)
Sierra Mar/S (L)
Silks (L)
Slanted Door (L)
Sonoma Mission/N (L)
Spenger's/E (L)
Spuntino (L)
Stars Cafe (L)
Station House/N (L)
Straits Cafe (L)
Suppenküche (B)
Swagat/S (L)
Swan Oyster Depot (L)
Sweet Heat (L)
Tadich Grill (L)
Tarpy's Roadhse./S (L)
Thirsty Bear (L)
Thornhill Cafe/E (B,L)
Ti Couz (B,L)
Timo's (L)
Ton Kiang (L)
Tortola (L)
Town's End (B)
Tra Vigne/N (L)
Trio Cafe (L)
Tu Lan (L)
Tutto Mare/N (L)
2223 Rest. (L)
Universal Cafe (B,L)
U.S. Rest. (L)
Valentine's Cafe (B)
Val 21 (B)
Vicolo (L)
Viognier/S (B)
Vivande Porta Via (L)
Vivande Rist. (B,L)
Wappo Bar/N (L)
Waterfront (L)
Wente Vineyards/E (L)

Wine Spectator/N (L)
Wu Kong (L)
Yank Sing (B,L)
Yoshi's/E (L)
Yoyo Bistro (L)
Yuet Lee (L)
Zachary's/E (L)
Zarzuela (L)
Zazie (B,L)
Zuni Cafe (L)

Sunday Dining – Best Bets

(B=brunch; L=lunch;
D=dinner; plus most hotels
and Asians)

Ajanta/E (L,D)
Alain Rondelli (D)
Alfred's (D)
Amber India/S (L,D)
Antica Trattoria (D)
Aqui/S (L,D)
Atlas Peak/N (D)
Avenue 9 (B,L,D)
Balboa Cafe (B,D)
Bay Wolf/E (D)
Beach Chalet (B,L,D)
Betelnut (L,D)
Bette's Oceanview/E (L)
Bistro Don Giovanni/N (L,D)
Bistro Ralph/N (D)
BIX (D)
Blackhawk Grille/E (D)
Boulevard (D)
Brava Terrace/N (L,D)
Bridges/E (D)
Brix/N (L,D)
Bubba's Diner/N (L,D)
Buckeye Roadhse./N (B,L,D)
Buffalo Grill/S (D)
Cafe Beaujolais/N (D)
Cafe de Paris (L,D)
Cafe Fanny/E (L)
Cafe For All Seasons (D)
Cafe Jacqueline (D)
Cafe Kati (D)
Cafe Marcella/S (D)
Cafe Marimba (L,D)
Carta (B,D)
Casa Aguila (L,D)
Casanova/S (B,D)
Chapeau! (B,D)
Charles Nob Hill (D)
Chateau Souverain/N (L,D)
Chez Michel (D)
Citron/E (D)
Club XIX/S (L,D)
Crustacean (L,D)
Cypress Club (D)
Doidge's (L)

Domaine Chandon/N (L,D)
Doug's BBQ/E (L,D)
Ebisu (L,D)
Eliza's (L,D)
El Paseo/N (D)
Eos (D)
Erna's Elderberry/S (B,D)
Evvia/S (D)
Farallon (D)
Firefly (D)
Flea St. Cafe/S (B,D)
Foothill Cafe/N (D)
French Laundry/N (L,D)
Fresh Cream/S (D)
Garibaldi's (B,D)
General's Daughter/N (B,L,D)
Grandview/S (L,D)
Greens (B,L)
Harris' (D)
Hawthorne Lane (D)
Hayes St. Grill (D)
Helmand (D)
Iberia/S (L,D)
Incontro (D)
Indigo (D)
Infusion (D)
Insalata's/N (D)
Johnny Love's (L,D)
Juban/S (D)
Kasbah/N (D)
Kate's Kitchen (L)
Katia's (B,L,D)
Kenwood/N (L,D)
Khan Toke Thai (L,D)
Kincaid's Bistro/S (D)
Kirala/E (D)
La Felce (D)
La Forêt/S (B,D)
Laghi (D)
La Ginestra/N (D)
Lalime's/E (D)
La Mediterranee (L,D)
La Mère Michelle/S (B,L,D)
La Pastaia/S (L,D)
La Petite Auberge/N (L,D)
Lark Creek/E (B,D)
Lark Creek Inn/N (B,D)
La Taqueria (L,D)
La Vie (L,D)
Left Bank/N (L,D)
Le Marquis/E (L,D)
Le Mouton Noir/S (D)
Le Papillon/S (D)
Long Life Noodle (D)
L'Osteria del Forno (L,D)
Maki (L,D)
Mama's Girl (L)
Mandalay (L,D)
Marnee Thai (L,D)

Massawa (L,D)
Mayflower (L,D)
Mecca (D)
Meetinghouse (D)
Mio Vicino/S (D,L)
Montrio/S (B,L,D)
Moose's (B,D)
Morton's of Chicago (D)
Mo's Burgers (L,D)
Moxie (D)
Murasaki (D)
Mustards Grill/N (L,D)
Napa Valley Grille/N (B,L,D)
Nightshade (B,D)
Nob Hill Cafe (L,D)
North Beach (L,D)
Oliveto/E (L,D)
Omnivore/E (D)
Pane e Vino (D)
Pauline's (D)
PJ's Oyster Bed (D)
Pluto's (L,D)
Pluto's/S (L,D)
Prima Trattoria/E (D)
Raw Living Foods (L,D)
Rest. Peony/E (L,D)
Rice Table/N (D)
Rio Grill/S (B,L,D)
Rivoli/E (D)
Rocco's (D)
Rooster (D)
Rose Pistola (L,D)
Rose's Cafe (L,D)
Sally's (L)
Sanraku (D)
Sent Sovi/S (D)
Seoul Garden (L,D)
Slanted Door (L,D)
Socca (D)
Spiedini/E (D)
Splendido (D)
Suppenküche (D)
Swagat/S (L,D)
Tarpy's Roadhse./S (B,L,D)
Terra/N (D)
Thep Phanom (D)
Thornhill Cafe/E (L,D)
Ti Couz (L,D)
Tommaso's (D)
Tommy Toy's Chinoise (D)
Ton Kiang (L,D)
Tra Vigne/N (L,D)
Tutto Mare/N (B,L,D)
2223 Rest. (B,D)
Universal Cafe (L,D)
Valentine's Cafe (D)
Val 21 (D)
Venezia/E (D)
Venticello (D)

Viognier/S (D)
Vivande Porta Via (L,D)
Vivande Rist. (L,D)
Wappo Bar/N (L,D)
Wente Vineyards/E (B,L,D)
Willowside Cafe/N (D)
Woodward's (D)
Yabbies (D)
Yank Sing (B,L)
Yoshida-Ya (D)
Yuet Lee (L,D)
Zinzino (D)
Zuni Cafe (B,L,D)

Senior Appeal

Alfred's
Alioto's
Cafe For All Seasons
Clement St. B&G
Courtyard B&G
Covey/S
Emile's/S
Fresh Cream/S
General's Daughter/N
Guernica/N
Harris'
House of Prime Rib
La Petite Auberge/N
Marin Joe's/N
Maye's Oyster Hse.
Scoma's
Scoma's/N
Sears Fine Food
Waterfront

Singles Scenes

Aqua
Balboa Cafe
Beach Chalet
Betelnut
Biscuits & Blues
BIX
Blue Light
Bruno's
Buchanan Grill
Buckeye Roadhse./N
Cadillac Bar
Cafe Flore
Cafe Marimba
Caribbean Zone
Crow's Nest/S
Cypress Club
Eleven Ristorante
Elite Cafe
Eos
Garibaldi's
Gordon Biersch
Gordon Biersch/S
Hamburger Mary's
Harry Denton's

Hayes & Vine
Infusion
Johnny Love's/E
Julie's Supper Club
LuLu
MacArthur Park
Max's Diner
Mecca
Palomino
Paragon B&G
Perry's
Pier 23 Cafe
Pluto's
Pluto's/S
Postrio
Prego
Sam's Anchor Cafe/N
Sol y Luna
Stars
Stars Cafe
Sweet Heat
Tavern Grill/S
Thirsty Bear
2223 Rest.
Washington Sq.
Zuni Cafe

Sleepers

(Good to excellent food,
but little known)
Amber India/S
Aqui/S
Beausejour/S
Bella Trattoria
Blue Point
Boonville Hotel/N
Café Chêneville/E
Cafe Marcella/S
Cafe Trio/S
Cafe 222
Casanova/S
Chez Renee/S
Chez T.J./S
Club XIX/S
Covey/S
Doug's BBQ/E
Dusit Thai
Emile's/S
Eulipia/S
Foothill Cafe/N
Fung Lum/S
Gibson/S
Great Eastern
Guernica/N
Hong Kong Villa
Korea House
La Felce
La Forêt/S
La Luna Bistro/S

La Mère Michelle/S
La Pastaia/S
La Petite Auberge/N
Las Camelias/N
La Traviata
Le Marquis/E
Le Mouton Noir/S
Le Papillon/S
Madrona Manor/N
Maki
Mama's Girl
Mama's Royal Cafe/E
Marrakech
Ma Tante Sumi
Mikayla/N
Mio Vicino/S
Moxie
Murasaki
Nan Yang/E
Ocean
Pacific
Paolo's/S
Pasta Prego/N
Picante/E
Plumed Horse/S
Prima Trattoria/E
Rest. Peony/E
Rice Table/N
Robata Grill/N
Rocco's
Rue de Main/E
Sanraku
Seoul Garden
Showley's/N
Siam Cuisine/E
Sierra Mar/S
Swagat/S
Tanuki
Thornhill Cafe/E
Trilogy/N
Uzen/E
Valentine's Cafe
Vic Stewart's/E
Yoyo Bistro
Yukol Place

Teflons

(Gets lots of business, despite so-so food, i.e. they have other attractions that prevent criticism from sticking)
Basta Pasta
Beach Chalet
Bocce Café
Cadillac Bar
Cal. Pizza Kitchen
Capp's Corner
Chevys
Chevys/E

Cliff House
Hard Rock Cafe
Mel's Drive-In
Picaro
Planet Hollywood
Sam's Anchor Cafe/N
Spenger's/E
Stinking Rose
Tommy's Joynt

Smoking Permitted

Alta Mira/N
Aqua
A. Sabella's
Auberge du Soleil/N
Bahia Cabana
Balboa Cafe
Basque Cultural Ctr./S
Basta Pasta
Bauhaus Art/Rest.
Biscuits & Blues
BIX
Blue Light
Bruno's
Buchanan Grill
Cadillac Bar
Cafe Bastille
Cafe Claude
Cafe de Paris
Cafe Majestic
Cafe 222
Campton Place
Capp's Corner
Caribbean Zone
Carnelian Room
Carpaccio/S
Castagnola's
Cha Am Thai
Cha Am Thai/E
Charles Nob Hill
Chef Chu's/S
City of Paris
Cliff House
Coconut Grove
Courtyard B&G
Crescent Park/S
Crustacean
Cypress Club
Dal Baffo/S
Duarte's Tavern/S
Duck Club/S
Eddie Rickenbacker's
Eleven Ristorante
Elroy's
Empress of China
Erna's Elderberry/S
Essex Supper Club
Fizz Supper Club
Fleur De Lys

Fly Trap
Gordon Biersch/S
Grand Cafe
Grissini/E
Hamburger Mary's
Hard Rock Cafe
Harry Denton's
Hawthorne Lane
House of Prime Rib
Imperial Palace
Iron Horse
Julie's Supper Club
Julius' Castle
Kansai
Kuleto's Tratt./S
Kyo-Ya
La Felce
La Mère Michelle/S
La Petite Auberge/N
La Scene
Le Central
Le Marquis/E
Leticia's
Little City
L'Olivier
London Wine Bar
LuLu
MacArthur Park
Mandarin
Marina Central
Marrakech
Matterhorn Swiss
Maxfield's
Max's Diner
Maye's Oyster Hse.
McCormick & Kuleto's
Mom is Cooking
Moose's
Morton's of Chicago
Moxie
Nightshade
North Beach
Occidental Grill
Old Swiss Hse.
O'Reilly's
Original Joe's
Original Old Clam Hse.
Paragon B&G
Park Grill
Pier 23 Cafe
Plumed Horse/S
Postrio
Prego
Puccini & Pinetti
Rick's
Rist. Ideale
Rist. Salute/E
Ritz-Carlton Din. Rm.
Ritz-Carlton Terrace

Rocco's
Rose Pistola
Rue de Main/E
Sam's
San Benito Hse./S
Schroeder's
Scoma's
Scoma's/N
Seoul Garden
Sol y Luna
Spiedini/E
Splendido
Stars Cafe
Storyville
Suppenküche
Tadich Grill
Tarantino's
Thirsty Bear
Timo's
Tommy's Joynt
Tonga
Top of the Mark
Tourelle/E
2223 Rest.
Vertigo
Vic Stewart's/E
Vintner's Court/N
Vivande Rist.
Wa-Ha-Ka
Washington Sq.
Waterfront
Wente Vineyards/E
Zinzino

Tasting Menus
Alta Mira/N
Aqua
Auberge du Soleil/N
Bok Choy/S
Catahoula/N
Chapeau!
Charles Nob Hill
Chez Michel
Crescent Park/S
Cypress Club
Fleur De Lys
French Laundry/N
Kasbah/N
La Folie
Le Mouton Noir/S
Madrona Manor/N
Masa's
Meadowood Rest./N
One Market
Pacific's Edge/S
Rubicon
Sukhothai
Terra/N
Timo's

Trilogy/N
Wu Kong
Zaré

Teas

Alta Mira/N
Bridges/E
Delancey St.
Fournou's Ovens
Garden Court
O'Reilly's
Panama Hotel/N
Park Grill
Rotunda
Vivande Rist.

Teenagers & Other Youthful Spirits

Alexander/E
Benihana
Bill's Place
Cacti/N
Cactus Cafe/N
Cafe de Bordeaux/E
Cal. Pizza Kitchen
Caribbean Zone
Clement St. B&G
Enrico's
Gira Polli
Hamburger Mary's
Hard Rock Cafe
La Taqueria
Mario's Bohemian
Maxfield's
Max's Diner
Mel's Drive-In
Mo's Burgers
Mozzarella Di Bufala
Nightshade
Olive's
Pancho Villa
Pauline's
Primo Patio
World Wrapps
World Wrapps/E
World Wrapps/S

Theme Restaurants

Alexander/E
Fat Apple's/E
Hard Rock Cafe
Planet Hollywood

Visitors on Expense Accounts

Big Four
Castagnola's
Essex Supper Club
Fleur De Lys
General's Daughter/N

Greens
Harris'
Harry Denton's
Izzy's
La Forêt/S
Le Mouton Noir/S
McCormick & Kuleto's
Moose's
North Beach
One Market
Park Grill
PlumpJack
Ritz-Carlton Din. Rm.
Rubicon
Stars
Tadich Grill

Wheelchair Access

(Most places now have wheelchair access; call in advance to check)

Wine/Beer Only

Acquerello
Adriana's/N
Ajanta/E
Albona
Alegrias
Aliotos
Allegro
Antica Trattoria
Aperto
Appam
Asimakopoulos
Aux Delices
Avenue 9
Babaloo Tapas
Babette's/N
Baker St. Bistro
Barnaby's/N
Bay Wolf/E
Bella Trattoria
Bette's Oceanview/E
Bill's Place
Bistro Aix
Bistro Clovis
Blowfish Sushi
Blue Nile/E
Blue Point
Bonta
Boonville Hotel/N
Brother's Deli/S
Bubba's Diner/N
Cactus Cafe/N
Cafe Akimbo
Cafe Beaujolais/N
Café Chêneville/E
Cafe/Chez Panisse/E
Cafe Claude

Cafe de Bordeaux/E
Cafe Fanny/E
Cafe Flore
Cafe For All Seasons
Cafe Jacqueline
Cafe Kati
Cafe Marcella/S
Café Mozart
Cafe Trio/S
Caffe Centro
Caffe Delle Stelle
Caffè Greco
Caffè Macaroni
Caffe Sport
Campo Santo
Carta
Cassis Bistro
Cha Cha Cha
Chapeau!
Chateau Souverain/N
Cheers Cafe
Chez Panisse/E
Chez T.J./S
Chow
Citron/E
Columbus Rist.
Correnti's
Curbside Cafe
dame
Delancey St.
Dottie's True Blue
Doug's BBQ/E
E'Angelo
Ebisu
El Balazo
Eliza's
Ella's
El Paseo/N
Emerald Garden
Empress Court/S
Eos
Eric's
Ernesto's
Esperpento
Estampas Peruanas/S
Fat Apple's/E
Firefly
Flea St. Cafe/S
Flying Saucer
Fook Yuen/S
Foothill Cafe/N
Fountain Court
French Laundry/N
Fung Lum/S
Fusilli Rist./N
Gertie's Chesapeake/E
Gira Polli
Gira Polli/N
Godzilla Sushi

Golden Turtle
Gordon Biersch/S
Grandview/S
Great Eastern
Greens
Hahn's Hibachi
Hamano Sushi
Hayes & Vine
Hong Kong Villa
House
House of Nanking
Hunan
Hungarian Sausage
Iberia/S
I Fratelli
Incontro
Indian Oven
Insalata's/N
Irrawaddy
Isobune
Isobune/S
Jackson Fillmore
Jade Villa/E
Jakarta
Jasmine House
Jessie's
Juban/S
Kasbah/N
Katia's
Kelly's on Trinity
Khan Toke Thai
Kim's of Saigon
Kincaid's Bistro/S
Kirala/E
Kirin
Kiss
Korea House
La Belle Saison
La Bergerie
La Cumbre
La Cumbre/S
Laghi
Lalime's/E
La Luna Bistro/S
La Mediterranee
La Mediterranee/E
L'Amie Donia/S
Las Camelias/N
La Taqueria
La Vie
Le Charm
Le Soleil
Leticia's
Lhasa Moon
Liberty Cafe
Lichee Garden
Little Henry's
Little Italy
Little Joe's

London Wine Bar
Long Life Noodle
Long Life Vegi/E
Los Gatos/S
L'Osteria del Forno
Madrona Manor/N
Mai's
Maki
Mama's Royal Cafe/E
Mangiafuoco
Mario's Bohemian
Massawa
Matsuya
Meetinghouse
Mel's Drive-In
Mescolanza
Michelangelo Cafe
Mifune
Mikayla/N
Milano Pizzeria
Millennium
Mio Vicino/S
Miss Millie's
Moa Room
Mo's Burgers
Mozzarella Di Bufala
Nan Yang/E
Narai
Neecha Thai
New Gulf Coast/E
Nob Hill Cafe
North India
North Sea Village/N
Ocean
O Chame/E
Olive's
Omnivore/E
Osome
Osteria
Osteria/S
Pacific Cafe
Pacific Fresh/S
Panama Hotel/N
Pane e Vino
Parkside Grille/S
Parma
Pasta Moon/S
Pasta Pomodoro
Pasta Pomodoro/E
Pasta Prego/N
Pauline's
Pauli's Cafe
Picaro
Pinot Blanc/N
Planet Hollywood
Plearn Thai/E
PlumpJack
Pluto's
Pluto's/S

Primo Patio
Pyramid Alehse./E
Radicchio
Rendezvous du Monde
Rest. Peony/E
Rice Table/N
Rist. Bacco
Rist. Fabrizio/N
Rivoli/E
Robata Grill/N
Roosevelt Tamale
Rooster
Rose's Cafe
Rosti
Rosti/S
Rue de Main/E
Samui Thai
San Francisco BBQ
Sanppo
Sanraku
Saul's/E
Savor
Sent Sovi/S
Showley's/N
Skylight Cafe/E
Slanted Door
Spuntino
Stars
Stelline
Sukhothai
Suppenküche
Terra/N
Thep Phanom
Thornhill Cafe/E
Ti Couz
Tommaso's
Ton Kiang
Tortola
Town's End
Tratt. Contadina
Trilogy/N
Tu Lan
231 Ellsworth/S
Universal Cafe
U.S. Rest.
Uzen/E
Valentine's Cafe
Val 21
Venezia/E
Vicolo
Vicolo/S
Vivande Porta Via
Wappo Bar/N
Wente Vineyards/E
Willowside Cafe/N
World Wrapps
World Wrapps/E
World Wrapps/S
Yabbies

Yank Sing
Yaya Cuisine
Yuet Lee
Yukol Place
Zachary's/E
Zaré
Zarzuela
Zax
Zazie
Zinzino
Zza's Trattoria/E

Winning Wine Lists

Acquerello
Aqua
Auberge du Soleil/N
Balboa Cafe
Bay Wolf/E
Blackhawk Grille/E
Brava Terrace/N
Carnelian Room
Catahoula/N
Chapeau!
Chez Panisse/E
Chez T.J./S
Covey/S
Dal Baffo/S
Domaine Chandon/N
El Paseo/N
Elroy's
Eos
Erna's Elderberry/S
Flea St. Cafe/S
Fleur De Lys
Fournou's Ovens
French Laundry/N
General's Daughter/N
Greens
John Ash & Co./N
Julius' Castle
La Pastaia/S
Lark Creek Inn/N
London Wine Bar
Masa's
Moose's
Mustards Grill/N
North Beach
One Market
Pacific's Edge/S
Park Grill
PlumpJack
Postrio
Prima Trattoria/E
Rist. Ecco
Rivoli/E
Rubicon
Sardine Factory/S
Stars
Terra/N
Tra Vigne/N
231 Ellsworth/S

Wente Vineyards/E
Willowside Cafe/N
Wine Spectator/N
Zuni Cafe

Worth a Trip

EAST
Berkeley
    Chez Panisse
    Zachary's
Oakland
    Oliveto
Walnut Creek
    Lark Creek
NORTH
Calistoga
    Catahoula
Larkspur
    Lark Creek Inn
    Left Bank
Napa
    Auberge du Soleil
    Brava Terrace
    Domaine Chandon
    French Laundry
    Meadowood Rest.
    Mustards Grill
    Terra
Sonoma
    Babette's
    General's Daughter
SOUTH
Big Sur
    Sierra Mar
Half Moon Bay
    Pasta Moon
Monterey/Carmel
    Fresh Cream
    Pacific's Edge
Oakhurst
    Erna's Elderberry
Pebble Beach
    Roy's/Pebble Beach
San Jose
    Emile's
San Mateo
    Lark Creek
    231 Ellsworth
Saratoga
    Sent Sovi

Young Children

(Besides the normal fast-food
places; * indicates children's
menu available)
Alta Mira/N*
Aperto*
Aqui/S*
A. Sabella's*
Barnaby's/N
Beach Chalet*

Benihana*
Benihana/S*
Bighorn Grill/E*
Bill's Place*
Blackhawk Grille/E*
Bok Choy/S*
Bubba's Diner/N*
Buckeye Roadhse./N*
Cactus Cafe/N
Cafe/Chez Panisse/E*
Cafe de Bordeaux/E*
Cafe Marimba*
Café Riggio*
Cafe Rouge/E*
Cafe 222*
Caffe Sport
California Cafe/N*
California Cafe/S*
Cal. Pizza Kitchen*
Capellini/S*
Capp's Corner
Casanova/S*
Castagnola's*
Cheers Cafe
Chevys*
Chevys/E*
Chevys/N*
Chez Panisse/E*
Clement St. B&G*
Club XIX/S*
Crow's Nest/S*
Duck Club/S*
Ernesto's*
Fat Apple's/E
Fournou's Ovens*
French Room*
Garden Court*
Ginger Island/E*
Hamburger Mary's*
Hard Rock Cafe
Horizons/N
House of Prime Rib*
I Fratelli*
Il Fornaio*
Il Fornaio/N*
Insalata's/N*
Izzy's
JoAnn's Cafe/S
Jordan's/E*
Kenwood/N
Kuleto's Tratt./S*
Lark Creek/E*
Lark Creek/S*
Lark Creek Inn/N*
Left at Albuquerque*
Left at Albuquerque/S*
Left Bank/N*
Los Gatos/S*
Marin Joe's/N

Maxfield's*
Max's Diner*
Max's Opera Cafe*
Max's Opera Cafe/S*
Mel's Drive-In*
Mescolanza
Montrio/S*
Mo's Burgers
Mozzarella Di Bufala
New Joe's*
Nightshade
North India*
Old Swiss Hse.
One Market
Pacific Fresh/E*
Pacific Fresh/S*
Pacific's Edge/S*
Palomino
Paolo's/S*
Park Grill*
Parkside Grille/S*
Pauline's
Perry's*
Piatti/N*
Piatti/S*
Picante/E*
Puccini & Pinetti*
Pyramid Alehse./E*
Rio Grill/S
Ritz-Carlton Terrace*
Rosti*
Rosti/S*
Roy's/Pebble Beach/S*
Rutherford Grill/N*
Sam's Anchor Cafe/N*
Sardine Factory/S*
Saul's/E*
Schroeder's*
Scoma's*
Scoma's/N*
Scott's/S*
Silks*
Spenger's/E*
Splendido*
Station House/N*
Tanuki*
Tarantino's
Tarpy's Roadhse./S*
Tortola
Tourelle/E*
Venezia/E*
Vic Stewart's/E*
Vintner's Court/N
Viognier/S*
Wente Vineyards/E*
World Wrapps*
World Wrapps/E*
World Wrapps/S*
Zza's Trattoria/E*

ALPHABETICAL PAGE INDEX*

* All restaurants are in the City of San Francisco unless otherwise noted (E=East of San Francisco; N=North of San Francisco; S=South of San Francisco).

NOTES

Wine Vintage Chart 1985-1996

This chart is designed to help you select wine to go with your meal. It is based on the same 0 to 30 scale used throughout this *Survey*. The ratings (prepared by our friend Howard Stravitz, a law professor at the University of South Carolina) reflect both the quality of the vintage and the wine's readiness for present consumption. Thus, if a wine is not fully mature or is over the hill, its rating has been reduced. We do not include 1987 because, with the exception of '87 cabernets, those vintages are not recommended.

	'85	'86	'88	'89	'90	'91	'92	'93	'94	'95	'96
WHITES											
French:											
Burgundy	27	28	20	29	24	18	26	19	25	25	26
Loire Valley	–	–	–	25	24	15	19	22	23	24	24
Champagne	28	25	24	26	28	–	–	24	–	25	26
Sauternes	22	28	29	25	26	–	–	–	18	22	24
California:											
Chardonnay	–	–	–	–	23	21	26	25	22	23	22
REDS											
French:											
Bordeaux	27	26	25	28	28	–	19	23	24	25	24
Burgundy	24	–	26	27	29	21	23	25	22	23	24
Rhône	26	20	26	28	27	26*	16	23*	23	24	22
Beaujolais	–	–	–	–	–	22	13	21	22	24	21
California:											
Cab./Merlot	27	26	16	22	28	26	25	24	24	23	22
Zinfandel	–	–	–	–	–	20	20	20	22	20	21
Italian:											
Tuscany	27	16	25	–	26	19	–	20	19	24	19
Piedmont	26	–	24	27	27	–	–	19	–	25	25

*Rating and recommendation is only for Northern Rhône wine in 1991 and Southern Rhône wine in 1993.

Bargain sippers take note: Some wines are reliable year in, year out, and are reasonably priced as well. These wines are best bought in the most recent vintages. They include: Alsatian Pinot Blancs, Côtes du Rhône, Muscadet, Bardolino, Valpolicella and inexpensive Spanish Rioja and California Zinfandel.